Mitchell's
Elementary Building Construction

Mitchell's
Elementary
Building Construction

Revised by

RAYMOND MOXLEY, A.R.I.B.A.

B. T. BATSFORD LTD · LONDON

Revised Edition © B. T. Batsford Ltd, 1959

Twenty-third Edition, 1959
Reprinted, 1961

PRINTED IN GREAT BRITAIN BY
THE WHITEFRIARS PRESS LTD, LONDON AND TONBRIDGE
AND BOUND BY KEMP HALL BINDERY, OXFORD, FOR THE
PUBLISHERS
B. T. BATSFORD LTD
4 FITZHARDINGE STREET, PORTMAN SQUARE, LONDON, W.1

Preface

THE student of building, whether he is a potential Architect, Engineer, Surveyor or Builder, must be literate in sound construction based on good design. This implies an appreciation of all the important aspects—appropriate use of materials, sufficient strength and permanence, maximum utility, and good proportion and grace. The appelations ' traditional ', ' modern ', ' contemporary ' or whatever, are immaterial in deciding what is good—principle and not fashion is the only legitimate yardstick.

Architecture is concerned with the design of buildings right down to the last detail and is much more a matter of teamwork than it was in the past because of the immense complexity of the task, and the innumerable variations made possible by the vast number of new materials and techniques available.

Many progressive architects have produced and are developing different grammars of construction, using modern techniques and materials. Leading journals are continually publishing good details from the offices of architects (some give excellent cost information); this stream of information is helping in the codification of modern construction. This transitional phase will last for some time and can only end when prices have been stable for a long time and international standards of modular co-ordination have been generally accepted.

Several channels of development are discernible, some of which demand mainly fitting techniques, e.g. the Hertfordshire schools or the Fuller domes; others which involve site or *in situ* casting of concrete. Both the economics of, and a more rational approach to, smaller building work is encouraging greater use of short bore piles, strip foundations and simple rafts for under structure; whilst frames and various spanning systems will become more widely known. The introduction of frostproof lightweight insulating block may give the bricklayer a new lease of life in external walling work as the importance of insulation is more generally appreciated. Cladding is now, quite wrongly, often a matter of fashion; timber siding is now ' out ', and some are tiring of the curtain wall. Once again choice should depend on principle, but the factors are sometimes so variable and involved that decision is difficult.

This edition has been completely rewritten with this background in mind. The matter is grouped in elements as far as practicable in the sequence of the building operation, but in some cases, for clarity, techniques relating to the same material have been taken together. It is not possible to be entirely comprehensive within the span of one volume, but it aims to describe the principles of elementary construction and the more important solutions to the problems raised by their application.

Very little of the material in previous editions is retained here. This may be missed by some of those schooled in earlier times. Even if it is thought that these forms of construction are met with now, there is no doubt they will very soon become obsolete.

For a fuller understanding of the subject, this book should be read in conjunction with the publications referred to in the text and footnotes.

This volume covers the work for the first stage of most professional examinations. More advanced work is covered in the two volumes of *Advanced Building Construction* published by Batsford.

I would like to thank the trade and development associations, manufacturers, government departments and official bodies who have supplied information for this book. The majority of these are acknowledged in the text footnotes and drawings.

In particular I would like to thank Denzil Nield, A.R.I.B.A., for undertaking the job of reading the MS and making many valuable suggestions. My thanks are also due to the draughtsmen of the many new drawings: Betty Blessley, A.A.Dipl., A.R.I.B.A., David Brown, Dipl. Arch.(R.W.A.), A.R.I.B.A., J. F. Price, A.R.I.B.A., A. A. C. Staples, Dipl. Arch.(R.W.A.), A.R.I.B.A., Bernard Knight and Michael Curnock.

RAYMOND MOXLEY

Bristol, 1959.

Contents

viii CONTENTS

1

General Considerations

BEFORE getting down to details of construction it is as well to have a clear idea of what happens before, during and after a building is constructed and who are the people involved.

Building Owner. May be one individual, a company or a committee of a local authority or some other body. He is usually referred to in the industry as the 'employer' and is so named in the R.I.B.A. Contract document. Frequently the employer has very little idea of precisely what he wants in the way of building or how much the space he wants will cost.

Architect. The employer calls in an architect to advise him. The architect will make a careful analysis of the employer's requirements and find out how much he is willing to spend on the project. From his own experience and by consultation with his quantity surveyor the architect will know approximately the average cost of buildings similar to that which the employer requires.*

The architect is trained to think of the building in three dimensions, i.e. as a series of volumes or envelopes which he carefully relates into a well-proportioned whole. To produce a building which is well constructed, is as efficient and useful as possible to the owner, and is delightful to look at, and walk in, is a highly skilled job needing many years of training and experience.

When the architect's sketch designs are sufficiently advanced a firmer check upon the cost is made.

Approvals. The architect prepares from the sketch designs, draft 1/8th scale working drawings, draft details and a specification. The specification describes all the work that has to be done, defining as far as possible the standard of workmanship and the quality of materials. The form and content of this document is undergoing a certain amount of change at the present time.

The 1/8th scale working drawings and specification, having been approved by the employer, are sent to the City Surveyor or Engineer, or the Urban or Rural District Council Surveyor for approval, by a special committee, under the local Building By-laws. Most local Building By-laws are based on the Ministry of Health Model By-laws which have recently been revised.

---

* The *Architects' Journal* prepares Cost Analyses of current buildings in a special form which is most useful to the architect when considering shape and volume, the choice of constructional system, materials, and finishes.

By-laws. Building by-laws ensure that the building is properly constructed of durable materials in such a way that it will be dry and healthy to live in. By-laws regulate details of drainage, damp-proof courses, foundations, the size of windows, size of opening vents, position and number of w.c.'s, the space about buildings, construction of flues, size of hearths and many other vital factors. The architect must ensure that his building conforms in every respect to the by-laws.

Planning Permission. Additional 1/8th scale drawings are sent to the local Planning Authority (County or City Planning Department), usually through the local council, for approval under the City or County Plan. The Planning Officer is interested in the siting of the proposed building, its relationship to the highway, whether the building is of ' suitable use ' for the neighbourhood, e.g. he would not permit a glue factory to be built in the middle of a residential neighbourhood, whether in his opinion the appearance of the building is satisfactory and whether or not the building will harm the ' amenity ' of the neighbourhood (' amenity ' can mean almost anything).

For a more complex building it is as well for the architect to consult with the By-law and Planning Authority to make sure that various points of his design are understood and appreciated properly.

Drawing Office Stage. This is a very vital stage which is not usually given sufficient time and thought. It is the architect's job to make the mistakes on paper so that as few as possible are made on the site. At this time the building owner is usually getting impatient and pressing the architect to get something started. It is vital that the working drawings, details, schedules, etc., are carefully and properly considered if the client is to build within his budget and the building is to be completed on time.

Bill of Quantities. When the architect has completed the working drawings, details and schedules, they are passed to the quantity surveyor (in cases where the job is big enough) so that he may prepare a bill of quantities. This is an involved process which results in a bill giving the quantity and a precise description of all the labour and materials shown, described, or indicated in the working drawings and other documents prepared by the architect. The bill of quantities has been used until recently solely for builders to prepare an estimate from. It is now being extended in certain cases to give additional information on labour content, or to assist the organisation of the job, or to assist the architect or quantity surveyor in producing a cost analysis of the job in comparison with other buildings.

The bill of quantities is then sent to several selected builders for them to prepare tender prices. In some cases one contractor is selected and a price is negotiated with him.

Smaller contracts, which do not have bills of quantities drawn up for them (under £4,000 value), are tendered for by builders on the architect's drawings, details and specification. This makes the job of the builder's estimator very much more difficult.

Estimator. Normally the estimator's job is to put rates against each of the items in the bill and to multiply these rates by the quantity of labour or materials shown in the bill. When this has been done, all the items are totalled up and with any necessary adjustments this total forms the contract sum submitted to the architect.

Where quantities are not provided, the estimator must do some measuring in order to arrive at a contract sum. To do the job thoroughly a great deal of work is involved. In many cases the job is 'supered' (i.e. the total number of square feet ascertained and multiplied by a rate which is known from experience to cover the cost of the type of work concerned). If the contract is a small one and any errors in judgment are made, the losses are relatively small.

Tenders. The architect usually specifies that all the estimates prepared by builders, i.e. the tenders, must be submitted by a certain day. On this day the architect, often in the presence of the employer, opens the tenders and usually the lowest tenderer is selected as the contractor. If the lowest tender is very much below the others it may indicate a mistake in the calculations. The owner is not obliged to accept any, or the lowest, tender.

Contract. This document lays out the respective rights and responsibilities of the employer and the contractor. It mentions the architect and the quantity surveyor, specifies the contract sum, states the date on which the site may be entered by the contractor, the completion date, the amount of money to be paid by the contractor if he fails to complete the building to time, and many other important details concerning the management of the contract. It is signed by the contractor and by the employer.

Builder's Planning. The builder must now be allowed a period in which to organise the work and to become familiar with the drawings, schedules and specification. He is usually unfairly expected to enter the site immediately and to start work straight away. But he cannot begin work efficiently unless he has spent a reasonable amount of time planning, at least, the first stages of the work.

Setting Out. The first action of the builder is to peg out roughly the shape of the building on the ground. He then carefully sets up one or two base lines from the architect's drawings and from this erects profiles at the corners of the main walls. He drives in pegs at the exact levels of the various floors. The architect is responsible for checking the main outlines of the walls of the building, but has no responsibility for setting out thereafter. If much excavation has to be done over the site, this must be completed by the earth-moving equipment before the precise setting out is undertaken. Excavation of the foundations is then undertaken, the basement, if there is one, by digging equipment and the foundation trenches by hand or by trenching equipment, if the ground is suitable. Alternatively, the foundations may rest upon short bore piles or normal piles, etc. (p. 18).

Drainage. If the building is unlikely to settle appreciably it is sometimes convenient to excavate and lay the drains at this stage. At this stage also it is usual to bring on services such as water and electricity so that the site is not cut up with service trenches during the main course of the work. If, however, the building is a heavy one and is likely to settle, it is as well to leave the drainlaying section of the work until the building has settled.

Concreting. Next, the foundations are concreted ready to receive the superstructure.

Superstructure. If the walls are to be of brick or block, the bricklayers now proceed to lay walls on the concrete foundations. If it is to be a frame structure, then the steel or concrete erectors move on to the site to complete their work.

Building Inspector. The Building Inspector of the local authority calls on the site from time to time to inspect the works to see that they conform with the by-laws.

Roof. When the walls or frame has been completed the next step is to cover the roof by erecting the roof carcassing and carpentry work or by progressing up each floor level with, for example, concrete floors until the roof concrete is complete. Once slates, tiles, felt or asphalt waterproofing work has been completed, the windows can be fixed and glazed and the fitting and finishing work put in hand.

Services. The electrician, plumber, gas fitter and the G.P.O. wiremen now attend to put the main runs of their service cables or pipes in the structure before the walls are plastered. These trades usually have to make a second visit to complete their installations once the plastering and other finishing has been completed. The heating engineer fixes his boilers and pipe runs, installs the radiators, heating panels or coils.

Plasterer. The plasterer then follows, plastering the walls and laying the floor screeds level and even, to receive the floor finishes.

Carpenter and Joiner follow to fix skirtings, door linings, doors, architraves, staircases, cupboards, panelling, and so on.

Painter and Decorator. The painters and decorators move in to paint or polish the woodwork, to decorate or paper the walls and ceilings.

Floorlayers and other Trades. The floorlayer likes to be the last on the job, but so does the painter and decorator. The floorlayer complains of the drops of paint from the ceiling and the decorator complains of the floorlayer's adhesive marks on his newly painted skirtings. Perhaps the last of all should be the electrician with his electric light fittings.

External Works. While the last stages of the job are in progress the paths, garden, drives, parking spaces and planting is put in hand so that by the time the internal work is complete so will be the external works.

Certificates. The quantity surveyor visits the job from time to time and values the amount of work that has been done and the value of the materials delivered to the site. From this he works out the amount of money due to be paid to the builder, less a percentage which is kept back in the ' retention fund '. Half of this fund is paid to the contractor on completion and the other half at the end of a period, usually six months after completion. This sum ensures that the builder will return to repair defects which are his responsibility during this defects liability period.

Supervision. During the course of the contract the architect makes regular visits to the site to inspect the quality of work and materials, and to check that the building is being properly constructed in accordance with his drawings. He often arranges site meetings with the building contractor, the quantity surveyor and any specialist contractors who are being employed to do specialist work, e.g. flooring, electrical work, plumbing work, special equipment, etc.

Clerk of Works. If the job is large enough the employer will appoint a clerk of works, nominated by the architect, to keep in close touch with the architect's office on all matters relating to the work on the site.

Foreman. The foreman is the builder's senior representative on the site and is responsible to him for the running of the job. Sometimes he is also expected to do the ordering of the materials, but this is more usually done in the builder's office. The foreman often has a checker to assist him, whose job it is to inspect all deliveries of materials to see that they tally with the orders and the invoices, and are up to the standard specified.

Final Certificate. When the building has been completed for six months, or whatever period is stated in the contract document, the architect and the quantity surveyor inspect the work and the builder is instructed to put right defects which are his responsibility. This having been done, the quantity surveyor prepares the final accounts, and from these, when they have been agreed with the builder, the architect prepares the final certificate for payment by the employer.

Maintenance. Now comes an aspect which is sometimes not properly considered. If the architect and builder have done their work properly, the amount of money that the building owner has to spend annually on maintenance will be relatively small. Too often committees and local authorities have regard at the building stage solely to the contract sum, i.e. first cost, and do not consider the value of paying a little extra for materials that need less maintenance and so save money in the long run.

2
Survey

Ordnance Survey. The first step is to obtain an Ordnance Survey map of the particular site. These maps are published in several different scales, the one which applies most in this case is that of 1/500th, i.e. 1 in. on the map equals 500 in. on the site.

It is frequently found that boundaries shown on the Ordnance Survey map, whilst reasonably accurate for the purposes of the map maker, are not sufficiently accurate for a building site. This is especially true of confined sites in towns.

Object. It is frequently necessary to make an accurate survey of a building site. It is necessary to know not only the shape of the site and the size and shape of any obstacles such as ponds or buildings that exist within the boundaries of the site, but it is also important to know how the site slopes. Surveys are required to produce this information. One is called a chain survey and the other a levelling survey.

CHAIN SURVEY

Engineer's Chain. This consists of a series of steel wire links each a foot long measuring altogether 100 ft exactly. At each end is a handle with a swivel so that when the chain is pulled tight it does not kink. At each 10 ft point is a characteristic tally.

Tape. For very accurate measurement a steel tape, usually 100 ft long, is used. Otherwise a linen tape may be used of similar length. The linen tape must be cleaned and dried at the completion of the survey, a steel tape must be cleaned and dried and lightly oiled.

Ranging Poles. These are used to mark important positions in a survey and to assist in keeping long chain lines straight and true. They are poles 6 ft, 8 ft or 10 ft long with a steel shoe or spike and are usually painted in foot-length bands red, white and black.

Field Book. This is like a narrow reporter's notebook, but instead of having horizontal lines drawn on it, it is divided vertically into three columns. It is usual to start the entries in a Field Book at the bottom of the last page. Entries are made upwards as the survey proceeds. The first entry is the date and the name of the surveyor followed by a sketch plan of the site which may be made from the Ordnance Survey, or from an inspection of the site. The central column is kept free of sketches and notes and is used for the entry of running dimensions. The columns on either side are used for offset distances and diagrams indicating the nature of boundaries, obstacles, etc.

Planning the Survey

The main survey lines usually can be laid out in many ways. The method employed depends upon the nature of obstacles in the site. When the method has been decided, the survey lines are drawn on the sketch plan at the beginning of the Field Book; the intersections or corners are lettered. The survey lines themselves can also be numbered. The ends of the survey or chain lines are known as stations. The longest chain line is known usually as the base line and is measured first.

Procedure

Place ranging poles at principal station points. The team consists of two men, the surveyor and the chainman. The chainman proceeds first and the surveyor, holding the other end of the chain, stands at the beginning of the line. When the chain is tight the surveyor lines the chainman up with the ranging pole at the end of the line. The chainman has in his hand ten arrows. These are 18 in. lengths of wire with a rag for identification tied at one end. He places one of these arrows into the ground at the 100 ft mark. The surveyor then proceeds up the chain line and measures any offsets that are necessary. The chainman then proceeds on towards the end of the baseline until the chain is once more tight. He places another arrow in the ground once he has been lined up with the ranging rod by the surveyor. The surveyor then removes the first arrow and proceeds to measure any offsets from the chain that are necessary. By this method of handling the arrows, a check is kept upon the number of chain lengths.

Offsets. Every irregularity in the shape of the boundary is plotted by measuring a line from it to the nearest chain-line. These lines are called offsets and must be at right angles to the chain-line. It is sufficient to judge these right angles by eye up to a distance of about 25 ft. Offsets of greater length than this should be set out by the 3 : 4 : 5 method or by a cross staff or by an optical square.

The 3 : 4 : 5 method is based on the fact that a triangle with sides 3 : 4 : 5 or multiples of these dimensions, contains a right angle. This can be set out easily with a tape.

Slopes. On ground that slopes any more than one in twenty it is important to make some allowance for the loss of length due to the slope. This may be done by stepping. This is achieved by holding as much of the chain or tape as is possible truly horizontal without appreciable sag. A ranging rod or a plumb line may be used to mark the foot of each step.

Station Pegs. It is sometimes necessary to place station pegs in station points in place of the ranging poles so that these may be removed safely. These station pegs are useful in relating the grid for the levelling survey, to the chain survey.

Plotting. The information written by the surveyor in his Field Book should be sufficiently complete so that any other person could plot the survey from the information without having to revisit the site. Do not use an unusual scale; do not forget the north point, the title and the scale. A small location plan is useful showing the relationship of the site to roads and other important features of the neighbourhood.

Triangulation. It is important to note that no station should be isolated, but that all stations should be tied up with at least two other ones by chain-lines. Thus the site is covered by a series of large triangles so that there is no doubt that the location of each station can be accurately plotted.

Other Features. It is almost always necessary to inspect the site and its surroundings from the point of view of future development. It may be necessary to provide as far as possible answers to the following questions :—

1. Any local electricity supply? 2. Water supply? 3. G.P.O. lines? 4. Any marshy or boggy ground? 5. Any made-up ground? 6. Which direction does the site slope? 7. Where is the view? 8. Is the site overlooked by other buildings? 9. Are there any trees on the site, what varieties, ages and condition? 10. Is the site in the lee of a factory? 11. If the site is not close to a main drainage system, is there sufficient room for a septic tank and filter bed and its effluent drain? 12. Are there any windows overlooking the site which may be the subject of an ancient light dispute? 13. What are the local amenities ?—buses—trains—shops.

LEVELLING SURVEY

Grid. A square grid is set up on the plotted chain survey, and as far as possible related to the stations used. The size of the grid depends upon what has to be done to the various parts of the site. For instance, where there is to be garden it may not be necessary to have a grid smaller than 100 ft. Where the building is to be placed it may be necessary to have the grid as close as at 10 ft centres. If the site is fairly even it may be satisfactory to have the grid as far apart as at 25 ft centres.

Setting-out on the Site. The ends of the grid lines are established by reference to the existing station pegs. Ranging rods are then set up at these points. The staffman then proceeds down the first grid line with the chain in the same manner as for a chain survey and he places the staff in turn at the grid points, i.e. 10 ft or 25 ft or at 100 ft intervals. The surveyor takes readings of the staff at each point with his dumpy or Quickset level.

Staff. A Sopwith staff is most usually employed. The telescope of the surveying instrument does not usually rectify the image, and so the surveyor must get used to reading the staff upside down. The staff is usually 14 ft high, but may be less and is either folding or telescopic. It must be held perfectly upright and steady and must face properly the surveying instrument. It is important that it should be placed on average ground, that is to say, not in a rabbit hole or on top of a molehill.

Level. One of the most common levels in use today is the Quickset level which consists of a telescope aligned with a bubble of long radius, and which is mounted on a universal ball joint that can be tightened by a ring screw. The bubble can be observed from the viewing position through a mirror. There are adjusting screws for focusing the telescope, for tilting the telescope, for traversing it and for releasing the traverse. There is a small circular bubble for getting the level roughly horizontal when initially setting up. There is also a traversing scale marked in degrees, with a pointer. The instrument is mounted on a tripod, which must be firmly positioned before commencing work.

Reading Procedure. First check to see that the vertical hair can be seen clearly. Put the telescope out of focus; then adjust the eyepiece so that the crosshair comes clearly into view. Then take readings as follows:—

1. Traverse the telescope until the staff comes into view.
2. Focus clearly on to the staff.
3. Level the instrument with the levelling screw.
4. Read the staff.

It should be noted here that the staff is divided up into decimals of a foot and not into inches.

Datum. It may be necessary to relate the levelling survey to Ordnance Survey datum. For this it is necessary to inspect the Ordnance Survey map. On the face of the Ordnance Survey map will be found numerous spot heights; these are represented on the ground by bench marks which consist of arrow heads under a horizontal line carved into steps, walls, plinths or other permanent objects.

Once the nearest bench mark to the site has been found it is then necessary to transfer this bench mark level to the site by means of a Flying Level.

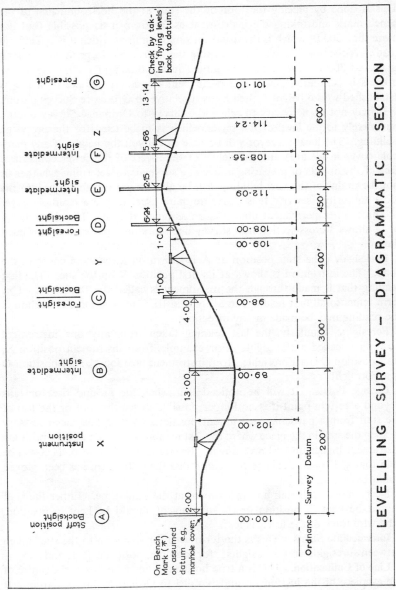

LEVELLING SURVEY – DIAGRAMMATIC SECTION

This is done by placing the foot of the staff at the horizontal line of the bench mark and taking the instrument as far from it as possible (but not more than 300 ft, which is the usual maximum limit at which it is possible to read). A reading is taken and, keeping the instrument in position, the staff is moved 300 ft beyond the instrument in the direction of the site. This process is continued until some permanent object on the site or a peg is established whose height is then known relative to Ordnance Survey datum.

It may not be necessary to relate the survey to Ordnance Survey datum, but merely to the level of the sewer which is to be used for the proposed building. The local surveyor will be able to tell you the height of any man-hole cover in his area and the depth of the invert of the sewer concerned. One of the objects of preparing a levelling survey is to determine whether or not the drains of the new building will be able to run satisfactorily into the local authority's sewer. It is therefore quite usual to use a manhole cover or some other permanent object as an assumed datum. The drawing on p. 11 shows a cross-section of a survey line working from such an assumed datum.

Backsight. The staff position at A is shown on a manhole cover in the road. The instrument is shown at its first position X on the site. The first reading that is made through the instrument is called the Backsight. This term refers to all first readings in all new instrument positions, even though the reading may be made in any direction.

Foresight. Similarly, the last reading taken from any one instrument position is called a Foresight. For example, from instrument position X, staff position C is a Foresight; from instrument position Y, staff position D is a Foresight.

Change Points. It will be noticed that when the ground rises or falls beyond a certain point it is no longer possible to see the foot or the top of the staff from a particular instrument position. It then becomes necessary to keep the staff in the place where the last reading was made and to move the instrument higher up or lower down. From the drawing on p. 11 it will be seen that C is such a change point and that the instrument has been moved uphill beyond to Y.

Never move both staff and instrument at the same time. Either the staff should be kept in position or the instrument should be kept in position, otherwise track of the levels is lost.

Intermediate Sights. This is the term used for sights on to the staff taken between foresights and backsights; for example, positions B, E and F.

Line of Collimation. This is a true horizontal line taken from the centre of the eyepiece of the instrument and parallel to Ordnance Survey datum. If the instrument is out of adjustment and the axis of the bubble is not parallel to the axis of the instrument, inaccurate readings will result.

Adjustments. There are two normal adjustments:—

A. The bubble axis may not be parallel with the line of collimation. In order to correct this, set the Level up, level it carefully by reference to the bubble, turn the telescope through 180°. If then the bubble is not in the centre of its run, bring the bubble half-way back to its central position by means of the levelling screw and bring it the remainder of the way with the capstan-headed adjusting screw attached to the bubble tube.

B. The axis of the telescope may be out of line with the line of collimation. In order to adjust this, set the Level up between two pegs 150 ft apart

RISE AND FALL METHOD

	Back-sight	Inter-mediate sight	Fore-sight	Rise	Fall	Reduced level	Distance	Remarks
A	2·00	—	—	—	—	100·00	—	Datum (assumed) manhole cover (instrument at X)
B	—	13·00	—	—	11·00	89·00	200 ft	—
C	—	—	4·00	9·00	—	98·00	300 ft	—
C	11·00	—	—	—	—	—	300 ft	Instrument moved to Y
D	—	—	1·00	10·00	—	108·00	400 ft	—
D	6·24	—	—	—	—	—	400 ft	Instrument moved to Z
E	—	2·15	—	4·09	—	112·09	450 ft	Top of hill
F	—	5·68	—	—	3·53	108·56	500 ft	—
G	—	—	13·14	—	7·46	101·10	600 ft	—
	19·24	—	18·14	23·09	21·99	—	—	—
	18·14	—	—	21·99	—	—	—	—
	1·10	—	—	1·10	—	—	—	—

N.B.—End each page with a backsight and carry out check.

on reasonably level ground. Place the staff on peg A and take a reading; for example, 5·30. Place the staff on peg B and knock the peg in until the reading is the same. The two pegs will then be level, despite the fact that the Level is out of adjustment. Now move the instrument 5 ft from peg B, take a reading on peg B and then take a reading on peg A. If the readings differ then adjust the diaphragm which contains the crosshairs until the readings are the same.

Booking. There are two methods of booking levelling readings. One is called the Rise and Fall method and the other is called the Collimation or Height of Instrument method. Special levelling books are printed with the appropriate number of columns for either method.

Rise and Fall Method. The difference between each succeeding reading is entered in either the Rise or the Fall column. If the reading is larger than the preceding one the difference is entered in the Fall column, if it is smaller the difference is entered in the Rise column.

If the site is not too far from the office it is usual to leave the calculations concerned in finding the rise and fall and working out the Reduced Level, i.e. the actual level of each staff position in relation to datum, until the surveyor returns to the office. If errors are found it is then possible to return to the site to repeat the necessary part of the survey. If, however, the site is difficult to reach from the office, it is advisable for the surveyor to work out the rise, fall, and reduced levels on the site.

It is advisable to attempt to end each page with a foresight and begin each page with a backsight. It is then possible to check each page as follows: add up the backsights, add up the foresights, and find the difference. Add the rise column and the fall column, the difference should equal the difference between the backsight and the foresight column.

The distance along each chain line or grid line should be entered as a running dimension in the distance column. Remarks should be kept to details of the survey.

Collimation Method. In this case each succeeding reading is subtracted from the last calculated collimation height, i.e. the instrument height from datum. This produces the reduced level at each staff position.

As before begin each page with a backsight and end with a foresight. In order to check add the backsights, add the foresights and find the difference. Then find the difference between the level of datum and the last reduced level. This should equal the difference between the backsight and the foresight totals.

It is advisable at the end of a site levelling survey to take flying levels back

COLLIMATION METHOD

	Back-sight	Inter-mediate sight	Fore-sight	Collimation or instru-ment height	Reduced level	Distance	Remarks
A	2·00	—	—	102·00	100·00	0 ft	(Instrument at X), datum (assumed) manhole cover
B	—	13·00	—	—	89·00	200 ft	—
C	—	—	4·00	—	98·00	300 ft	—
C	11·00	—	—	109·00	—	300 ft	(Instrument moved to X)
D	—	—	1·00	—	108·00	400 ft	—
D	6·24	—	—	114·24	—	400 ft	—
E	—	2·15	—	—	112·09	450 ft	Top of hill
F	—	5·68	—	—	108·56	500 ft	—
G	—	—	13·14	—	101·10	600 ft	—
	19·24	—	18·14	—	100·00	—	—
	18·14	—	—	—	1·10	—	—
	1·10	—	—	—	—	—	—

N.B.—End each page with a foresight and carry out check.

to the datum point in order that the degree of accuracy of the survey may be checked. On very small sites where no change points are necessary, it is difficult to put a check on the survey. It may then be necessary to introduce a change point in order that the survey may be checked.

OTHER SURVEYING TECHNIQUES

Plane surveying may be done with the use of a plane table. This consists of a small drawing board mounted on a tripod which can be levelled. A piece of drawing paper is fixed on to the drawing table and the equipment set up over the first station. A site rule or alidade is then used so that other station points can be sited and plotted directly. There are several methods of using the plane table: (a) radiation, (b) intersection, (c) traversing, (d) resection.

Plane surveying is a quick and effective method more suitable for drier climates.

Theodolite. This instrument is used for measuring horizontal and vertical angles. It is used more in civil engineering work where the difficult nature of the ground may make simpler methods of surveying impracticable.

SURVEYING EXISTING BUILDINGS

It is often necessary to make accurate surveys of existing buildings for the purposes of planning alterations or additions. Confusion can arise if a definite method is not followed. The following is a description of one of the methods which can be used.

Reconnaissance. It is first necessary to inspect the building on all floors to get to know the general layout. Find out which walls are structural and which are merely partitions. Structural walls usually pass up through several storeys but they may not do so on some of the upper floors. It is possible to get some idea of the construction of walls by sounding them—that is to beat them with your fist, or to tap them. A stud wall will sound hollow in parts and solid in others. A thin breeze partition will vibrate. Partitions 3 in. and over are usually too solid to give any indication of their nature. The actual measurements of the survey will reveal a good deal of information as to the construction of the various walls.

There is a convention that plans are drawn 4 ft up from floor level, if there are clearstory (high level) windows these should be dotted on plan.

Equipment. Use a sketch book of tracing paper, fairly large, say 10 in. × 6 in. It should have a stiff sheet of card hinged at the side to fold under each sheet of tracing paper as it comes into use. The point of tracing paper is, that once the ground floor plan has been traced, it is easier to sketch in the upper floors by using the ground floor plan on the lower sheet as a basis. It is therefore wise to start at the back of the book as is the case with the field book. A ball-point pen is very useful as it produces a line which is easy to read and which does not smudge; otherwise use a fairly hard pencil, say 2H.

When possible an assistant saves a great deal of time. The equipment used may consist of a 50 ft tape, a 5 ft rod and a 2 ft rule. If there is a likelihood of mouldings to be copied in the new building work, strips of 3 or 4 lb lead are useful for taking full sizes of these mouldings. The strips of lead are pressed around the contours of the mouldings and are then carefully placed on the sketch pad and traced around. The exact location where the moulding was taken is noted on the elevation and plan.

Procedure. The ground floor entrance hall is measured first. Start on the left-hand side of the front door measuring in a clockwise direction. Finish on the right-hand side of the front door and then measure the door opening itself. Whenever possible take running dimensions, i.e. put the end of the tape in the corner of the room and at each projection, window, door opening, etc., note the dimension on the tape without moving the tape. This is much more accurate than measuring each configuration on its own. Always check the main rooms of the building for squareness, i.e. take both diagonal dimensions. If the principal rooms of the building are true then there is no need to check the other rooms unless they are obviously irregular.

Check then the floor-to-ceiling height, putting this in a circle towards the centre of the room. All the entries of feet and inches should be thus: 5/6 or 2/3. Start with the left-hand room and proceed in a clockwise direction until all the rooms have been measured. Subsidiary rooms, e.g. stores or larders in kitchens should be measured with the kitchen.

Next measure the staircase. This is done by measuring the horizontal distance between the top riser and the bottom riser, noting this and then noting the number of risers in the flight. At the staircases it will be possible to measure the thickness of the floors.

After measuring the ground floor measure the first floor, then the second floor and so on to the top of the building, and then measure the basement and note any associated building works immediately outside.

Elevations. Having made a sketch of each elevation fill in the dimensions by using the 5 ft rod. This can be done usually by leaning out of windows, or from the ground. Where this is impossible a weight may be attached to the end of the tape and lowered from the windows of the top floor.

Construction and Materials. Note as far as possible the direction of floor joists in suspended floors. Make notes of roof finishes, wall finishes and any other points.

Drainage. Note position of vent pipes and rainwater pipes on the first-floor plan and note gullies and manholes on the ground-floor plan. Remove manhole covers and measure the depths of the manholes, noting the size of the drain. Trace the drains by flushing w.c.'s and running taps in sinks in turn so that every run is accounted for. Note the general condition of the drainage installation.

3
Excavation

THE contractor must first decide whether it will be more economical to employ mechanical equipment (plant) or hand excavation. Plant should normally be used where it can be kept fully occupied, the ground is not too boggy, the excavation is not too ' fussy ', there is room to manoeuvre, and the transport costs to and from the site can be paid for from the savings over the cost of hand excavation.

The choice of plant is a matter for the expert. Generally speaking it is most economical to have the largest available equipment that can reasonably handle the work. If the excavated material is not being removed from the site by lorry or dumper, and it has not to be moved very far, then Bulldozers will probably be used. If the spoil heaps are at a distance then Drag-lines or Face Shovels loading into dumpers may be used. If there is a large area of excavation, then a Scraper may be used. A Trenching Machine is useful where the trenches are in straight runs for fairly long lengths, and the ground does not contain boulders or large roots.

Base Lines. If plant is being employed, it is usual to set up pegs at the ends of the base lines. Base lines are drawn on the layout plan, and may consist of two lines at right angles, coinciding with the principal walls of the structure.

The pegs marking the ends of the base line must be sufficiently far away from the building so that they are not knocked over by the plant, and they must be concreted in. A nail driven into the tops of these pegs indicates the correct position of the base line. Between the nails a wire or a line can be tightly stretched, from which the vital dimensions may be made.

Profiles. These consist of poles with cross bars fixed to them at a height related to datum. If a particular part of the excavation has to be say, 90·00 ft, then the cross bars of the profiles may be fixed at 95·00 ft. The bulldozer (or other) driver carries a boning rod, which is like a T-square and which is exactly 5 ft long. From time to time he stops his machine and checks to see how much further he must excavate in order to get the crosspiece of his boning rod level with the cross-pieces on the profiles. He does this by sighting along the cross-bars. The profiles must be sited so that they do not obstruct the movement of the plant unduly.

Topsoil. This is usually of considerable value and has to be carefully removed by the plant or by hand to a topsoil heap out of the way of the

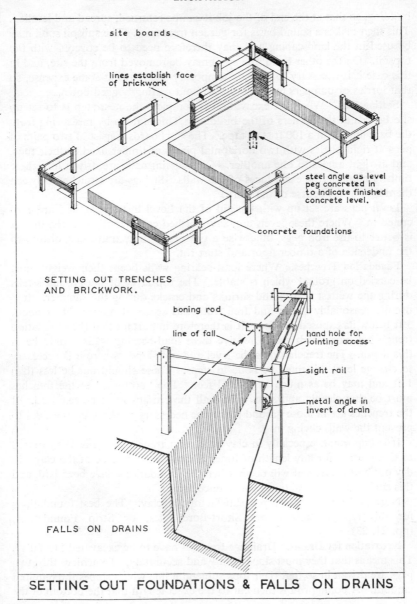

site boards

lines establish face
of brickwork

steel angle as level
peg concreted in
to indicate finished
concrete level.

concrete foundations

SETTING OUT TRENCHES
AND BRICKWORK.

boning rod

line of fall

hand hole for
jointing access

sight rail

metal angle in
invert of drain

FALLS ON DRAINS

SETTING OUT FOUNDATIONS & FALLS ON DRAINS

building, so that at the end of the job it can be returned, spread and levelled. This then makes a sound basis for garden treatment. The subsoil spoil may be used in the landscaping and may therefore need to be covered with the topsoil. On the other hand, the spoil may be removed from the site, and in this case it is necessary to provide temporary site roads at some expense, so that lorries or dumpers may operate without getting bogged down.

Setting Out. When the excavation is complete the next step is to set up site boards at the corners of the building. This is done by measuring from the base lines with a 100 ft steel tape. The site boards consist of two pairs of pegs at right angles with two horizontal pieces of timber fixed to their tops, and at right angles to one another. Once again, nails are driven into these timbers marking the exact faces of the walls. Strings are stretched between them during the course of the work.

Level pegs are set up with the aid of the Level instrument and are concreted in. Where these levels are, say, finished concrete floor levels, then it is better to use iron pegs, otherwise a timber peg may transmit moisture to the underside of a timber floor and start rot.

Foundation Trenches. Where load-bearing walls occur their weight must be carried on ground which is stable. The top layer of the ground swells during the wettest season and shrinks and cracks during the summer. It is usually reasonably stable and free from this seasonal movement at about 3 ft below its exposed surface. It is therefore important that the foundation trench bottoms which are to receive these load-bearing walls should be at this depth. The trenches must be level and not slope—where it is necessary to change level this must be done in steps. These should not be less than 1 ft and may be as much as several feet. The ' bottoms ' of the trenches must be dug cleanly and square, and all the crumbs must be removed. If the trenches are in loose ground it may be necessary to shore up the sides to prevent the walls caving in.

It is important, especially in clay soils, that trenches are not left exposed to the weather for any length of time, otherwise the surface of the clay will dry out and movement will occur when the foundations have been laid, and this surface becomes wet and swells once again.

Normal foundations are not satisfactory in clay. The best foundations for this type of subsoil are Short-Bore Piles, or Strip Foundations (pp. 21, 23).

Excavation for Drains. Drainage trenches have to be excavated ' to falls '. This means that they must slope evenly and accurately. To achieve this, two pegs are driven in so that their tops subtend a line which slopes the required amount. A boning rod is then cut to the exact length that the bottom of the drain requires to be from this sloping line. The man excavating the trench can then use this boning rod to sight along to the two pegs so as to check the depth of his excavation.

Curtain Drains. It is often wise to dig a land drain across the uphill side of the site to intercept ground water flowing towards the new building. It is as well to tackle this job at the excavating stage to reduce the risk of the excavations becoming flooded.

Pumping. If water is troublesome then a sump must be dug in the corner of the foundations at the lowest point, into which the foot-valve of a pump can be placed. It may be necessary to keep the pumps going continuously so as to avoid the foundation work being spoilt by incoming water.

FOUNDATIONS

The design of foundations depends upon the nature of the structure which they have to carry and the properties of the soil in which they are carried. The structure may consist mainly of load-bearing walls which have to have continuous support, or the structure may consist of a framed building supported from the ground at isolated points. It may be cheaper to build a light structure on a concrete raft, which in effect floats on the ground; if the ground shrinks or swells, the whole building moves together.

Design. The first step is to calculate the weight at the base of a wall or at the foot of a column to see how much the ground must support. Then the subsoil must be inspected to gauge its bearing ability. Trial holes will indicate whether the ground has been disturbed and the strata in them must be carefully examined in case the site contains ' made-up ' ground.

Seasonal Movement. As pointed out earlier seasonal movement is likely to occur especially in clays down to a depth of 3 ft or 3 ft 6 in. This occurs when the clay dries in summer and shrinks. This movement goes down to a depth of at least 3 ft and occurs whether foundations are present or not, wherever the surface of the ground is exposed. If the building is not going to crack it is important that the foundations are built on stable ground. The achievement of stability in the foundations can be attained in several ways:—

Types of Foundations

Traditional Strip. This is the most usual variety and consists of concrete say 9 in. thick laid at the bottom of a trench 3 ft deep. The width that the concrete extends beyond the faces of the wall depends upon the bearing ability of the soil. Model By-laws lay down that where the load is $\frac{3}{4}$ tons

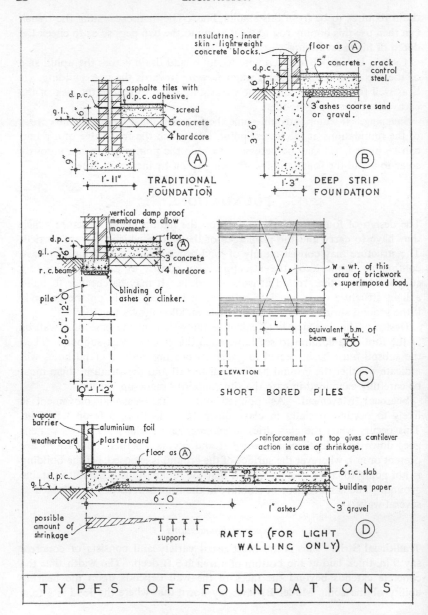

(A) TRADITIONAL FOUNDATION

- d.p.c.
- asphalte tiles with d.p.c. adhesive.
- screed
- 5" concrete
- 4" hardcore
- g.l.
- 6"
- 9"
- 1'-11"

(B) DEEP STRIP FOUNDATION

- Insulating · inner skin · lightweight concrete blocks.
- floor as (A)
- d.p.c.
- g.l.
- 6"
- 5" concrete · crack control steel.
- 3" ashes coarse sand or gravel.
- 3'-6"
- 1'-3"

(C) SHORT BORED PILES

- vertical damp proof membrane to allow movement.
- d.p.c.
- g.l.
- 6"
- floor as (A)
- r.c. beam
- 3" concrete
- 4" hardcore
- blinding of ashes or clinker.
- pile
- 8'-0" – 12'-0"
- 10" – 1'-2"
- W = wt. of this area of brickwork + superimposed load.
- L
- equivalent b.m. of beam = $\frac{W.L.}{100}$
- ELEVATION

(D) RAFTS (FOR LIGHT WALLING ONLY)

- vapour barrier
- aluminium foil
- weatherboard
- plasterboard
- floor as (A)
- d.p.c.
- g.l.
- reinforcement at top gives cantilever action in case of shrinkage.
- 6" r.c. slab
- building paper
- 6'-0"
- 1" ashes
- 3" gravel
- possible amount of shrinkage
- support

TYPES OF FOUNDATIONS

per foot run, the width of the foundation may be the same as that of the wall; where the load is 1½ tons per foot run, the projection may be 3½ in. on each side and the thickness of the concrete 6 in. These dimensions apply to building on stiff clay. The brick walls are built from this concrete strip, and in the case of a cavity wall, the cavity is filled with concrete to ground level.

It is good concrete practice to put a layer of building paper in the trench before pouring the concrete so that the cement is not washed out into the ground and inferior concrete produced as a result. In clay sites the concrete must be poured immediately after the trench is dug so that the clay has no opportunity to dry out and cause movement trouble later on. The bottoms of the trenches must be sound and all soft patches must be cut out and filled with concrete. Where the bottoms are changeable, i.e. varying from, say, gravel to clay, or to shale, it is often advisable to thicken the footings and to include some steel reinforcement in them (A, page 22).

Deep Strip Foundations.* This method is particularly recommended in areas of firm shrinkable clay. For the normal two-storey house a trench of 15 in. in width is all that is required. This is most satisfactorily achieved by machine. The depth of the external wall footings should preferably be 3 ft 6 in. Footings under internal walls should not be less than 24 in. deep and 15 in. wide. If the floors are not suspended timber, and there is a 6 in. thickness of oversite concrete, then the internal walls may be supported directly on this concrete. This oversite concrete should be reinforced with chicken wire or other light steel mesh to reduce cracking (B, page 22).

Short Bored Piles.† These consist of auger holes in the clay, at strategic points, which are filled with concrete. Their tops are joined by a shallow beam, cast in a shallow trench, upon which the walls are built. It is an economic and effective method, but it cannot be used where the clay contains boulders which may interrupt the passage of the auger. It is a clean method on the site; it saves a considerable amount of concrete and produces stable foundations. Where there are boulders and tree roots in the ground, strip foundations are a better solution.

For small jobs a hand auger may be used. It is advisable to choose the larger-sized augers, as these will pass small stones more easily than the small augers. The spoil from the auger should be emptied straight into a wheelbarrow so avoiding spoil heaps and double-handling of the spoil. Where the site warrants it, a mechanical auger mounted on the back of a lorry should be employed. The concreting team should follow directly behind the auger.

* See *Building Research Station Digest*, No. 3.
† See *Building Research Station Digest*, No. 42.

Their first job is to tamp a little dry concrete mix into the bottom of the hole and then to fill the hole up with 1 : 2 : 4 concrete. (This will be described in the chapter on concrete.)

The concrete must be carefully tamped as the hole is filled up so that no gaps are left. Soil must not fall into the hole as the concrete is poured in. It is advisable to arrange that the concreting team is able to cast sufficient concrete to fill all the holes that have been augered in the course of the day's work.

The holes are bored to a depth of 8 to 12 ft as follows:

LOAD BEARING CAPACITY AND LENGTH OF PILES

Strength classification	Diameter of pile (in.)	Length of pile (ft)			
		6* ft	8 ft	10 ft	12 ft
Firm at 2 ft and stiff at 8 ft .	10	2 tons	4 tons	5 tons	5 tons
	12	3 tons	5 tons	6 tons	7 tons
	14	4 tons	6 tons	7 tons	8 tons
Stiff at 2 ft and hard at 8 ft .	10	4 tons	6 tons	8 tons	—
	12	5 tons	7 tons	9 tons	—
	14	6 tons	9 tons	11 tons	—

* *Note.*—6 ft piles are advised only for internal situations given adequate shelter by a solid concrete floor or the oversite concrete.

When all the piles have been cast, then shallow trenches 6 in. deep and 1 ft wide are dug between the pile heads, under where the walls are to be built. Concrete with light steel reinforcement is then placed in these trenches to form the foundations for the wall. These are called ground beams. Corner piles should have several 4 ft lengths of ¾ in. reinforcing rod set half into their tops, and bent over in the direction of the ground beams. The walls are built direct on to the ground beams.†

† Where openings in walls are near the supports the bending moment used in the design of the beams may be taken as $\frac{WL}{50}$; where there are no openings, or openings are the centre of the span, the bending moment may be taken as $\frac{WL}{100}$. Where W is the weight of the rectangle of brickwork immediately above the beam, plus the superimposed loads on the span. When these ' equivalent bending ' moments are used, the ratio of depth beam to span must lie between $\frac{1}{15}$th and $\frac{1}{20}$th. Do not stress the steel more than 7 tons per sq. in. The reinforcement should have an inch of cover and top reinforcement should be placed 1 in. below the upper surface of the concrete immediately above the pile heads and extending each side as far as the quarter span points.

Where doors occur at the end of the span, shear reinforcement is necessary.

This method should only be used with the 'firm' or 'stiff' class of clays unless there is special information available concerning softer clays (C, page 22).

Bases. Point loads from columns at widely separated intervals are usually carried on bases. For these it is necessary to excavate to stable ground where a rectangular concrete base suitably reinforced is cast of a size sufficient to carry the load; e.g. if a column transmits a load of 6 tons and the ground is only capable of carrying $\frac{1}{2}$ ton per sq. ft, a base of 12 sq. ft will be necessary. If the columns are of concrete they bear on to the base in a variety of ways: (a) by being cast as part of the base; (b) by being grouted into a hole formed in the base; (c) bearing on to a steel plate cast at the foot of the column. This may be bolted into the concrete base.

If the column is of steel, a thick metal plate or bloom base is welded or riveted to its foot, which in turn is bolted to the concrete base.

Timber. It is inadvisable to cast timber into concrete bases, e.g. posts, or timber frames for houses, etc. Unless the timber has been very thoroughly treated with a preservative, the centre of the timber member will eventually rot. It is, therefore, advisable to cast in metal support stub columns to which the timber members can be fixed out of contact with the ground.

Rafts. Where the ground is very soft, as in the case of made-up ground, or where the structure is a light one, e.g. a timber house, raft foundations in reinforced concrete are often an economical solution to the foundation problem.

For a light single-storey timber building, one method is to put down a blinding layer of ashes followed by a 3 in. layer of gravel. Over this is spread building paper; and over the general body of the raft a layer of light reinforcing steel fabric is placed to prevent cracking and to distribute any stresses that may build up. Under load-bearing partitions an extra band of reinforcement is placed an inch from the bottom surface of the slab. The margin to the edge of the raft is provided with a 6 ft wide band of heavy reinforcement near the surface so that if the ground under the 3 ft outer edge of the raft shrinks back in summer, the raft will not crack. It is also usual to turn the edge of the raft down to contain the gravel and, if necessary, to keep the edge below the varying ground line (D, page 22).

4

Concrete

In this chapter consideration will be given to making, placing, and some of the more common applications.

MAKING CONCRETE *

When concrete sets, complicated chemical reactions take place. If the components of the mix are not present in the correct proportions many things can go wrong: the chemical reactions may not take place properly; there may be too much water present, producing voids; there may be impurities which may spoil the reaction or prevent proper adhesion of the particles, or there may be insufficient fine material to fill in the spaces formed by the coarse material—in other words bad grading.

It is important, therefore, that concrete should be mixed properly, the ingredients being properly measured in accordance with a designed specification.

Designing the Mix. Generally speaking, the less cement there is, the weaker the concrete will be. There must be sufficient cement to cover the particles of the aggregates throughout the mix. In a given volume of aggregate, the finer the aggregate the larger the total surface area. Thus a mix containing an unusual amount of very fine aggregate will require a large amount of cement to produce concrete of equivalent strength.

It is usual to specify a concrete mix by stating the proportions of cement to fine aggregate to coarse aggregate; e.g. 1 : 1½ : 3 or 1 : 2 : 4 or 1 : 3 : 6, etc. A 1 : 1½ : 3 mix is an unusually strong one, whilst a 1 : 2 : 4 mix is frequently used for normal reinforced concrete. A 1 : 3 : 6 mix is often used for mass concrete used in filling rather than for beams or stanchions, etc. It is also important when specifying a mix to mention the water cement ratio required and to take into account the fact that sand bulks when it is damp. When the aggregates are measured out by volume, additional sand must be added in some cases to allow for this bulking.

Cement. B.S. No. 12 covers cements in normal use such as Normal Portland Cement and Rapid Hardening Portland Cement. It is sometimes necessary to specify special cements; for instance, ones which do not

* See *Building Research Station Digest*, No. 44.

generate much heat when setting, for very large concrete structures which may be adversely affected by this; or cements which resist the presence of sulphates in the ground.*

The cement should be stored on a damp-proof floor in the dry and should not be stored for long periods of time. Eventually cement will harden as a result of the action of the moisture in the air. This is known as air-hardening. Lumps of air-hardened cement should not be harder than can easily be broken between the thumb and forefinger. Otherwise it should be discarded.

Aggregates. There are many varieties of suitable aggregates. For example: sand, gravel, limestone chips, and other crushed rocks. When used for concrete they should be free of clay and silt and impurities such as acids or alkalies. The coarse aggregate should have strong particles and should be considerably smaller than the size of any reinforcing mesh which is to be incorporated in the mix. A typical specification would be 1 of cement to 2 of a specified sand; 4 of ¾ in. to ¼ in. limestone chippings by volume. A sand with a large proportion of fine dust in it will be wasteful in cement.

The grading of aggregates is very important. This refers to the ability of the fine aggregate to fill entirely the spaces between the larger lumps of coarse aggregate. It is not good to have too much fine aggregate, otherwise, once again, the cement will be wasted in covering the unnecessarily large surface area of the ' surplus ' fine aggregate.†

The shape of the particles in the aggregate affects the workability but not the strength of the mix. The rounder the particle the easier it is to compact the mix. A rough test as to whether there are any impurities in the aggregates is to place a sample of the aggregate in a beaker of water and to shake up and then allow to settle. The impurities will separate out.

The mixing water will be satisfactory if it is potable, that is to say if it is drinking water.‡

If there is any doubt a test may be carried out using the proposed water supply by making a standard mix with it and comparing the setting time to a similar mix made with pure water.

Quantity of Water. (Water : cement ratio.) Of equal importance to the proportions of the mix is the proportion of water in the mix. The graph indicates the relationship between the crushing strength and the water/cement

* Presence of sulphates in ground-waters or in clay can be very damaging over a period of time to concrete structures, and it is as well to have the ground-water analysed before cement is specified. See *Building Research Station Digest*, No. 31.

† B.S. No. 882 specifies the method in which the grading of aggregates should be carried out.

‡ See p. 4 of *Building Research Station Digest*, No. 90, entitled ' Analysis of Water Used or Encountered in Construction '.

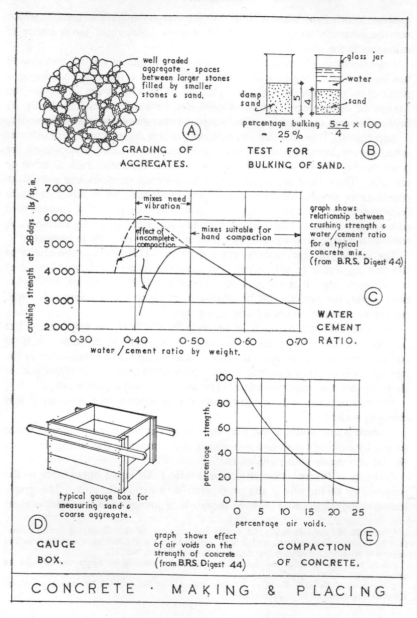

well graded aggregate - spaces between larger stones filled by smaller stones & sand.

(A) GRADING OF AGGREGATES.

glass jar
water
damp sand
sand

percentage bulking $\frac{5-4}{4} \times 100$ = 25%

(B) TEST FOR BULKING OF SAND.

mixes need vibration
effect of incomplete compaction
mixes suitable for hand compaction

crushing strength at 28 days . lbs/sq. in.
7000 6000 5000 4000 3000 2000
0·30 0·40 0·50 0·60 0·70
water/cement ratio by weight.

graph shows relationship between crushing strength & water/cement ratio for a typical concrete mix. (from B.R.S. Digest 44)

(C) WATER CEMENT RATIO.

typical gauge box for measuring sand & coarse aggregate.

(D) GAUGE BOX.

percentage strength.
100 80 60 40 20 0
0 5 10 15 20 25
percentage air voids.

graph shows effect of air voids on the strength of concrete (from B.R.S. Digest 44)

(E) COMPACTION OF CONCRETE.

CONCRETE · MAKING & PLACING

ratio for a typical 1 : 2 concrete mix.   Notice that where the water/cement
ratio increases above 0·50 the strength falls off rapidly.   The ratio is worked
out as follows:

$$\text{The water : cement ratio} = \frac{\text{Weight of water in the mix}}{\text{Weight of cement in the mix.}}$$

For example, a concrete mix containing 112 lb cement and total water
content of 5½ gals (approximately 56 lb) has a water cement ratio of 56 : 112
which equals 0·50.

Another vital factor closely allied to the water content is the method of
compaction.   If the mix is compacted by hand, the minimum water : cement
ratio of 1 : 2 : 4 mix is 0·50.   If the mix is compacted by mechanical vibration, greater strengths are obtainable by using a lower water : cement ratio,
i.e. 0·40.

The strength of the concrete is usually measured by testing its crushing
strength.   On important concreting jobs the contractor is requested to make
test cubes of a standard size at specified intervals, and these are tested in a
crushing machine, either seven or twenty-eight days after mixing.

Concrete which is too wet has an additional disadvantage that when it is
being placed, a slurry of cement and water will rise to the surface or seep
through the joints in the formwork, thus depriving the bulk of the mix of
cement, and thereby producing weakness.   This cement-rich slurry dries to
form a cement-rich skin which is in itself weak, and must be removed before
subsequent mixes are placed against it.

The amount of cement in the mix also affects the ease of working;   the
richer the mix the easier it is to compact.

A good rule is that the best concrete is made from the *driest mix that can
be fully compacted with the means available on the job.*

Measuring Materials.   It is not satisfactory to measure the materials by
counting the number of shovelfuls.   Shovelfuls differ very widely and will
vary according to the operative, the size of the shovel, the moisture content
of the aggregate, the shape of the particles, and other factors.   Measuring
by the shovel only is bound to cause either a waste of cement or insufficiently
strong concrete.   The following are the alternatives:

Gauge Boxes.   Gauge boxes have four handles, sides, but no bottom or
top.   They are placed on the mixing surface which should be hard and
clean.   They are filled and struck off level.   The box is then lifted by means
of the handles, and the resulting accurately-measured pile of aggregate is
shovelled into the mixer.   The size of the gauge box is calculated from the
mix specified, e.g. if a 1 : 2 : 4 mix is required the hundredweight bag of

cement is used complete (never divide bags of cement as a general rule). Cement occupies 1¼ cu. ft per bag, therefore a gauge box for 2½ cu. ft of sand will be required, and another box for 5 cu. ft of coarse aggregate. The volume of the coarse aggregate will not change according to its moisture content appreciably, but sand will bulk when damp.*

Cement is frequently wasted when the bulking test for sand is not made.

Mixing Machines with Hoppers may have adjustable divisions in the hopper so that it acts as a gauge box. It is not sufficient to heap the aggregate in the hopper on each side of the division, but the aggregate must be struck off level each time, so that accurate measurement is made. The larger machines have cisterns for water, which must be tested from time to time to see that they deliver the correct amount. Larger construction jobs will warrant the use of a Weigh-Batcher. In this method the weights of the appropriate volumes of material must be calculated each day to take account of the water content of the aggregates.

Mixing. When mixing by shovel only, it is necessary to ' turn over ' the materials together dry a couple of times before the water is added. It is then necessary to mix the wet materials thoroughly so that the cement is completely incorporated with the aggregates.

When mixing by machine, the mixer should not be going too fast, mixing time being about two minutes. The water, if the mixer is not equipped with a cistern, should be added through a watering can fitted with a rose. Add some of the coarse aggregates first in each new batch so that the drum is kept clear from clogging. Clean the mixer out thoroughly at the end of each day's work.

Transporting the Mixed Concrete. The mixer site should be as close as possible to the job. If barrowing has to be undertaken, barrows or carts with pneumatic tyres should be used, so that unnecessary vibration does not cause the ' laitence ' to come to the surface. Concrete may be conveyed by shute, but it must not be dropped from a height, otherwise this will cause the separation of the constituents. Concrete may also be pumped, and on larger jobs this is an effective way of moving concrete from a central mixing plant.

In the larger cities it is possible to purchase concrete already mixed to

---

* The bulking test should be made as follows: In a straight sided glass jar place a quantity of the sand. Level it *lightly*, measure its height. Pour water into the jar and stir. Allow to settle and then measure the height of the sand under the water. The difference between the two measurements expressed as a percentage indicates the percentage bulking: e.g. ' Damp ' Measurement = 5 in.; ' Submerged ' Measurement = 4 in.; Difference = 1 in.; then $\frac{1}{4} \times 100 = 25\%$. From this it will be seen that an extension to the sand gauge box will be required increasing its volume by 25%.

your specification by a mixer lorry, which delivers the concrete straight to the job. When this method is used it is important that the site can be approached by good roads, as the lorries are heavy and are liable to churn up the site.

Placing. Concrete must be placed immediately after mixing. Do not add water to the mix in order to make it easier to compact. Wherever possible use mechanical vibrators to ensure proper compaction and the elimination of voids. Where this is not possible, tamp by thoroughly rodding, especially round reinforcement and in awkward corners. Once the voids have been removed stop tamping or vibrating, otherwise segregation may occur and laitence will appear on the surface. This indicates a weakening of the concrete.

Construction Joints. The first operation at the beginning of the day is to remove any hardened laitence off the previous day's concreting. Thoroughly roughen the surface and dust off, then paint on some cement grout to receive the new mix. If this is not done a weak joint will result.*

Curing. Concrete which dries too quickly does not develop its full strength. Green concrete should be kept moist by protecting it from drying winds or the sun with canvas, straw, or sawdust which is kept watered. Continue protection for three days.

Concreting in Cold Weather †

Temperature affects speed of setting. Cold weather slows setting speed down. If the water in the concrete freezes, it will expand and break up the concrete, that is, if it is in the process of setting. In cold weather a thermometer must be kept on the site so that the danger of freezing can always be avoided.

Two types of cement are useful in cold weather. One is rapid hardening cement which reduces the setting time during which the concrete can be damaged by frost. The other is high alumina cement, which not only develops strength rapidly, but produces a lot of heat at the same time. In any case, concrete should be kept covered up to keep the heat in. Do not mix high alumina cement with any other type of Portland cement. One possible disadvantage of using high alumina cement is that the additional heat that it produces in setting may cause undue expansion in bulky sections causing cracking.

In order to reduce the amount of time when frost precautions have to be taken with concrete, the setting time may be speeded up by the addition of 2% by weight of calcium chloride to the mix (that is; 2–2½ lb to 1 cwt bag

* Excellent advice on making good concrete is given in *Ministry of Works Advisory Leaflet*, No. 26, ' Making Concrete '.
† See *Ministry of Works Advisory Leaflet*, No. 7.

of cement)*. Do not use with high alumina cement. Do not use less than this or there will be little effect, if you use too much the concrete will set too quickly. Mix the calcium chloride with water before adding by putting 1 cwt into 23 gallons of water through a sieve; 4–5 pints of this solution will then be necessary for each hundredweight bag of cement. (Make sure that all the calcium chloride has been dissolved.)

When the concrete has been placed, insulate against cold winds and from the night sky by clean straw, timber shuttering, several layers of building paper, dry sacks, but not by corrugated iron.

It is usually safe to concrete when the thermometer reads 38° F. Stop if the temperature starts to drop. If the morning temperature reaches 34° F. and the thermometer rises, concreting may be started, but should be stopped if 38° F. is not reached by midday. Take antifrost precautions directly concreting stops.

Heaps of aggregate on the site may freeze and may have to be thawed out with steam hoses; a common fault is to assume that a pile of aggregate is frost free when in fact only the surface has thawed and much frozen material remains inside.†

Piles of aggregate on the site should be kept covered with tarpaulins or other insulating material, in severe conditions the mixing water may be warmed so that the temperature in the mixer is not above 70° F. (over 100° F. there is risk of a flash set). The mixing water can therefore be heated to 120° F. so long as the mix has cooled below 100° F. before the cement is added in the mixer.

Concreting Paper. Wherever concrete comes in contact with the ground, place subsoil grade building paper on the ground so that the cement content of the mix cannot wash away into the ground.

Formwork. The formwork whether it is of timber or steel should be supported sufficiently frequently that it does not sag or distort under the weight of the wet concrete. Formwork should be painted, before the cement is poured, with mould oil to prevent the concrete adhering to it. Formwork should be cleaned thoroughly before use so that the face of the concrete is not defaced with unnecessary pits and pockets. In special cases the formwork can be faced with material to produce a decorative texture on the struck face. This can be done with moulded rubber to form numerous patterns, the rubber being pulled back from the face when the concrete has set sufficiently.

* A flake form of calcium chloride may be used added dry to the aggregate (*not* to the cement).

† See *National Building Studies Bulletin*, No. 3. ' Concreting and Bricklaying in Cold Weather ' (H.M.S.O., 6d.).

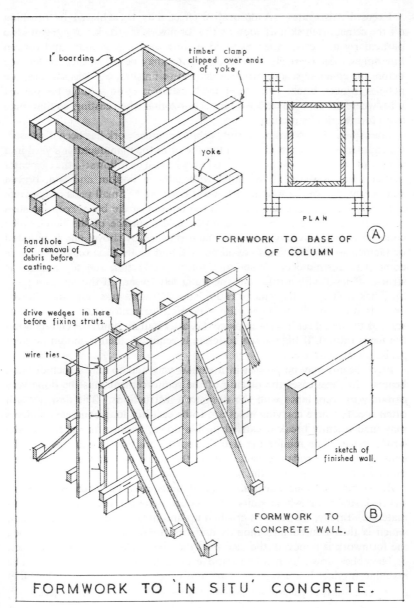

1" boarding

timber clamp
clipped over ends
of yoke

yoke

handhole
for removal of
debris before
casting.

PLAN

FORMWORK TO BASE OF (A)
OF COLUMN

drive wedges in here
before fixing struts.

wire ties

sketch of
finished wall.

FORMWORK TO (B)
CONCRETE WALL.

FORMWORK TO 'IN SITU' CONCRETE.

Exposed Aggregates. A decorative effect may be achieved by brushing off the cement-rich skin as soon as the formwork is struck. Aggregates are particularly attractive when exposed in this way, e.g. granite, and certain limestones. Alternatively, special aggregates may be rolled into the surface before the concrete sets to produce decorative finishes, e.g. washed seashore pebbles, broken brick. This ' applied ' texture is more suitable for precast units where the exposed textured face is horizontal when casting, so that there is no formwork obstruction.

Precasting. Up to this point only *in situ* concrete work has been discussed. Concrete may be precast either on the site or in the manufacturer's yard in a variety of ways. For example, a lintel may be cast as follows:—the carpenter makes a box the size of the lintel with sides, a bottom and end, braced sufficiently to take the weight of the wet concrete.* Small pads of concrete are cast 1 in. thick and are placed in the bottom of the box; keep the steel reinforcing bars 1 in. from the exposed under surface of the lintel. The concrete is then carefully placed in the formwork by shovel and is vibrated or tamped so that the voids are eliminated and so that the reinforcement is completely surrounded. When the formwork is full, the top surface is struck off level with a rule, and the lintel left to set. If the mix is a good one, has a 40% water/cement ratio, and vibrators are used, and if the lintel is not too big, it is sometimes possible to remove the formwork as soon as the initial set has taken place (i.e. after half an hour, depending upon the temperature). If high-grade concrete is required, then it should be kept moist for at least a week.

Floor beams may be precast in a similar way and so may stanchions and beams. In these cases the placing of the reinforcement must be done very carefully in accordance with the designer's instructions. The designer will often specify where carrying holes are to be cast-in; long concrete members may inadvertently break if carried upside down, because the steel is in the wrong place. The reinforcing steel is kept in position by stirrups and the ends of the main rods are bent over in the shape of ' standard hooks ' so that they cannot slip when the member is loaded.

Reconstructed Stone Facings. Precast units may be faced with reconstructed stone, or whole units may be constructed complete from this material. Briefly, the stone is crushed up and mixed with coloured cement, which is then poured into moulds and cast to the desired shape. When the formwork is removed, the face may then be treated with abrasive discs, or be rubbed down by hand to remove the cement-rich surface skin. The resulting product has a very even texture which some consider to be ' life-

---

* The box may be painted with mould oil to prevent the concrete from sticking.

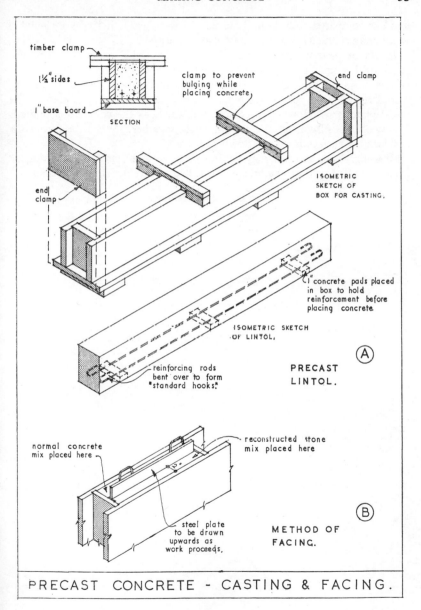

timber clamp

1¼" sides

1" base board

SECTION

clamp to prevent
bulging while
placing concrete

end clamp

ISOMETRIC
SKETCH OF
BOX FOR CASTING.

end
clamp

1" concrete pads placed
in box to hold
reinforcement before
placing concrete

ISOMETRIC SKETCH
OF LINTOL.

reinforcing rods
bent over to form
"standard hooks."

(A)

PRECAST
LINTOL.

normal concrete
mix placed here

reconstructed stone
mix placed here

steel plate
to be drawn
upwards as
work proceeds.

(B)

METHOD OF
FACING.

PRECAST CONCRETE - CASTING & FACING.

less ' as compared with natural stone. In some cases it has more reliable weathering characteristics and may also be cheaper.

In situ or precast concrete may be faced with this material as follows. A removable metal plate is placed in the formwork say 2 in. from its exposed surface. As the normal concrete is poured in the bulk of the formwork, reconstructed stone concrete is placed in the front of the metal plate. The metal plate is withdrawn progressively upwards as the concrete is poured. The two types of concrete bond completely together. When the formwork is struck the surface is rubbed down as before.

Dressing. New concrete may be dressed at various stages of its setting by mason's tools,* or it can be brushed or rolled to produce unique finishes.

* See chapter on Masonry.

5

Walling

THE FUNCTIONS OF THE WALL

WHEN designing a wall, many factors should be taken into consideration, such as durability and composition, strength and stability, exclusion of rain, heat insulation, changes in volume under changing conditions of temperature and moisture content, fire resistance, sound insulation and appearance.*

There are many materials from which walls can be made, e.g. brick, stone, concrete, enamelled steel panels, forms of asbestos, etc. The wall may carry loads from floors and roofs, or it may be an in-filling—steel or concrete stanchions (posts) carrying the loads.

Durability. This must be judged in relation to the expected life of the building and capital cost. For example, certain bricks and stones may last for many centuries with little maintenance, whereas painted panels may need repainting every few years. Many walling materials are covered by British Standard Specifications. It is therefore wise to make sure that proposed materials are up to these standards.

In general the durability of walling materials depends upon mechanical strength, chemical composition and pore structure.

Frost. The degree with which a walling material may be saturated with water is a partial indication as to its resistance to frost. As important is the structure of the material, i.e. whether the pores are isolated from one another or whether the texture is ' lamina '—the latter often being prone to frost failure. The parts of the wall most liable to frost damage are those which are liable to be saturated with water and exposed to freezing, for instance, below the damp-course and in parapets. Elementary tests may be made in a refrigerator by freezing and thawing samples many times, but it is always best to examine similar materials that have been used in buildings for a number of years (see Table 1, p. 38).

Solubility. Most common walling materials are insoluble, but some renderings, for example gypsum plasters, are slightly soluble and should not be used externally.

* These factors are dealt with in detail in *Principles of Modern Building*, Vol. I, published by H.M.S.O. and in *Building Research Station Digest*, No. 25, ' The Selection of Clay Building Bricks '.

TABLE 1

SUSCEPTIBILITY OF MATERIALS TO DETERIORATION AS THE RESULT OF FROST ACTION

Class of material	How affected
Natural stone	Variable. Best stones unaffected. Some stones with pronounced cleavage along bedding planes are unsuitable for copings or cornices.
Bricks and clayware generally	Generally highly resistant. Certain products made by extrusion processes may develop lamina structure when the manufacturing conditions are badly adjusted.
Cast-stone and concrete	Material of good quality is rarely affected.

Note.—Any material having a lamina structure is liable to deterioration.

TABLE 2

SUSCEPTIBILITY OF MATERIALS TO ATTACK BY ACID GASES IN POLLUTED ATMOSPHERES

Class of material	How affected
Clay bricks and blocks	Rarely affected, but may retain soot.
Terra-cotta	Rarely affected.
Siliceous sandstones	Rarely affected, but retain soot.
Cast-stone and Portland cement concrete	Only slightly affected. Dense mixes desirable for high degree of pollution.
Sand-lime bricks Limestones	Very slightly affected. All attacked to some extent. The more durable stones have a long life in the worst environment. Care needed in selection.
Calcareous sandstones	Liable to be badly attacked.

Acid Attack. In industrial atmospheres containing sulphur gases from solid fuels and oil burning, very dilute sulphuric acid forms in the rain and will attack limestones, sand-lime bricks and some concretes (see Table 2).

Crystallisation of Salts in the Pores. ' Acid ' rain may take into solution certain salts present in the walling material (usually calcium sulphate) which may crystallise out in the pores of the material in fine weather. When this occurs *behind* the surface of the wall, the surface may be pushed away from the main part of the wall * (see Table 3).

Often parts of the wall which are most sheltered suffer most severely as elsewhere the rain tends to wash out the crystallised salts. The calcium sulphate may be washed from limestone walling into brickwork underneath and disrupt the brickwork. Similarly, it may be washed out of the mortar. Sandstone may also be affected by adjacent limestone.

TABLE 3

SUSCEPTIBILITY OF MATERIALS TO DETERIORATION DUE TO
CRYSTALLISATION OF SOLUBLE SALTS

Class of material	How affected
Clay bricks	Good bricks rarely affected. Under-fired bricks may be badly attacked.
Terra-cotta	Rarely affected.
Sand-lime bricks Cast-stone and Portland cement concrete	Good bricks rarely affected.
Sandstones	Rarely affected. Vary very much in resistance. The best stones are excellent.
Limestones	Vary very much in resistance.

Note.—Decay of a moderate or poor brick or stone may be much accelerated by the use of impervious mortar for pointing. Salts may be washed from a limestone or concrete into sandstone or brick and lead to decay.

These three tables are from *Principles of Modern Building*, Vol. I, published by H.M.S.O.

Strength and Stability. Building by-laws lay down maximum widths and heights for various thicknesses of walling. These are rule of thumb methods for determining the thickness of the wall for safety. Invariably economies in material and an increase in efficiency can be achieved if the wall is designed in relation to its function and the characteristics of the proposed materials.

The loads may come squarely on to the top of a wall or they may be concentrated along one edge, i.e. eccentrically. It will be seen that the taller a wall is and the greater the eccentricity of the loading, the more likely the

* Sometimes called exfoliation. The salts may crystallise on the surface producing the unsightly whitish efflorescence which may be washed off in time by rain.

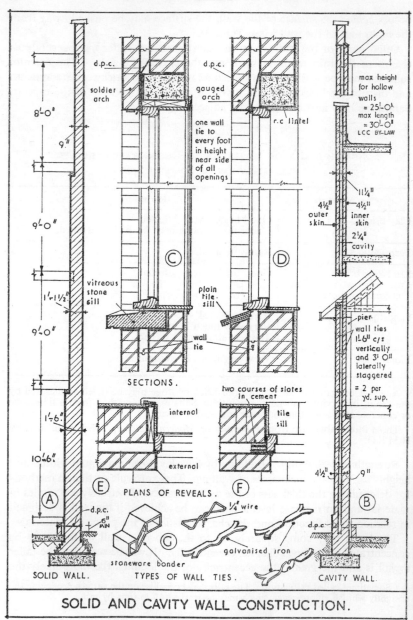

8'-0"

9."

9'-0"

vitreous stone sill

1'-1½"

9'-0"

1'-6"

10'-6"

d.p.c.
6"
MIN

SOLID WALL.

A

d.p.c.
soldier arch

gauged arch

d.p.c.

r.c lintel

one wall tie to every foot in height near side of all openings

C

plain tile sill

D

wall tie

SECTIONS.

internal

two courses of slates in cement

tile sill

external

E

PLANS OF REVEALS.

F

stoneware bonder

G

¼" wire

galvanised iron

TYPES OF WALL TIES.

max height for hollow walls = 25'-0"
max length = 30'-0"
LCC BY-LAW

11¼"

4½"
outer skin

4½"
inner skin

2¼"
cavity

pier.

wall ties 1'-6" c/s vertically and 3'-0" laterally staggered = 2 per yd. sup.

4½"

9"

d.p.c.

B

CAVITY WALL.

SOLID AND CAVITY WALL CONSTRUCTION.

wall will fail by buckling. Floors may help to support the walls and reduce their effective height so that their thickness may be reduced and economy achieved.

Weather Resistance. This is affected by the degree of exposure of the wall. If it faces south-west and there are no overhangs the wall is likely to get very wet at certain times of the year. A common form of providing a wall with ability to resist weather penetration is to build the wall with a cavity, i.e. in two leaves. Care is then taken that no water can find its way from the wet outer leaf to the dry inner leaf. Dampness is liable to rise up in the walling material from the ground and this must be prevented by a course of damp-proof material.*

Sometimes the thickness of a wall will determine the amount of moisture that can get through it. ' Sandwich ' construction may be employed where several materials are bonded together with an impervious membrane incorporated to prevent the ingress of moisture. The wall may be rendered or treated with special paints or chemicals, but these are very unlikely to keep the wall free from penetration for any length of time. The material, on the other hand, may be glass or enamelled steel or aluminium which are impervious. Consideration must also be given to the path that water will follow as it washes down the face of the wall.

Heat Insulation. Habitable buildings must almost always be designed so that the four walls and roof lose as little heat as possible during the winter and do not heat up uncomfortably in summer. This particular building problem is only just beginning to have the attention it deserves. All the heat that is lost through a wall in winter has to be paid for.

Invariably, the incorporation of insulation will be paid for by the fuel saved during the first two or three winters. Some materials transmit heat rapidly, e.g. concrete, brick and stone. Others transmit heat very slowly and are therefore good insulators, e.g. lightweight blocks, timber, cork, glass fibres. Insulation may also be affected by the colour of the surfaces, i.e. the way the heat or cold is reflected. (Black absorbs cold or heat readily, white does not.)

A considerable amount of heat is lost through air leakage, that is, by badly fitting doors and windows, and by the draught up flues. Areas of glass (single glazing) are another major source of heat loss.†

Moisture Movement (Drying Shrinkage). Most materials expand slightly when they are wet and shrink when they are dry. This moisture move-

---

* Damp-proof course—D.P.C. (see p. 73).
† Very roughly it may be said that in the average house a third of the heat is lost through the walls, a third through the windows and a third through air leakage.

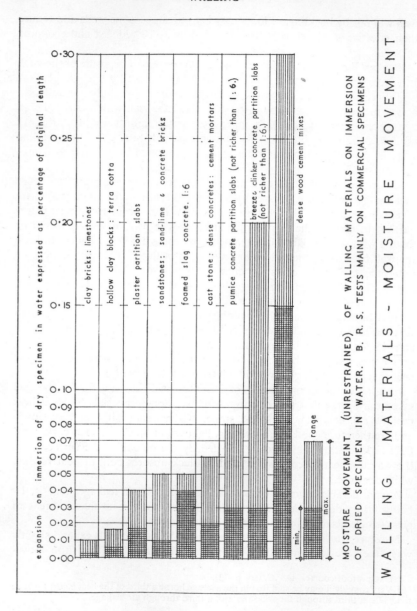

WALLING MATERIALS – MOISTURE MOVEMENT

MOISTURE MOVEMENT. (UNRESTRAINED) OF WALLING MATERIALS ON IMMERSION OF DRIED SPECIMEN IN WATER. B. R. S. TESTS MAINLY ON COMMERCIAL SPECIMENS

ment may cause cracking in renderings or to internal finishings, e.g. plaster.*

TABLE 4

MOISTURE MOVEMENT AND MATERIALS

Materials having very small moisture movements	Well-fired bricks and clay goods. Igneous rocks. Most limestones. Calcium sulphate plasters.
Materials with small moisture movement	Some sand-lime bricks. Some sandstones.
Materials with considerable moisture movement calling for precautions in design and use	Well-proportioned ballast concretes. Cement mortars and renderings. Lime mortars. Concrete bricks and some sand-lime bricks. Some sandstones.
Materials with large moisture movement which call for special precautions in proportioning and handling	Most lightweight concretes.
Materials with large moisture movement calling for special technique of treatment at joints and surrounds	Wood-cement materials. Fibrous slabs and wallboards. Asbestos cement sheeting. Plywoods and timber in direction of the grain.
Materials with very large moisture movement which must be accommodated by allowing freedom for movement in framing up	Timber across the grain. Hard fibrous wallboards.

Note.—Extract from *Principles of Modern Building*, Vol. I, published by H.M.S.O.

Expansion (Thermal). Most building materials expand when the temperature rises and contract again when the temperature falls. If the building is a small one, the total movements caused by the temperature difference between summer and winter may be sufficiently small to be taken up in the structure without any noticeable damage. As a rough guide, for example, concrete roofs over 100 ft long, or walls of brick or stone exposed to the sun over 100 ft long should be provided with expansion joints, so that the expansion and contraction of each section can take place independently.†

* British Standards lay down the maximum ' drying shrinkage ' permissible for many building materials, e.g. B.S. 1257 : 1945—Clay Building Bricks; B.S. 187 : 1942—Sandlime Bricks.
† See ' The Design of Flat and Concrete Roofs in Relation to Thermal Effects,' *Building Research Station Digest*, No. 12.

Condensation. This is a common source of trouble and will occur in a wall or a roof where the temperature of the inside surface falls below the dew point (condensation point) of the air in contact with it. For instance, condensation will form on the inside of the window pane on a cold night when the glass has been chilled to below the dew point of the air in the room.*

If walls (or roofs) are built of materials which can be cooled down easily (i.e. poor insulators) for example 9 in. brickwork or a single leaf of ordinary concrete blocks, the risk of condensation is great.

Cavity walling will overcome some of the trouble, especially if the inner leaf is of an insulating block. However, in panel construction of, for example, a stoved-enamelled steel panel outer-surface, with insulating board stuck to it as the insulator, moisture-carrying air will diffuse through the insulating board, and condensation will take place on the inside surface of the steel, when the steel has been chilled below the dew point of the air. The insulating board will then become soggy and will deteriorate rapidly.† Not only do the surfaces have to be impermeable, but there must be no route by means of cracks and joints where the inside air may find its way to a cold surface.

Great care must be taken to insulate steelwork and metal trim so that condensation cannot occur and cause rust and deterioration within the building structure where maintenance is impossible.

* † This matter is dealt with fully in *National Building Study*, No. 23, published by H.M.S.O.

6

Masonry—Brickwork

Bricks. Bricks are blocks of clay, or shale, moulded to suitable dimensions while in a plastic condition, then burnt to harden and vitrify. There are three types—commons (backing bricks), facings, and engineering bricks. The composition and method of manufacture of many well-known bricks are dealt with in *Advanced Building Construction* (*Structures*).

Brickwork. The art of the bricklayer consists in arranging and bedding bricks in mortar to form a homogeneous mass and to bond them in such a manner that point or other loads and stresses are dispersed and distributed through the mass without tending to disintregrate the structure.

Dimensions of Bricks. Bricks are moulded to standard dimensions which admit of their being laid to a number of regular arrangements to obtain the maximum lap or bond. For this purpose the breadth to length should be approximately in the ratio of one to two. The dimensions are usually such that:

> Length + one mortar joint = 9 in.
> Width + one mortar joint = $4\frac{1}{2}$ in.
> Depth + one mortar joint = 3 in.
> (On average a mortar joint is $\frac{3}{8}$ in. thick.)

As it is not possible to ensure that all bricks when burnt in the kiln will be exactly the same size, a certain tolerance is permitted in the British Standard Specification 657 : 1936.

Frog. In hand-made and machine-pressed bricks, indentations, known as frogs, are formed in the bedding surfaces of the bricks. In the former brick one frog only is formed, in the latter two. The object of the frog is twofold: first, to reduce the weight; secondly, to form a key for the mortar. Frogs are not formed in wire-cut bricks, the method of manufacture renders this impossible.

Instead of frogs, some bricks are perforated from bed surface to bed surface to attain the same advantages.

Normally the frog should be laid downwards, especially if the frog is a deep U-frog. This saves mortar and produces a wall which is well within the requirements of the Third Schedule of the Model Building By-laws, 1952.*

* See *Building Research Station Digest*, No. 71, entitled ' Frog up or Frog Down'.

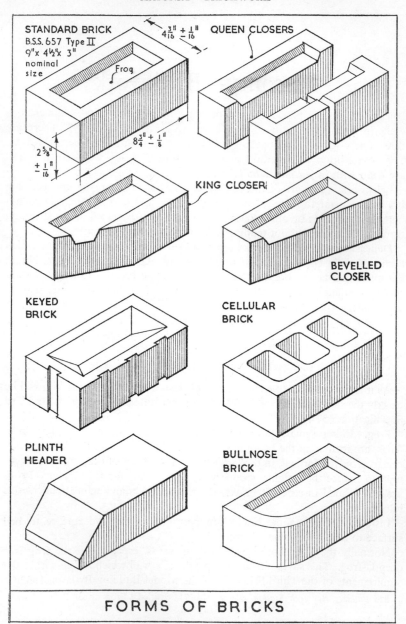

STANDARD BRICK
B.S.S. 657 Type II
9" x 4½" x 3"
nominal size

Frog

$4\frac{3}{16}" + \frac{1}{16}"$

$8\frac{3}{4}" + \frac{1}{8}"$

$2\frac{5}{8}" + \frac{1}{16}"$

QUEEN CLOSERS

KING CLOSER

BEVELLED CLOSER

KEYED BRICK

CELLULAR BRICK

PLINTH HEADER

BULLNOSE BRICK

FORMS OF BRICKS

Bricks laid frog down have no noticeable effect upon rain penetration and, although it reduces sound insulation by virtue of reducing weight slightly, it does in fact also slightly increase the thermal insulation of the wall. The only difficulty here is that bats (half-bricks) cannot be laid easily frog down because the bearing then becomes uneven and must, therefore, be laid frog up.

Course. This is the name given to the row of bricks between two bed joints, and the thickness is taken as one brick plus one mortar joint; in this work, unless otherwise stated, it will be considered as 3 in. or, as technically described, four courses to a foot.

Bed Joints. The mortar joints should always be normal to the pressure:

(*a*) In walls with vertical faces, the bed joints should be horizontal.

(*b*) In battered walls they should be at right angles to the batter.

(*c*) In arches, the joints should be normal to (i.e. at right angles to) the curve of the arch.

Quoins. These are the external corners of walls. The name is sometimes applied to the bricks or stones which form the quoins, e.g. quoin brick, quoin stone.

Perpends. The vertical joints of the face of the wall. In plain walling it is necessary for good bond that these joints in alternate courses should be vertically one above the other.

Stretchers. Bricks laid with their lengths of 9 in. on the face of the wall or parallel to the face of the wall.

Headers. Bricks laid with the width of $4\frac{1}{2}$ in. on the face of the wall or parallel to the face of the wall.

Bats. Pieces of bricks, usually known, according to their fraction of a whole brick, as $\frac{1}{2}$ or $\frac{3}{4}$ bats, or snap headers.

Lap. The horizontal distance between the vertical joints in two successive courses. This should be one-fourth the length of a brick.

Queen Closers. Bricks made the same length and thickness as ordinary bricks, but half the width, placed usually next to the quoin header to obtain the lap. Closers are not usually specially moulded; bricklayers form the closers economically by cutting their broken bricks into $\frac{1}{4}$-brick bats and placing two together to form closers. This is done with the edge of the trowel.

King Closers. Bricks cut so that one end is half the width of the brick. They are used in the construction of reveals to avoid having any face bricks less than $4\frac{1}{2}$ in. on the bed.

Squint Quoins. Bricks cut or moulded to form angles other than right angles in plan. They are cut to show a three-quarter brick on one face and a quarter brick on the return, no closers are then used on the front of the work.

Keyed Brick. The keyed brick is used to provide an effective key for plaster.

Cellular Brick. Is used where it is necessary to lighten the weight of a wall and to increase the thermal insulation. Although, in fact, their use decreases bearing strength slightly, walls built of cellular bricks are usually well within normal strength requirements and their use should be encouraged.

Plinth Bricks. Bricks moulded with a splay or moulding of a projection of $2\frac{1}{4}$ in. and used to form the top member of a projecting plinth.

Bullnose. Bricks moulded with a rounded angle employed to form rounded quoin. The radius for the curve lies on the long centre line of the brick.

Cownose. A double bullnose on end.

MORTAR

Mortar may be defined as a material composed of fine aggregate (say below $\frac{3}{16}$ in. in size), and cementing materials which forms a hardened mass after admixing with a suitable proportion of water. It is used in the beds and side joints of brickwork in order to bind the bricks together, to distribute the pressure throughout the brickwork and, by filling the joints, to increase the heat and sound insulation. Sand is the aggregate commonly used for mortars; but old bricks, burnt ballast, or stones ground in a mortar mill are sometimes used as substitutes. It is doubtful if the shape of the individual grains, whether rounded or angular, has any significant effect upon the quality or strength of the mortar; the essential requirements for a good mortar aggregate are as follows:

(a) The particles should be evenly graded from fine to coarse.

(b) The aggregate should be clean and free from all clay or earthy matter, and from the presence of soluble salts. These last may give rise to efflorescence and dampness in the wall, and for this reason a degree of care should be exercised if either sea sand, ashes and clinker, or bricks contaminated with old plaster are used as an aggregate. The use of a loamy or soft sand to increase workability and plasticity produces an inferior and weak mortar, and should never be permitted.

The cementing material used in brickwork or masonry may be either Portland cement or lime or a mixture of the two. The constituents of all mortars should be mixed thoroughly to ensure uniformity of composition. Thorough mixing should entail turning over twice dry and twice wet if hand mixed. Mixing proportions for mortars given below are by volume.

The strongest mortar is obtained when the whole of the voids are completely filled with the cementing material, and this condition will generally be obtained with a well-graded aggregate when the ratio of cementing material to aggregate is about 1 : 2–3. Strong mortar is not always necessary, and may be detrimental. It is advisable that the strength of the mortar should be slightly less than the strength of the bricks. Limes and cements, their characteristics and properties, and the mixing of mortars, are dealt with in Mitchell's *Advanced Building Construction* (*Structures*).

Cement Mortar. The ratio of Portland cement to sand often adopted is 1 : 3. This is suitable only for the strongest engineering bricks. As the setting action commences soon after wetting, the mortar should be used at once; any subsequent disturbance will greatly reduce the strength. Cement mortar should never be retempered and, if not used within two hours of the addition of the water, should be discarded.

Cement-Lime Mortars (or Gauged Mortar). Suitable proportions for cement-lime mortars vary according to conditions and requirements from 1 : 1 : 6 to 1 : 3 : 12, cement : lime : aggregate. A 1 : 1 : 6 mix should be suitable for use under most conditions of severe exposure and is a near equivalent to Roman cement. Mixes containing a larger proportion of lime become progressively more liable to suffer damage from frost and exposure; although the workability and plasticity of the mortar increases with the increase of lime content. A 1 : 2 : 9 mix should be suitable for all normal work except under conditions of severe exposure; but a 1 : 3 : 12 mix should be used for internal work only. As with cement mortar, cement-lime mortar should never be retempered and, if not used within two hours of the wetting of the cement, should be discarded.

Mortar with Plasticiser. It is often an advantage to use a proprietary plasticiser with the cement and the sand instead of using lime. Its effect is to increase the ' wetting ' of the cement particles, increasing the effectiveness of the cement, permitting a weaker mix and improving the workability of the mix. It also tends to entrain air bubbles in the mix, making the mortar more elastic when set, reducing cracking. The recommended mixes vary, but an average is one part of cement to six parts of sand plus the amount of plasticiser (usually added to the mixing water) recommended by the manufacturer.

Wetting of Bricks. The presence of water in mortar is necessary for the setting action to take place; precautions should therefore be taken to prevent the work drying too quickly; as a means to this end, especially in hot weather, all the bricks should be saturated before bedding, except during frost, to prevent them absorbing the moisture from the mortar, and also to remove all loose dust from the surfaces that are to be in contact with the mortar.

Brickwork which has not been thoroughly wetted can be detected by a thin crack between the brick and the mortar joint. Such work should be pulled down and rebuilt.

Building During Frosty Weather. All brickwork should be suspended during frosty weather (below 37° F.) unless adequately protected, as stability is endangered by the disintegration of the mortar by the frost while it is wet. When the work is urgently required it can be carried up in the intervals between the frost; but all the freshly built portions should be carefully covered and protected on any recurrence of the frost, and always during the suspension of work for the night.*

Bedding of Bricks. Great care should be taken when bedding bricks that both the bed and side joints are thoroughly flushed, or filled up with mortar. This is done in three ways: (1) by the trowel; (2) by larrying; (3) by grouting. The first method is that usually adopted in all thin walls. The second, larrying, is largely adopted in thick walls. The face bricks are first laid upon a bed of mortar; the mortar, in a semi-fluid condition, is then poured in the space between the face bricks; the bricks are then pushed rapidly horizontally for a short distance into their position; a certain amount of the mortar is thus displaced, this rises in the side joints, and completely fills all the interstices; should the mortar not rise to the top of the joints, the vacant spaces are filled up when the next course is larried. (3) Grouting is an operation used in brickwork, generally for gauged arches and similar work, where fine joints are required; it consists in mixing the mortar to a fluid condition, of about the consistency of cream, this being poured into the joints of the work after the latter has been placed in position.

JOINTING

Flush. An excellent, straightforward joint formed by slicing the surplus mortar from the face of the brickwork.

Raked Joint. Here the mortar is raked out $\frac{1}{4}$ in. or $\frac{3}{4}$ in. so that the joint is in shadow. It looks effective when the perpends are flushed.

Weathered Joint. Perhaps the best joint for reducing the ingress of water. It is formed by drawing the point of the trowel at a slight angle along the course.

---

* See p. 31 for the warming of aggregates and mixing water when concreting in frosty weather; the same principles apply.

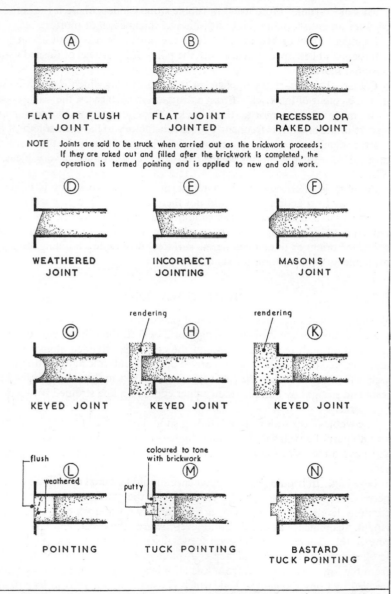

NOTE Joints are said to be struck when carried out as the brickwork proceeds; If they are raked out and filled after the brickwork is completed, the operation is termed pointing and is applied to new and old work.

VARIOUS TYPES OF MORTAR JOINTS

Masons' V-joint. More usual in rubble stone walling where it is desired to produce an even-looking joint with uneven thicknesses of mortar.

Pointing—Flush or Weathered. Here the mortar is raked out about $\frac{3}{8}$ in. and the joint filled up and struck with the point of the trowel or flushed with a coloured mortar.

Colour. It is invariably unpleasant to use a mortar which is much lighter than the colour of the brick. From a distance, in such cases, the wall appears to be made of more mortar than brick. Depending upon the colour and texture of the brick, it is frequently more satisfactory to have the colour of the mortar slightly darker than the colour of the brick. If brick dust is available, this, mixed with the mortar instead of sand, can produce a very pleasant effect.

Pointing is often employed to refurbish old brickwork but is liable to damage by frost action and should not therefore be used in new work.

Raked joints and keyed bricks should be used for brickwork that is to be rendered. If rendering has to be applied to a brick with bad suction (e.g. a vitrified brick) or to dense concrete surfaces, proprietary bonding fluids are available as a preparation for rendering.

BUILDING WALLS

Where new walls are erected the usual procedure is to build the corners or the extremities of the walls to a height of 2 or 3 ft, the bricks being carefully plumbed on both faces. The base of the corner is extended along the wall, and is racked back as the work is carried up. The intermediate portion of the wall is then built between the two corners, the bricks in the courses being kept level and straight by building their upper edges to a line strained between the two corners.

The whole of the walling of a building should be carried up simultaneously, and no part of a wall should be built higher than 3 ft above the remainder so as to avoid the risk of unequal settlements before the mortar has sufficiently set.

Levelling. In bedding bricks, great care should be taken to keep all courses perfectly level. To do this, the footings and the starting course should be carefully levelled through, using a spirit level with a stock at least 10 ft in length. Commence at one end and level towards the other, and take care to reverse the level each time at each forward step. Complete the length to be levelled in an even number of steps. A piece of slate or iron is left projecting from the lowest course, and from this all other courses at the corners can be levelled by using the gauged rod, which is usually about 10 ft in length, and has the courses marked on it. The work should then be again tested by the level, and the operation repeated. The levelling of brickwork is most efficiently accomplished with a surveyor's level, particularly where the walls are long.

Boning Method of Levelling. Boning rods are used for levelling trenches, ground work, paving, etc. Boning rods are similar in form to a T-square, and consist of an upright about $3' \times 3'' \times 1''$ and a white painted tee or sighting rail about $1' \, 3'' \times 3'' \times 1''$. There are three rods in a set; two of these are levelled at a distance of about 10 ft apart; a third rod is then levelled at a similar distance, taking care to reverse the long level. The centre rod is then removed, and the level transmitted to any point along the line by sighting or boning over the first and third rods. (See p. 20 for another way of using boning rods.)

Toothing. The usual method of leaving a brick wall which is to be continued at some future time is to tooth it. This consists in leaving alternate stretchers projecting $2\frac{1}{4}$ in. beyond the stretching courses above and below to allow the new work to be bonded to the old, as shown on p. 54 D.

The usual practice in joining new cross walls to old main walls is to cut out a number of rectangular recesses in the main walls equal in width to the width of the cross wall, three courses in height, and half a brick in depth, a space of three courses being left between the sinkings, as shown on p. 54 B; the new cross wall is then bonded into the recesses with cement mortar to avoid any settlement. It is necessary that the sinkings should not be less than 9 in. apart, as, in the cutting, the portion between is likely to become shaken and cracked. This is termed block-bonding.

Thicknessing. Where old walls have to be thickened, it is usual to cut recesses $9'' \times 9'' \times 4\frac{1}{2}''$ deep, one in every yard super * of the surface of the old wall. The new work is then built against the old and block-bonded to it at every recess. The surface of the old work is well cleaned, brushed and wetted before the new work is added. This is also termed block-bonding (see p. 54 A).

Racking. Racking is the term applied to the method of arranging the edge of a brick wall, part of which is unavoidably delayed while the remainder is carried up. The unfinished edge must not be built vertically or simply toothed, but should be set back $2\frac{1}{4}$ in. at each course, with a maximum of twelve courses, to reduce the possibility and the unsightliness of defects caused by any settlement that may take place in the most recently built portion of the wall (see p. 54 c).

* Yard super = square yard in area. ' Super ' is an abreviation of ' superficial '.

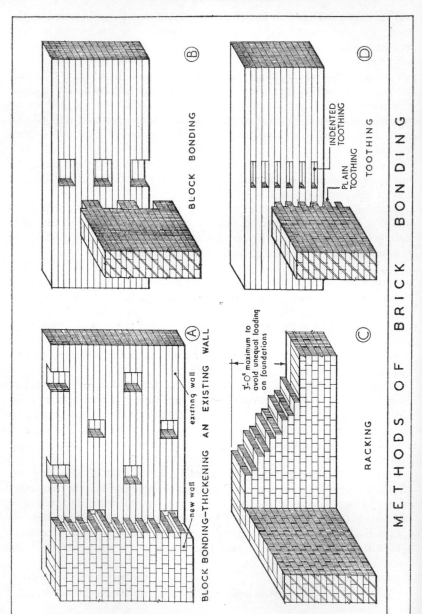

Ⓑ BLOCK BONDING

Ⓓ TOOTHING

INDENTED TOOTHING

PLAIN TOOTHING

Ⓐ BLOCK BONDING—THICKENING AN EXISTING WALL

existing wall

new wall

Ⓒ RACKING

3'-0" maximum to avoid unequal loading on foundations

METHODS OF BRICK BONDING

Stability of Brickwork. The stability of brickwork is affected in three general ways:

(1) By loading a given area of ground beyond its ultimate resistance, by the irregular concentration of great pressures on a soft subsoil, by the tendency of the substratum to slide, or by eccentrically loading: the walls are thrown out of the upright, crack, or disintegrate.

(2) By bad bonding, resulting in disintegration. One must also add: by no bond at all. In some old buildings this is frequently found.

(3) By side thrusts; these may be distributed or concentrated, and their tendency is to overturn the walls; they are provided for by designing the walls of a sufficient thickness, or by placing buttresses at regular intervals, so that the weight of wall or buttress has the effect of deflecting the thrust into a more vertical line. This ' resultant ' should fall within the base of the wall. Mortars are not considered to be effective in tension and tension in brickwork is therefore avoided. Great care should be taken when cutting openings for new doors or windows in old brickwork. The stresses will redistribute themselves and some sections of brickwork will be loaded more heavily than before. This may cause dangerous cracks to appear without warning.

WALL CLASSIFICATION

Walls are divided into two main types:

(*a*) Load-bearing walls.

(*b*) Non-load bearing walls.

Under section (*a*) include all solid house walls supporting a continuous load from the roof and floors, and also retaining walls for earth and water.

Under section (*b*) include all ' panel-filling ' walls which carry no superimposed load but which keep out wind and weather. See p. 56, A, ' Walling to Framed Structures '.

Retaining Walls. The design of walls to retain earth is based on the fact that few subsoils will keep to an unsupported vertical face, but assume their natural slope, beyond which they no longer move. The angle that this slope makes with horizontal is called the Angle of Repose and varies with the type of earth. Chalk newly cut will remain almost vertical. Dry sandy soil will not. It is the wedge of earth resting on the line of the natural slope which has to be supported by the retaining wall.

This is done by walls which rely on their own weight to resist this thrust or by walls which rely on leverage.

All vertical mass brick or mass concrete walls rely solely on their weight.

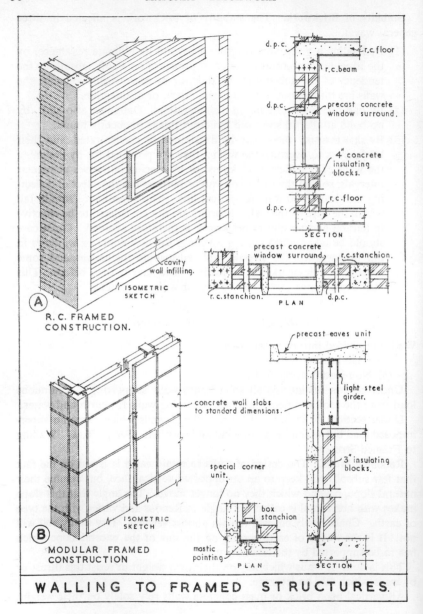

d.p.c.

r.c. floor

r.c. beam

d.p.c.

precast concrete window surround.

4" concrete insulating blocks.

d.p.c.

r.c. floor

SECTION

ISOMETRIC SKETCH

cavity wall infilling.

(A) R.C. FRAMED CONSTRUCTION.

precast concrete window surround.

r.c. stanchion.

r.c. stanchion.

d.p.c.

PLAN

precast eaves unit

light steel girder.

3" insulating blocks.

concrete wall slabs to standard dimensions.

special corner unit.

box stanchion

mastic pointing

PLAN

SECTION

ISOMETRIC SKETCH

(B) MODULAR FRAMED CONSTRUCTION

WALLING TO FRAMED STRUCTURES.

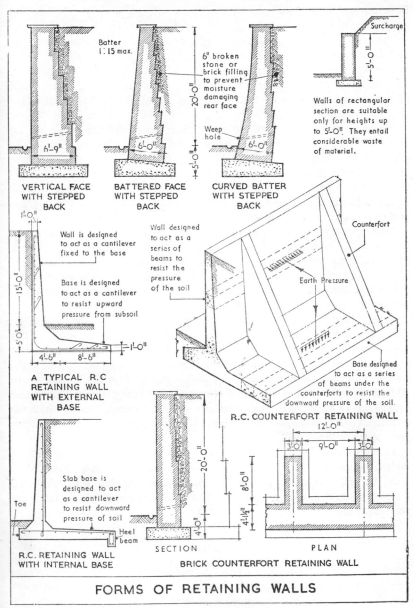

Batter 1:15 max.

6" broken stone or brick filling to prevent moisture damaging rear face

20'-0"

Weep hole

6'-9"

6'-0"

6'-0"

5'-0"

VERTICAL FACE WITH STEPPED BACK

BATTERED FACE WITH STEPPED BACK

CURVED BATTER WITH STEPPED BACK

Surcharge

5'-0"

Walls of rectangular section are suitable only for heights up to 5'-0". They entail considerable waste of material.

1'-0"

Wall is designed to act as a cantilever fixed to the base

Base is designed to act as a cantilever to resist upward pressure from subsoil

15'-0"

5'-0"

1'-0"

4'-6"   8'-6"

A TYPICAL R.C. RETAINING WALL WITH EXTERNAL BASE

Wall designed to act as a series of beams to resist the pressure of the soil

Counterfort

Earth Pressure

Base designed to act as a series of beams under the counterforts to resist the downward pressure of the soil.

R.C. COUNTERFORT RETAINING WALL

Slab base is designed to act as a cantilever to resist downward pressure of soil

Toe

Heel beam

R.C. RETAINING WALL WITH INTERNAL BASE

20'-0"

8'-0"

4'-1½"

4'-0"

SECTION

12'-0"

3'-0"   9'-0"   3'-0"

8'-0"

4'-1½"

PLAN

BRICK COUNTERFORT RETAINING WALL

FORMS OF RETAINING WALLS

Battered walls rely mostly on weight and partly on leverage. Reinforced concrete walls rely on leverage.

The first three retaining walls on p. 57 are subjected to continuous pressure and therefore each has a constant cross-section throughout its length.

The battered face is more economical and stable than the vertical face. Any curved work in building is costly and therefore the curved batter is not often used although it more nearly approaches the theoretical section for retaining walls.

Provision should be made to drain water from the retained earth by inserting drains, known as weep holes, through the walls near their bases. They are, however, often distributed over the wall face. Outlets should be at least 6 in. to 9 in. above ground level; 6 in. of hardcore filling behind the wall allows a quick flow of any surface water to the weep hole outlet. Gutters at the feet of such walls should be constructed to carry off all surplus water, and thus prevent the softening of the earth about the foundations.

A brick counterfort retaining wall is also shown. Where it is necessary to have a wall with a plain face the counterforts are constructed at the back of the wall; there is a slight saving in brickwork over the ordinary method of building retaining walls by adopting this arrangement. The counterforts must be securely tied to the main wall with internal iron ties to counteract any tendency to fracture at the junction.

Concrete is now largely employed for retaining walls, especially in localities where the materials—sand, ballast or broken stone—are plentiful. They may be formed as mass concrete walls similar to the brick sections, or as reinforced concrete walls. Of the latter, there are two types: (1) the plain wall of continuous section, with a wide projecting base for heights up to 20 ft, and (2) thin curtain walls and counterforts for heights over 20 ft; these usually have a toe of small projection and a rear horizontal base to which the counterforts are attached. The weight of the earth resting on the base adds great stability to the wall.

The concrete walls of continuous section are of two types, namely with an internal or an external base. The heel beam is used to resist sliding. Weep holes are also provided. There is greater tendency to slide with reinforced concrete walls than with mass brick or mass concrete walls as the latter are very much heavier.

BOND

Bond is the name given to any arrangement of bricks in which no vertical joint of one course is exactly over the one in the next course above or below it, and having the greatest possible amount of lap, which is usually one-fourth the length of a brick.

Bonds in Brickwork. To ensure good bond the following rules should be rigidly adhered to:

(1) The arrangement of the bricks must be uniform.
(2) As few bats as possible be employed.
(3) The vertical joints in every other course to be perpendicularly in line on the internal as well as the external face.
(4) Stretchers are only to be used on the faces of the wall, the interior to consist of headers only, as also in footings and corbels.
(5) When bedded, the length of a brick should equal twice the width, plus one mortar joint.
(6) Lateral lap between perpends to be ¼ of brick length.

There are several kinds of bond used in brickwork, those described in this chapter being as follows: (1) English, (2) Double Flemish, (3) Single Flemish, (4) Stretching, (5) Heading, (6) Garden Wall, (7) Facing, (8) Raking, (9) Hoop-iron.

English Bond. Consists of one course of headers and one course of stretchers alternately (see p. 60). In this bond, bricks are laid as stretchers only on the boundaries of courses, thus showing on the face of the wall, and no attempt should be made to break the joints in a course running through from back to front of a wall. That course which consists of stretchers on the face is known as a stretching course, and all in course above or below it would be headers with the exception of the closer brick, which is always placed next to the quoin header to complete the bond. These courses would be called heading courses.

It may be noticed that in walls the thickness of which is a multiple of a whole brick, the same course will show either:

(*a*) Stretchers in front elevation and stretchers in back elevation.
(*b*) Headers in front elevation and headers in back elevation.

But in walls in which the thickness is an odd number of half bricks, the same course will show either:

(*a*) Stretcher in front elevation and header in back elevation.
(*b*) Header in front elevation and stretcher in back elevation.

In setting out the plan of a course to any width, draw the quoin or corner brick; then next to the face (which in front elevation shows headers) place closers to the required thickness of wall, after which set out all the front headers, and, if the thickness is a multiple of a whole brick, set out headers in rear: the intervening space, if any, is always filled in with headers.

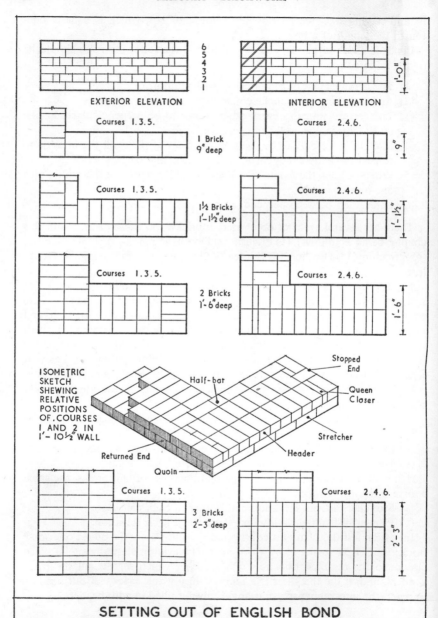

EXTERIOR ELEVATION

INTERIOR ELEVATION

6
5
4
3
2
1

1'-0"

Courses 1.3.5.

Courses 2.4.6.

1 Brick
9" deep

9"

Courses 1.3.5.

Courses 2.4.6.

1½ Bricks
1'-1½" deep

1'-1½"

Courses 1.3.5.

Courses 2.4.6.

2 Bricks
1'-6" deep

1'-6"

ISOMETRIC
SKETCH
SHEWING
RELATIVE
POSITIONS
OF COURSES
1 AND 2 IN
1'-10½" WALL

Half-bat

Stopped
End

Queen
Closer

Stretcher

Returned End

Header

Quoin

Courses 1.3.5.

Courses 2.4.6.

3 Bricks
2'-3" deep

2'-3"

SETTING OUT OF ENGLISH BOND

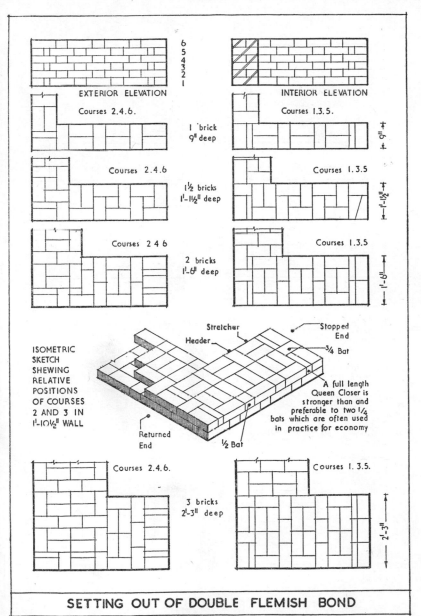

EXTERIOR ELEVATION

INTERIOR ELEVATION

Courses 2.4.6.

Courses 1.3.5.

1 brick
9" deep

Courses 2.4.6

Courses 1.3.5

1½ bricks
1'-1½" deep

Courses 2 4 6

Courses 1.3.5

2 bricks
1'-6" deep

ISOMETRIC SKETCH SHEWING RELATIVE POSITIONS OF COURSES 2 AND 3 IN 1'-10½" WALL

Stretcher

Header

Stopped End

¾ Bat

A full length Queen Closer is stronger than and preferable to two ¼ bats which are often used in practice for economy

Returned End

½ Bat

Courses 2.4.6.

Courses 1.3.5.

3 bricks
2'-3" deep

SETTING OUT OF DOUBLE FLEMISH BOND

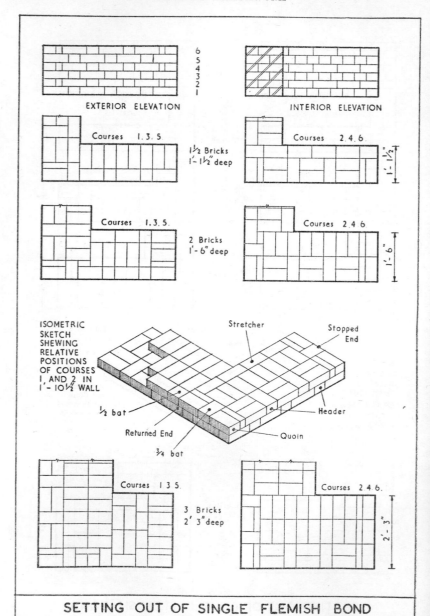

EXTERIOR ELEVATION   INTERIOR ELEVATION

Courses 1.3.5   Courses 2.4.6.
1½ Bricks
1'-1½" deep   1'-1½"

Courses 1.3.5.   Courses 2.4.6
2 Bricks
1'-6" deep   1'-6"

ISOMETRIC SKETCH SHEWING RELATIVE POSITIONS OF COURSES 1 AND 2 IN 1'-10½" WALL

Stretcher   Stopped End
½ bat
Returned End   Header
¾ bat   Quoin

Courses 1 3 5.   Courses 2.4.6.
3 Bricks
2' 3" deep   2'-3"

SETTING OUT OF SINGLE FLEMISH BOND

Double Flemish Bond. Has headers and stretchers alternately in the same course, both in front and back elevations. It is weaker than English Bond, owing to the greater number of bats and stretchers, but is considered by some to look better on the face. It is also economical, as it admits of a greater number of bats being used, so that any bricks broken in transit may be utilised. By using Double Flemish Bond for walls one brick in thickness, it is easier to obtain a fair face on both sides than with the English Bond.

Single Flemish Bond. Consists in arranging the bricks as Flemish Bond on the face, and English Bond as backing. This is often done on the presumption that the strength of the English Bond as well as the external appearance of the Double Flemish is attained, but this is questionable. It is generally used where more expensive bricks are specified for facing. The thinnest wall where this method can be introduced is $1\frac{1}{2}$-brick thick. Plans of alternate courses are given. The front elevations are the same as in Double Flemish Bond.

Stretching Bond. Stretching Bond is used for walls half-brick thick, such as partition walls, bricknogging in partitions and in 11 in. cavity walls. All bricks are laid as stretchers upon the face.

Heading Bond. All bricks show as headers on face. Used chiefly for rounding curves, for footings, corbels and cornices.

Facing Bond. Modifications of the rules given for bonding are necessary, first, where the thicknesses of the facing and backing bricks vary: there is one heading course only to several stretching courses and the distance between the heading courses being the least common multiple of the backing and facing bricks. There should be at least one course of headers to every foot in height.

The second case where modification of the rules is necessary is where the facing bricks are expensive and it is desired to economise by the usual practice of having three courses of stretchers to one course of headers.

This is also known as *Garden Wall* or *Boundary Wall Bond* and is used for walls one brick thick (9 in.) of which each side can be seen, as it is easier to adjust the back face by decreasing the number of headers, the lengths of which usually vary.

Raking Bonds. Walls as they increase in thickness increase in transverse strength, but become proportionally weaker in a longitudinal direction, owing to the fact that stretchers are not placed in the interior of a wall. This defect is remedied by using raking courses at regular intervals, of from four to eight courses in the height of a wall. The joints of bricks laid in this position cannot coincide with the joints of the ordinary courses directly above or below, the inclination to the face usually being determined by

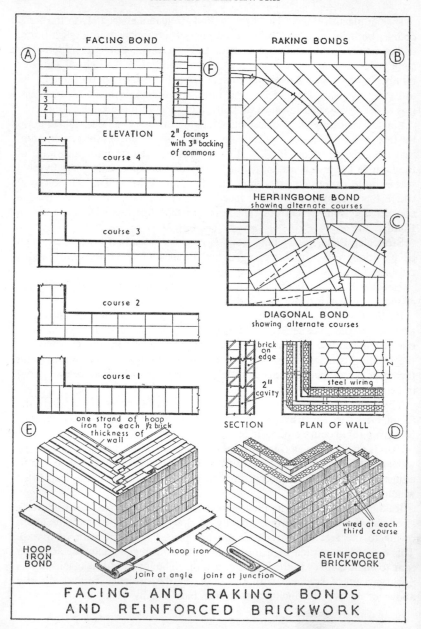

FACING BOND

RAKING BONDS

ELEVATION

2″ facings with 3″ backing of commons

course 4

course 3

course 2

course 1

HERRINGBONE BOND
showing alternate courses

DIAGONAL BOND
showing alternate courses

brick on edge

2″ cavity

steel wiring

2″

SECTION   PLAN OF WALL

one strand of hoop iron to each ½ brick thickness of wall

wired at each third course

HOOP IRON BOND

hoop iron

joint at angle   joint at junction

REINFORCED BRICKWORK

FACING AND RAKING BONDS
AND REINFORCED BRICKWORK

making the longitudinal distance between the opposite corners equal to the length of a brick. It is not advisable to use one raking course directly above another, as there is always a weakness at the junction of the raking with the face bricks.

Raking bonds are most effective when placed in the stretching courses in walls of an even number of half-bricks in thickness, in order that they may be effective over a greater area than would be the case if they were placed in the heading courses.

The alternate courses of raking bonds should be laid in different directions, in order to make the tie as perfect as possible. There are two varieties of raking bonds, viz. herring-bone and diagonal.

Reinforced Brickwork. Brickwork may advantageously be reinforced by iron and steel. Hoop-iron bond has been used for a considerable time, but probably it is true to say in many cases without any exact knowledge of its true value.

The reinforcement of brickwork skilfully applied adds considerable tensional strength to the brickwork. The mortar should be of good Portland cement, one to three of sand, and the reinforcement should be effectively bedded and surrounded with the mortar so that all air may be excluded, to prevent the rusting of the metal. All rods should be treated with two coats of bituminous paint.

Where structures are erected on soils of unequal bearing value, or on the side of a hill where sliding of the substratum may take place, proper reinforcement of brickwork is of great value to resist unequal settlement or the dislocation of the parts of the brickwork.

There are several proprietary makes of brick reinforcement, all of which are coated with bitumen to avoid rusting. They are made in several widths and lengths up to 300 ft (see p. 64).

Hoop-iron Bond. An additional longitudinal tie, termed hoop-iron bond, is sometimes inserted in walls, being usually lengths of hoop iron 1 in. by $\frac{1}{16}$ in., one row for every half brick in the thickness of the wall. It should be either tarred and sanded, or galvanised (see p. 64). It is hooked at all angles and junctions. This bond is inclined to be a clumsy expedient. Where such a strong tie is needed, it is generally better to use reinforced concrete.

Rod Reinforcement. Pages 66 and 67 show illustrations of reinforced brickwork lintels and piers. The lead weathering or tile creasing shown on p. 66 prevents any accumulation of moisture on the offset from penetrating the joints below. In frosty weather this moisture would freeze and expand, breaking up the mortar in the joints and spalling the bricks.

Vertical rod reinforcement is sometimes used in brick walls, but *one should*

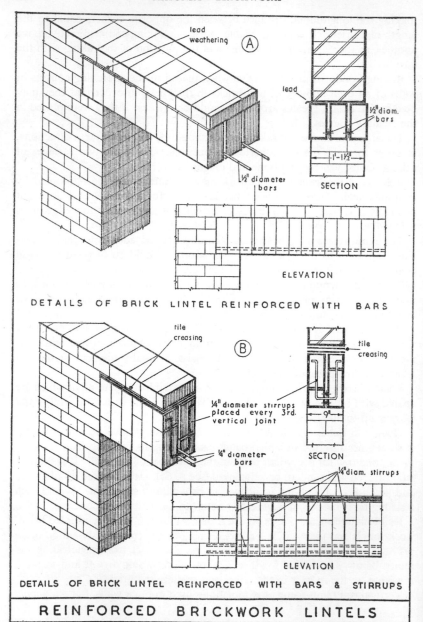

DETAILS OF BRICK LINTEL REINFORCED WITH BARS

DETAILS OF BRICK LINTEL REINFORCED WITH BARS & STIRRUPS

REINFORCED BRICKWORK LINTELS

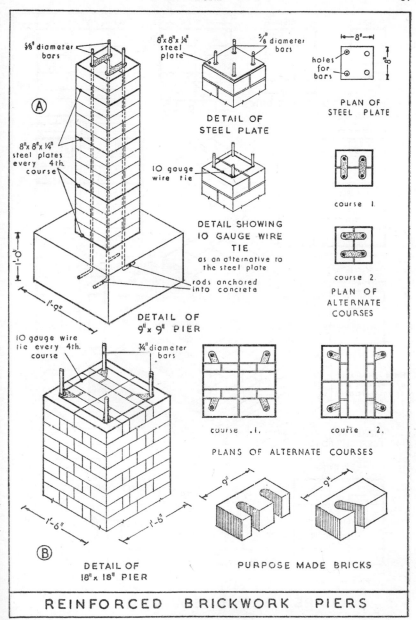

Ⓐ

⅝" diameter bars

8" x 8" x ¼" steel plates every 4th course

10 gauge wire tie

rods anchored into concrete

1'-0"

1'-9"

DETAIL OF 9" x 9" PIER

8" x 8" x ¼" steel plate

⅝" diameter bars

DETAIL OF STEEL PLATE

10 gauge wire tie

DETAIL SHOWING 10 GAUGE WIRE TIE
as an alternative to the steel plate

8"

8"

holes for bars

PLAN OF STEEL PLATE

course 1.

course 2.

PLAN OF ALTERNATE COURSES

Ⓑ

10 gauge wire tie every 4th. course

¾" diameter bars

1'-6"

1'-6"

DETAIL OF 18" x 18" PIER

course .1.

course .2.

PLANS OF ALTERNATE COURSES

9"

9"

PURPOSE MADE BRICKS

REINFORCED BRICKWORK PIERS

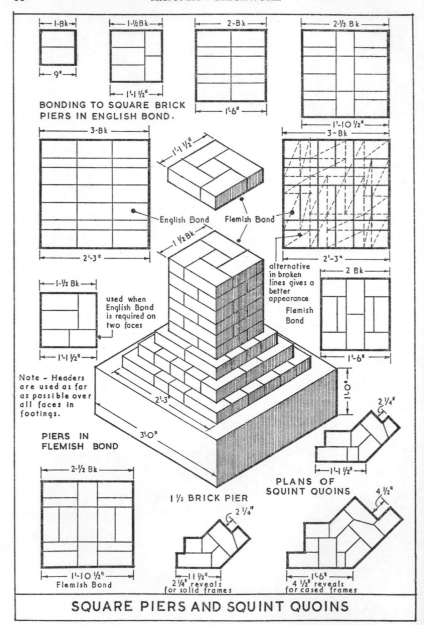

BONDING TO SQUARE BRICK
PIERS IN ENGLISH BOND.

1-Bk   1-½Bk   2-Bk   2-½ Bk

9"   1'-1½"   1'-6"   1'-10½"

3-Bk

English Bond   Flemish Bond

2'-3"

1'-1½"

1 ½Bk

1-½ Bk   used when
English Bond
is required on
two faces

alternative
in broken
lines gives a
better
appearance
Flemish
Bond

2'-3"

2 Bk

1'-1½"

Note – Headers
are used as far
as possible over
all faces in
footings.

PIERS IN
FLEMISH BOND

2'-3"

3'-0"

1'-0"

1'-6"

PLANS OF
SQUINT QUOINS

2¼"

1'-1½"

2-½ Bk   1 ½ BRICK PIER

4½"

1'-10½"
Flemish Bond

2¼"

11½"
2¼" reveals
for solid frames

4½"

1'-6"
4½" reveals
for cased frames

SQUARE PIERS AND SQUINT QUOINS

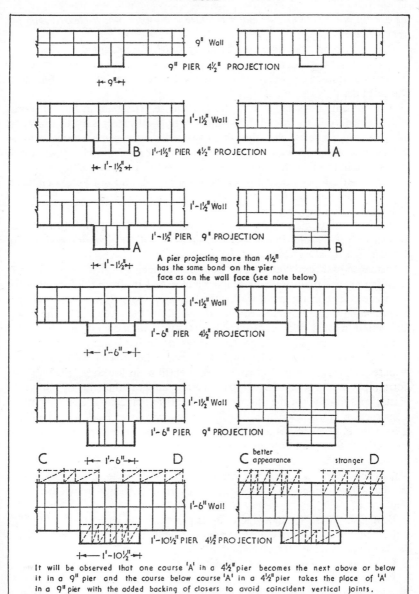

9" Wall

9" PIER 4½" PROJECTION

9"

1'-1½" Wall

B 1'-1½" PIER 4½" PROJECTION A

1'-1½"

1'-1½" Wall

A 1'-1½" PIER 9" PROJECTION B

1'-1½"

A pier projecting more than 4½"
has the same bond on the pier
face as on the wall face (see note below)

1'-1½" Wall

1'-6" PIER 4½" PROJECTION

1'-6"

1'-1½" Wall

1'-6" PIER 9" PROJECTION

C 1'-6" D   C better appearance   stronger D

1'-6" Wall

1'-10½" PIER 4½ PROJECTION

1'-10½"

It will be observed that one course 'A' in a 4½" pier becomes the next above or below
it in a 9" pier and the course below course 'A' in a 4½" pier takes the place of 'A'
in a 9" pier with the added backing of closers to avoid coincident vertical joints.

ATTACHED PIERS IN ENGLISH BOND

be careful not to attempt to make brickwork do work which clearly calls for reinforced concrete.

Piers. Piers in brickwork, as shown on p. 68, are rectangular pillars constructed to support loads transmitted to them by beams and girders, or to receive the thrusts of two or more arches, the resultant of which falls in a vertical line.

The illustration (p. 68) shows plans of square piers built in English Bond and Flemish, one to three bricks square. It is only necessary to draw the plan of one course, as the adjoining courses have the same arrangement of bricks, but placed in such a manner that those in the front elevation of one course are in the side elevation of the next, above or below.

The height of any isolated brick or stone pier should not exceed eighteen times its least dimension, or have a width of less than 13 in.

Squint quoins are also shown.

Attached Piers. Attached piers in English and Double Flemish Bonds are shown on pp. 69 and 71. These strengthen a wall at given intervals along its length, a usual spacing being 10 or 12 ft.

Junctions of Cross Walls. The bond is obtained in cross or party walls abutting against main walls by placing a closer $4\frac{1}{2}$ in. from the face in every alternate course in the main wall, thus leaving a space $2\frac{1}{4}$ in. deep and of a length equal to the thickness of the cross wall for the reception of the $2\frac{1}{4}$-in. projection in every other course of the cross wall, as shown on p. 72.

Projecting Courses. There are three cases in which it is necessary to enlarge the horizontal areas of walls: first, to increase the area of the base to distribute the pressure over a greater area of earth as in footings; secondly, to form a projection to afford a bearing area to support the ends of girders or joists; and thirdly, for the purpose of obtaining architectural effect, as in the construction of strings or cornices. The following two rules must be complied with in order to obtain the greatest efficiency. First, in any course the projection should not exceed one-fourth the length of the brick. This is to prevent the bricks from overturning, provided they are properly weighted at their back ends. Secondly, all bricks as far as possible should be laid as headers; this renders the bricks more secure from being drawn from the wall.

Footings. These are the wide courses placed at the base of a wall to distribute the pressure over a greater area of foundation. They are now obsolescent as concrete has taken their place.

Foundations are dealt with in Chapter 3.

Corbelling. It is sometimes necessary to support loads by the method of brick corbelling, which consists of one or more courses projecting a distance

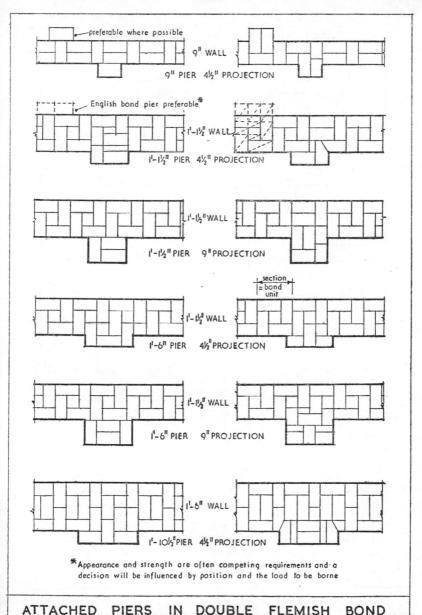

preferable where possible

9" WALL

9" PIER 4½" PROJECTION

English bond pier preferable*

1'-1½" WALL

1'-1½" PIER 4½" PROJECTION

1'-1½" WALL

1'-1½" PIER 9" PROJECTION

section
= bond unit

1'-1½" WALL

1'-6" PIER 4½" PROJECTION

1'-1½" WALL

1'-6" PIER 9" PROJECTION

1'-6" WALL

1'-10½" PIER 4½" PROJECTION

*Appearance and strength are often competing requirements and a
decision will be influenced by position and the load to be borne

ATTACHED PIERS IN DOUBLE FLEMISH BOND

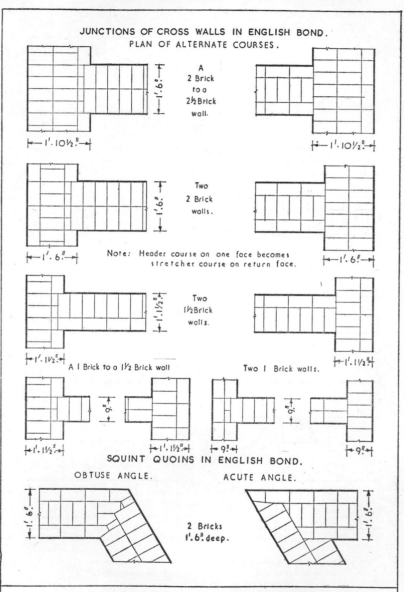

JUNCTIONS OF CROSS WALLS IN ENGLISH BOND.
PLAN OF ALTERNATE COURSES.

A
2 Brick
to a
2½ Brick
wall.

1'. 6"

1'. 10½"

1'. 10½"

Two
2 Brick
walls.

1'. 6"

1'. 6"

1'. 6"

Note: Header course on one face becomes
stretcher course on return face.

Two
1½ Brick
walls.

1'. 1½"

1'. 1½"

1'. 1½"

A 1 Brick to a 1½ Brick wall

Two 1 Brick walls.

9"

9"

1'. 1½"

1'. 1½"

9"

9"

SQUINT QUOINS IN ENGLISH BOND.

OBTUSE ANGLE.

ACUTE ANGLE.

1'. 6"

1'. 6"

2 Bricks
1'. 6". deep.

BONDING AT JUNCTIONS OF CROSS OR PARTY WALLS

sufficient to afford the required bearing area for the load. The L.C.C. By-laws require a wall to be corbelled out to an extent not more than one-third the thickness of the wall immediately below. Chimney breasts may, however, corbel out to a projection not more than the thickness of wall immediately below.

The two conditions given on p. 70 for projecting courses must be rigidly adhered to. Corbelling renders the walls less stable by bringing the centre of gravity of the mass away from the centre of the wall, causing a greater compression on the side of the wall under the load than on the side remote from the load. (The distance of the centre of bearing from the centre of the wall is known as the eccentricity of the load.) Where the loads are light and distributed along the length of the wall, as in the case of ordinary bridging joists, the stresses caused by eccentricity are usually negligible. In the case of concentrated loads transmitted by the ends of main girders, the centre of pressure should always be arranged to come within the middle third of the wall or pier, to avoid tensional stresses being set up on the side of the wall remote from the load.

Plinth. A horizontal and usually projecting course built at the bases of walls, to protect them from injury and give additional strength. A recessed plinth is termed undercut.

String Course. The name given to horizontal courses, sometimes projecting and moulded, built in the faces of walls, anywhere between plinth and cornice, to act as a tie, and architecturally to emphasise the horizontal divisions of a building.

DAMP PROOFING

Damp-proof Courses. Walls are liable to become damp in four ways. First, by dampness rising up the wall from the ground and by being forced through the substructure into the basement; secondly, by dampness passing through from the faces of walls; thirdly, by dampness passing down through from the tops of walls; fourthly, by internal condensation due to the deposition of moisture on cold walls by a warm humid atmosphere.

A. *Rising Damp.* Many common building materials, e.g. brickwork, blockwork, concrete (except in special cases), will absorb water from the ground by capillary attraction. Apart from being unhygienic for the occupants of the building, damp materials are liable to frost attack, and the drying of the moisture from the outside surface may cause damage by exfoliation and produce unsightly efflorescence.*

* See p. 39.

The damp-proof course must be kept at least 6 in. above ground level, and in the case of a cavity wall construction, the cavity must carry on down at least 6 in. below the damp-proof course. This is so that mortar droppings produced when the wall is in course of construction cannot build up to form a bridge between the outside wet leaf and the inside dry leaf. No timber, e.g. wall plates, should be fixed below a damp-course in contact with damp brickwork or concrete.*

Suitable materials are flexible ones, e.g. sheet lead or copper, heavy bitumen felt, sandwich of lead, copper, or aluminium in felt.

In the past, asphalt has been used, but this is liable to squeeze out under load. It is not advisable to use slate, as any very slight building movement will cause capillary cracks, which are inclined to draw up moisture. A course of vitrified (engineering) bricks may be used, using a waterproofed mortar, but slight movement is unavoidable in any length of wall and capillary cracks are bound to occur.

B. *Weather Protection.* This is usually achieved by building a wall in two independent leaves each leaf being $4\frac{1}{2}$ in. thick, the outer one often of brick and the inner one being of an insulating material such as lightweight concrete blocks. Leaves are tied together by ties of galvanised steel placed 1 ft 6 in. apart vertically and 3 ft apart horizontally. In the case of 3 in. thick leaves 3 in. apart, the ties should be 1 ft 6 in. apart both vertically and horizontally. Great care must be taken that at lintels and sills, damp-proof courses are placed so that no water can run down the surface of the outside face of the inside leaf.

A less effective method of keeping water out is to render the wall. The rendering should be weak, 1 : 6 cement-sand. A strong rendering only makes matters worse, as the rain will wash down the surface until it finds a capillary crack, formed by the shrinkage of the strong rendering, where it will gain entry into the body of the wall.† The weak rendering will be slightly elastic and avoid forming capillary cracks. There is no such thing as a completely waterproof rendering.

Water may be discouraged from entering the building by tile hanging. This is carried out in a similar manner to roof tiling except that the gauge is usually very much bigger. The wall is battened out with creosoted or otherwise rot-proofed battens plugged to the walls and the tiles hung and nailed thereto. If the outer leaf is of lightweight fly ash blocks, the tiles may be nailed to the blocks, without the use of battens.

* See Model Building By-laws 27, 28, 29 and 30.
† See *Building Research Station Digest*, No. 23, and *National Building Study*, No. 10. H.M.S.O.

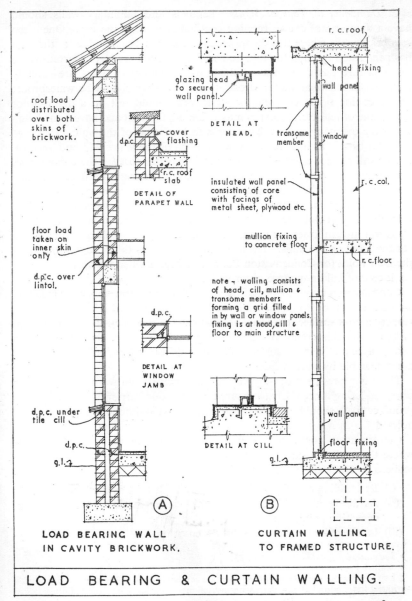

roof load distributed over both skins of brickwork.

d.p.c.

cover flashing

r.c. roof slab

DETAIL OF PARAPET WALL

floor load taken on inner skin only

d.p.c. over lintol.

d.p.c.

DETAIL AT WINDOW JAMB

d.p.c. under tile cill

d.p.c.

g.l.

glazing bead to secure wall panel.

DETAIL AT HEAD.

DETAIL AT CILL

g.l.

r.c. roof

head fixing

wall panel

transome member

window

insulated wall panel consisting of core with facings of metal sheet, plywood etc.

r.c. col.

mullion fixing to concrete floor

r.c. floor

note – walling consists of head, cill, mullion & transome members forming a grid filled in by wall or window panels. fixing is at head, cill & floor to main structure

wall panel

floor fixing

A

B

LOAD BEARING WALL IN CAVITY BRICKWORK.

CURTAIN WALLING TO FRAMED STRUCTURE.

LOAD BEARING & CURTAIN WALLING.

F 2

C. *Dampness at Tops of Walls*. Parapets and boundary walls should have a damp-proof course running continuously along the top. One often sees brick walls where this damp-proof course has been omitted; the rain has penetrated through the top, and severe efflorescence has occurred where this moisture has dried out on the surface. Many parapets are severely damaged in a similar way by frost action. Copings should be waterproof; or the coping brick, concrete, or stonework should rest on a damp-proof membrane of felt, etc. Copings may overhang the wall and have a throating under the overhang so that the water is thrown clear of the wall. This is of doubtful benefit as if there is any wind much of the water will be blown on to the wall surface eventually. It is possibly better to keep the coping flush with the wall surface so that the rain can wash the unsightly efflorescent salts and the grime that usually collects under such overhangs away.

D. *Condensation*. Warm air can hold more invisible water vapour than cold air. If you chill the walls of a room containing warm humid air, these walls will in turn lower the temperature of the air, and moisture will start to condense out on the walls. The temperature at which this occurs is known as the Dew Point (or Condensation Point) and occurs when the air is saturated, i.e. it cannot hold any more water vapour.

Condensation may be stopped by preventing the warm, moist air reaching a cold surface; or it may be controlled by arranging that if warm, moist air reaches a cold surface, the water formed cannot run back to the inside face of the wall—this commonly happens in cavity walling, the condensation taking place on the inside surface of the outside leaf. Most building materials are permeable by water vapour.*

There is a pressure† causing vapour movement from warm areas to cold ones, rendering it necessary to ensure that a vapour barrier (a form of damp-proof course) should be absolutely continuous (without cracks, joints or holes).‡

Condensation commonly occurs, for example, in badly built kitchens where the walls are only 9 in. thick and there is no insulation. It can be reduced or eradicated:

   (i) By building a cavity wall with insulating blocks as the inner skin; or
   (ii) As above plus the painting of the inside plaster with an anti-condensation paint.
   (iii) In framed or panelled walls by ensuring that a continuous damp-

---

* See *National Building Study*, No. 23.
† Called *Vapour Pressure*.
‡ Lap joints are permissible if the condensate can be drained safely away to the outside —without lodging on battens, damaging insulation; or running into the building.

proof membrane is applied on the *inside* surface of the main insulation (e.g. continuous aluminium foil behind 1 in. of insulation board). This will normally ensure that the surface temperature of the vapour carrier on the inside face of the insulation is above the Dew Point of the warm air within the building.

D.P.C.s and Model By-laws. Damp proof courses through cavity walls must be at least 6 in. above external ground level in the outside leaf. This is to reduce the possibility of earth in flower beds being banked up so that moisture can travel into the brickwork above the D.P.C. from the ground.

The cavity must be carried down at least 6 in. below the D.P.C. (see p. 74). It is advisable to arrange for bricks to be removed at intervals along the base of cavities, preferably at quoins, so that at completion of the bricklaying work the cavity can be raked clear of mortar droppings. The loose bricks are finally set in mortar when the cavities have been cleared. It is also necessary to leave an open perpend at the base of the cavity or immediately above flashings every 3 ft to allow the escape of moisture which might otherwise collect in the cavity.

Any lintel bridging the cavity should have a flashing placed above it under the outside leaf and then stepping up across the cavity at least 4 in. and tucked in to a course of the inside leaf. This flashing or D.P.C. will conduct moisture to the outside and prevent the inside leaf getting wet.

Where suspended timber ground floors are provided, it is necessary to put in air bricks through both leaves of the wall so that the under floor space is properly ventilated and so that rot cannot start. (Rot usually starts in an atmosphere of high humidity as a result of poor ventilation.) Between floor joists and the oversite concrete, where this is provided, there should be a gap of at least 3 in.; the distance between the underside of the joists and the ground, where no oversite concrete is provided, should be at least 9 in. Sleeper walls should be built in honeycomb fashion, i.e. perpends 4 in. wide to allow through ventilation.

Where the floor level is below ground level, then continuous tanking in asphalt or bituminous felt must be provided connecting with the D.P.C. across the walls. There must be absolutely no break in this tanking. It should be protected on the outside either by a layer of weak concrete or by a single skin of block or brick, with a structural wall (taking the vertical and lateral loads) on the inside of the tanking. In deeper basements where water pressure may be expected, a loading layer of concrete, suitably reinforced, must be provided to prevent the floor being broken upwards by the pressure of the water.

CHIMNEYS

The function of the chimney flue is to remove smoke and other products of combustion *only*, from the fire to a position well above surrounding windows. Unfortunately large quantities of air, which the fire has just warmed up, are also removed by the draught up the chimney.

Flues require careful designing so that fires do not smoke and so that the acids, which are liable to form in flues to slow combustion appliances, cannot cause damage to the mortar in the chimney stack.

Flues must be designed to suit the type of fire.

Type of Fire	Size and Type of Flue
Open fires:	Minimum diameter 7 in., traditional size 9″ × 9″ (Flues must be parged, i.e. rendered with mortar or lined with clay or other fired liners.)
Domestic boilers, slow-combustion stoves, etc., burning non-smokeless fuels:	6 in. diameter with salt-glazed liners.
Domestic boilers, slow-combustion stoves, etc., burning exclusively smokeless fuels:	4 in. diameter flue with salt-glazed liners.

Draught. An open fire requires roughly four to six times the volume of the air in a room per hour to keep it going satisfactorily. Only two air changes per hour are needed for health, so that two to four times as much air as is really required has to be heated up to produce comfortable conditions. This additional air comes from cracks round windows, under doors and between floor boards, which is why draughts are one of the characteristic discomforts of rooms warmed by open fires. If these cracks are draught-proofed then the fire may be starved of air and the fire may smoke.

Air supply to the fire should therefore be provided independently of the air in the room by means of pipes laid beneath the floor communicating with the outside air. These pipes should be 4 to 6 in. in diameter and should be arranged so that they can draw air from both sides of the house. (In a wind, the leeside of a house is in reduced pressure, and air is then sucked along any ventilation pipe opening to one side only.) Ventilation pipes should be arranged to supply air to the space immediately below the grate.

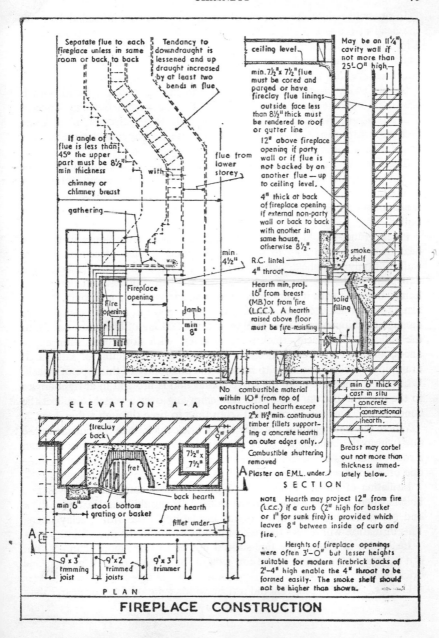

Separate flue to each fireplace unless in same room or back to back

Tendancy to downdraught is lessened and up draught increased by at least two bends in flue

ceiling level

May be an 11¼" cavity wall if not more than 25'-0" high.

min. 7½" x 7½" flue must be cored and parged or have fireclay flue linings

outside face less than 8½" thick must be rendered to roof or gutter line

12" above fireplace opening if party wall or if flue is not backed by an another flue — up to ceiling level.

If angle of flue is less than 45° the upper part must be 8½" min thickness

with

flue from lower storey

4" thick at back of fireplace opening if external non-party wall or back to back with another in same house, otherwise 8½".

chimney or chimney breast

gathering

min. 4½"

smoke shelf

R.C. lintel

4" throat

fire opening

Fireplace opening

Hearth min. proj. 18" from breast (MB) or from fire (LCC). A hearth raised above floor must be fire-resisting

solid filling

jamb

min 8"

ELEVATION A·A

No combustible material within 10" from top of constructional hearth except 2" x 1½" min. continuous timber fillets supporting a concrete hearth on outer edges only. Combustible shuttering removed

Plaster on E.M.L. under.

min 6" thick cast in situ concrete constructional hearth.

Breast may corbel out not more than thickness immediately below.

SECTION

fireclay back

fret

7½" x 7½"

min 6"

stool bottom grating or basket

back hearth
front hearth
fillet under.

A

A

NOTE Hearth may project 12" from fire (LCC.) if a curb (2" high for basket or 1" for sunk fire) is provided which leaves 8" between inside of curb and fire.

Heights of fireplace openings were often 3'-0" but lesser heights suitable for modern firebrick backs of 2'-4" high enable the 4" throat to be formed easily. The smoke shelf should not be higher than shown.

9" x 3" trimming joist

9" x 2" trimmed joists

9" x 3" trimmer

PLAN

FIREPLACE CONSTRUCTION

In order to reduce the wastage of air up the chimney, immediately above the head of the fire, the bottom of the flue should be formed into a throat 8 in. to 10 in. wide, 4 in. from front to back, and 6 in. deep. Precast throat units can be purchased, also cast-iron throat units with registers (doors) which ensure that the throat is formed to the right dimensions.

Smoke Shelf. Immediately above and to the back of the throat unit is the traditional site for the smoke shelf. To quote from *Building Research Station Digest*, No. 18: ' It does not appear to be essential if all other features are properly designed.' In fact some people consider that it is a trap for soot and may cause chimney fires.

There must be a smooth transition from the fireplace opening through the throat unit to the beginning of the flue with no cavities exposed at the back of the fireplace surround. The throat unit, of course, is not necessary where the appliance has its own flue connection as in the case of a stove or boiler.

Flues. Flues should generally be positioned within the house so that the heat from them can help to warm the building. Flues placed on outside walls not only waste heat, but the brickwork is liable to get chilled below the dew point of the flue gases, and water vapour will condense out on the flue lining, bringing with it sulphur compounds, tar, acids or ammonia. These can and do attack the lime or the cement in the mortar, and can cause severe damage to chimney stacks, as well as causing leaking of flue gases back into the building. This acid attack is more severe with slow combustion appliances, and that is why it is necessary to provide a flue lining of salt-glazed drainpipes (sockets upwards) to remove the possibility of this type of attack. When these liners are used, the stove connection is brought in at right angles to the flue, the bottom end of the flue emptying over a vessel to collect the condensate. This can be removed from time to time through a flue door.

Where the walls of a flue are only half a brick thick, then the outside of the flue (within the building) must be plastered. Where the flue passes through a roof of shingles or thatch, the flue must be thickened out to at least $8\frac{1}{2}$ in.— one brick thickness—to a distance of at least 4 in. above and below.

Insulation of Flues. Brickwork to flues to slow combustion stoves and boilers where they are exposed to the outside air should be at least 9 in. thick and are preferably constructed of an insulating block with fireclay liners. This insulation will reduce the risk of condensation in the flue.

Inclination of Flues. The flue should not be inclined more than 45°, but if it is, then the thickness of the top side of the slope should be at least one brick thick.

Fixings. Wooden plugs should not be within 9 in. of a flue or nearer than

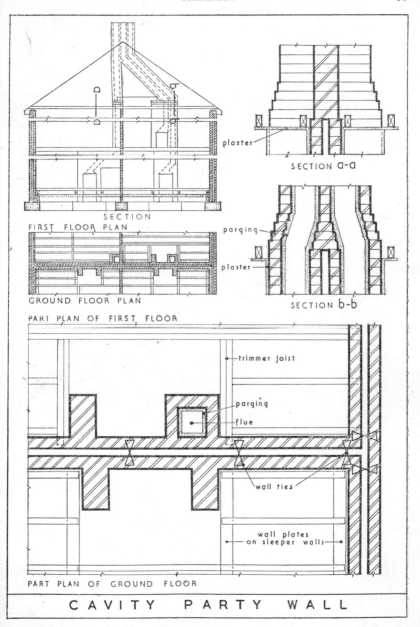

SECTION

SECTION d-d

FIRST FLOOR PLAN

plaster

parging

plaster

SECTION b-b

GROUND FLOOR PLAN

PART PLAN OF FIRST FLOOR

trimmer joist

parging

flue

wall ties

wall plates
on sleeper walls

PART PLAN OF GROUND FLOOR

CAVITY PARTY WALL

6 in. to a fireplace opening. Similarly, metal fastenings should be kept at least 2 in. away from a fireplace opening.

Hearths. Hearths should be constructed so that there is no danger of any fire spreading to combustible structure. By-laws lay down that the hearth must project 16 in. from the front of the fireplace; it must be 6 in. thick and must extend beyond the sides of the opening at least 6 in. The jambs to the fire should be at least 9 in. thick. The thickness at the back of the fireplace opening can be reduced to $4\frac{1}{2}$ in. except on party walls.

Chimneys through Roofs. Where the slope of the roof is not less than 10°, by-laws require that the chimney shall project above the ridge at least 2 ft. Where the chimney stack comes through the roof other than at the ridge, then it must project through the roof a distance of 3 ft, measured from the highest point of its junction with the roof.

Chimney Pots and Flaunching. There is no need for the chimney pot to project more than 2 in. or 3 in. from the top of the brick or stonework. The pot is merely a convenient termination to the flue and should not be exposed. The top of the brick or stonework should be flaunched to throw the water to the side to prevent undue penetration of the rain into the brickwork. It is better to cap the top of the stack with an impervious material such as a concrete cap.

D.P.C.s at Roof Level. Where the stack passes through the roof it is necessary to provide stepped flashings (see Plumber), soakers and aprons to make sure that rain does not penetrate into the joint between brick or stonework and the roof. The flashings, dressed into the brickwork, should connect with a damp proof membrane through the stack of an incombustible material, e.g. copper, lead. Alternatively a D.P.C. can be taken straight through the stack immediately above the highest flashing.

Down-Draughts. These draughts may be caused by air pressure in the vicinity of the top of the chimney stack caused by:

(*a*) High buildings in close vicinity.

(*b*) Bad positioning and height of the stack, e.g. on the windward side of the house where the stack rises close to the eaves and terminates well below the ridge. In this case there will be a greater pressure of air at the top of the stack which is liable to overcome the upward draught in the flue. In such a case it is necessary to carry the stack above the height of the ridge.

ARCHES

One method of spanning an opening in the brickwork is by forming an arch. A curved templet of wood is placed in position and the voussoirs (bricks

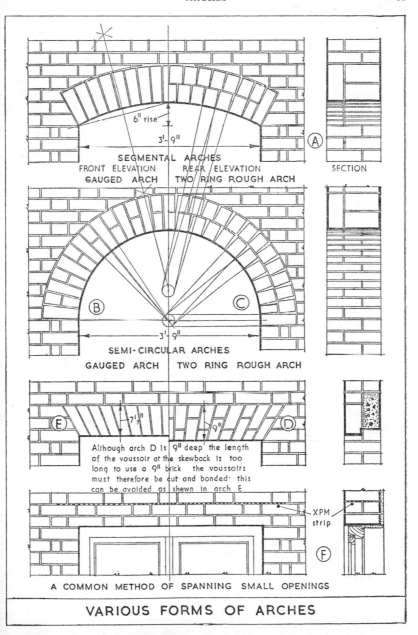

6" rise
3'-9"

SEGMENTAL ARCHES
FRONT ELEVATION   REAR ELEVATION
GAUGED ARCH   TWO RING ROUGH ARCH

Ⓐ   SECTION

Ⓑ   Ⓒ

3'-9"

SEMI-CIRCULAR ARCHES
GAUGED ARCH   TWO RING ROUGH ARCH

Ⓔ   7½"   9"   Ⓓ

Although arch D is 9" deep the length
of the voussoir at the skewback is too
long to use a 9" brick the voussoirs
must therefore be cut and bonded· this
can be avoided as shewn in arch E

XPM
strip

Ⓕ

A COMMON METHOD OF SPANNING SMALL OPENINGS

VARIOUS FORMS OF ARCHES

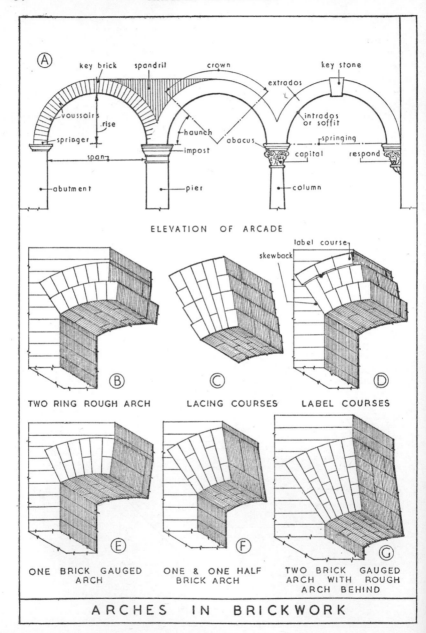

Ⓐ key brick spandril crown key stone extrados voussoirs rise springer haunch abacus intrados or soffit springing impost span capital respond abutment pier column

ELEVATION OF ARCADE

Ⓑ TWO RING ROUGH ARCH

Ⓒ LACING COURSES

Ⓓ LABEL COURSES — label course, skewback

Ⓔ ONE BRICK GAUGED ARCH

Ⓕ ONE & ONE HALF BRICK ARCH

Ⓖ TWO BRICK GAUGED ARCH WITH ROUGH ARCH BEHIND

ARCHES IN BRICKWORK

forming the arch) are bedded together on it. Properly speaking, arches are curved and transfer the weight of the walling above into the abutments. Lateral thrust is produced, the amount of which depends upon the span, the rise of the arch and the load of the brickwork above. This lateral thrust must be taken up by either producing a sufficiently wide and heavy abutment or buttress, or by placing a similar arch alongside to balance the thrust.

Confusion often arises in the minds of students because reinforced concrete or steel lintels are faced with bricks which are unhappily called flat arches (vertical brick arches, Dutch arches, or tiled arches). The sooner the word arch in this context falls out of use, the better.

If a square opening is cut in a plain brick wall, the brickwork within a 60° triangle above will tend to fall out, forming a triangular arch. This formation results from the diagonal support which each brick provides to the brick above. Any lintel provided need only support the weight of this triangle. If, however, floor joists come into the wall immediately above the opening, the lintel will have to be strong enough to carry these additional loads.

Rough Arches. These are made from bricks which are not specially shaped to fit the curve of the arch. So that the wedge-shaped mortar joints do not get too unpleasantly thick near the top, stretchers are usually replaced by half bricks, the perpends overlapping. This form of construction is often used behind gauged arches so that the rather untidy appearance of the half bricks is not seen.

Gauged Arches. Here the bricks are formed to the tapered shape necessary to make neat jointing in the arch. A saw cut of $\frac{1}{8}$ in. is first made in the brick to give a precise line of finish, and then the unwanted part of the brick removed by axing (with a bricklayer's axe or scutch). Alternatively, softer bricks may be used and instead of axing they may be rubbed with a rubbing stone or a file.

Relieving Arches. In the past, relieving arches were often built over square openings to take most of the load. The flat head of the opening was then carried on timber joists. It would, of course, be nonsense to provide both a relieving arch and a reinforced concrete or steel lintel.

LINTELS

Normal practice for spanning openings is to provide a lintel of wood, steel or concrete to support the triangle of brickwork which would otherwise fall out. Wood lintels are sometimes suitable for light loads internally. Unless they are rather oversize for the load they have to carry, they tend over a long period of time to sag, cracking the brickwork above. In any case they should be treated with a preservative to prevent attack by beetle and rot.

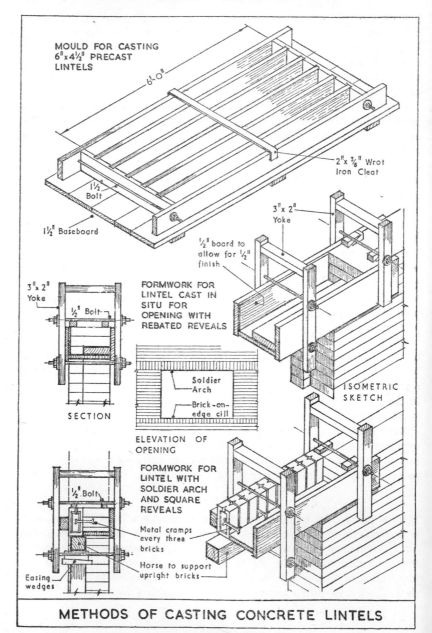

MOULD FOR CASTING
6"x4½" PRECAST
LINTELS

6'-0"

2"x ⅜" Wrot
Iron Cleat

3"x 2"
Yoke

1½"
Bolt

1½" Baseboard

½" board to
allow for ½"
finish

3"x 2"
Yoke

½" Bolt

FORMWORK FOR
LINTEL CAST IN
SITU FOR
OPENING WITH
REBATED REVEALS

ISOMETRIC
SKETCH

Soldier
Arch

Brick-on-
edge cill

SECTION

ELEVATION OF
OPENING

FORMWORK FOR
LINTEL WITH
SOLDIER ARCH
AND SQUARE
REVEALS

½" Bolt

Metal cramps
every three
bricks

Horse to support
upright bricks

Easing
wedges

METHODS OF CASTING CONCRETE LINTELS

Steel Lintels. For smaller openings, these may take the form of unequal angles and are used for holding up the outside leaf over an opening. Where they cannot be readily painted they should be galvanised or treated with several coats of a reliable bituminous paint. The advantage of angle lintels is that they are easy to position and are inconspicuous.

Alternatively, rolled steel joists may be used for larger openings. It is then customary to case these joists in concrete to protect them from corrosion and to render them resistant to fire. Steel collapses quickly at the outset of fires unless protected by a casing of concrete or asbestos. Unprotected steel should not be exposed in inaccessible cavities where corrosion can occur through condensation. This mistake is frequently made.

Reinforced Concrete Lintels. Casting lintels is dealt with in the chapter on concrete, p. 34. They may be either cast *in situ* or precast (see drawing on p. 35). Concrete lintels are perhaps the most satisfactory form of construction because they resist fire effectively and, so long as the reinforcement is kept at least 1 in. from the surface, the concrete itself being dense and of high quality, there will be no troubles from corrosion. (High grade vibrated concrete is practically waterproof.)

Where appearance is not a major factor, the lintel can go straight through the wall and be expressed on the front of the building for its full width, including the bearing of the brick jambs. Otherwise, the lintel may be faced with a mixture of stone dust and cement or it may be faced with brickwork (see p. 66). Another method is to form a boot lintel the toe of the boot being recessed from the face of the brickwork by about 1 in. for added protection. This is a most satisfactory form. The toe is stepped back in plan at the jambs. In cavity wall construction, the toe must be strong enough to support the leaf above.

Alternatively, ties (galvanised) may be cast projecting from the face of the lintel so that the brick face is supported at the vertical joints (see bottom right hand illustration, p. 66).

Whatever form of lintel is used, it is most important that a stepped D.P.C. is placed in such a way that any moisture running down the inside surface of the outside leaf of brickwork is conducted safely outside the head of the window.

Where a concrete lintel or a rendered soffit is provided, a throating should be formed near the outside edge of the soffit to prevent the wind driving drops of water back along the soffit and on to the top wood or metal member of the window.

SILLS

One of the most vulnerable parts of a wall is the window sill. It must be weathered to throw the water towards the outside. If the sill member over-hangs the wall below then a throating must be formed in it to prevent the ' run back ' of drops of water. A properly detailed water bar prevents the seepage of water back under the sill and helps to fix the sill in position. Damp proofing materials must be applied in such a way as to prevent moisture penetrating to internal sills and the internal leaf.

Sills may be formed in stone, reinforced concrete, tiles, pressed metal, slate and timber.

The drawings on pp. 132, 213 and 218 show various forms of sill construc-tion. Where the window is relatively far back from the face of the wall, then the window frame usually has its own weathering and stands so as to overhang the sill proper. The sill is then weathered fairly steeply to run the water off to the outside. Where the window is close to the outside surface, the wood sill may overhang the wall on its own.

Water Bar. This is often made of galvanised steel and is available in sizes varying from $\frac{1}{8}'' \times \frac{3}{4}''$ to $\frac{1}{4}'' \times 1\frac{1}{4}''$. It is bedded into a groove on the table of the sill and in the underside of the window frame, and is bedded in white lead or bituminous mastic. It is still liable to seepage if a strip of lead or super-purity aluminium is not folded over the top of the water bar and carried to the outside of the joint (see detail on p. 216).

Overhangs of sills are often provided and may be beneficial if they effec-tively throw the water clear of the wall. Observation shows that the wind frequently blows the large drops of water falling from sills back on to the wall surface. Furthermore, dirt, soot and grime frequently collect under sills and cannot be washed off by the rain, producing disfiguring uneven dark bands. It is well worth observing the effectiveness of sill overhangs. It will be seen that the sills usefulness is shown by the depth of this band of grime.

It is sometimes desirable that the wall is washed by the rain to keep it clean, and where the outer leaf is properly designed and built of a suitable brick it may be satisfactory to eliminate the overhang of the sill.

Large windows may cause an excessive amount of water to wash over the wall surface below the sill. The bricks and D.P.C.s must be able to stand up to this.

FIXING TO BRICKWORK

It is frequently necessary to fix joinery to the inner leaf of brickwork. Creo-soted wood plugs are built in, but these should not be so big that their eventual shrinkage would cause damage to the brickwork. Alternatively, clinker concrete blocks are built in. Whilst these do not shrink, they are not good at nail-holding. Lightweight fly-ash blocks are a great improvement in this respect.

A lot of fixing difficulties are eliminated if lightweight fly-ash blocks are used for the inner leaf instead of brickwork.

7

Masonry—Blockwork

CONCRETE BLOCKS

CONCRETE building blocks are suitable for the construction of walls using very similar techniques as in brickwork.

Types.* Many varieties are obtainable:

Dense. Weighing over 100 lb per cu. ft and made of normal aggregates.

Light Weight. Weighing under 100 lb per cu. ft and made with aggregates of a cellular nature such as clinker, expanded clay, foamed slag, or pumice, or by foaming or by air entraining (aerated, cellular or foamed concrete).

No-fines. Made with aggregates of one size (fairly large, say ½ in.) producing a very open structure and weighing about three-quarters that of ordinary dense concrete.

The lighter the weight of a concrete block, the better the thermal insulation, and the poorer the ability to withstand compressive stress.

For facing blocks, tooling, spraying, brushing, scraping, etching with acid, or casting in patterned moulds, can give a great variety of surface treatment. Alternatively, a special mix can be cast integrally with the concrete (see p. 34).

Sizes. Similar principles apply as with brickwork:

Lengths plus one mortar joint, i.e. $17\frac{5}{8}'' + \frac{3}{8}'' = 18''$.

Height plus one mortar joint, i.e. $8\frac{5}{8}'' + \frac{3}{8}'' = 9''$.

Thickness—2 in., $2\frac{1}{2}$ in., 3 in., $4\frac{1}{4}$ in., 6 in. are the most usual, the commonest being 3 in., $4\frac{1}{4}$ in. and 6 in.

Strength. The minimum compressive strength for an ' A ' type block is 375 lb per sq. in. and for ' B ' block 300 lb per sq. in. The average (of 12

---

* B.S. 2028 covers precast concrete blocks. B.S. 1364 covers aerated concrete building blocks dimensions.

British Standards divide the blocks as follows:

Type A. Dense aggregate blocks for: external walls (rendered), inner leaf of cavity walls, internal walls, partitions, infilling panels in framed buildings.

Type B. Light-weight aggregate blocks for load-bearing walls, and generally as type A.

Type C. Light-weight aggregate blocks for: non-load-bearing walls, and non-load-bearing internal panels in framed buildings.

The following Codes of Practice apply: C.P. 121.201—Masonry Walls, Ashlared with Natural Stone, or with Cast Stone; and C.P. 122.—Walls and Partitions of Blocks and of Slabs.

blocks) should be 500 lb and 400 lb per sq. in. respectively. The constructional principles are the same as for brick walls.*

Weather Resistance. Flashings and D.P.C.'s must be carried out exactly in the same way as for brickwork. A 9 in. nominal brick wall cannot be regarded as waterproof unless the outside surface has some additional protection. Even so, rendering cannot be regarded as absolutely waterproof (see p. 74), and an external grade emulsion paint (2 coats) or some similar paint system is recommended in addition.

Thermal Insulation. Lightweight concrete blocks can be very valuable as insulators. For instance, a cavity wall constructed with two 3 in. leaves of lightweight fly-ash block and rendered externally has a thermal resistance equal to over 40 in. of solid brickwork.†

MORTAR MIXES

Purpose	Mix			
	Masonry cement	Normal Portland cement	Hydrated lime	Sand
For use in winter, or when exposed to severe conditions, or when dense concrete blocks are used	—	1	1	6
	1	—	—	3½–4
For use in warmer weather, and for normal degrees of exposure; with either dense or lightweight blocks	—	1	2	9
	1	—	—	4–4½
For internal work, in warm weather, with lightweight blocks only	—	1	3	12
	1	—	—	4½–5

Note.—From *Concrete Block Walls*, the Cement and Concrete Association. The use also of air entraining or plasticising agents is recommended with cement : sand mortars.

* The following Codes of Practice apply : C.P. 3 (1950) Chapter 5 Loading ; C.P. 111 (1948) ; C.P. 122 (1952).

† At the time of writing an Act is before Parliament to make thermal insulation obligatory in certain classes of buildings. It is probable that the Egerton Committee's recommendation: U value = 0·2, will be required. E.g. this can be attained by constructing a cavity wall as follows:—Outer leaf of brick or dense concrete block, cavity, and an inner leaf of lightweight concrete block (75 lb per cu. ft) internally plastered, one of many variations possible.

Storage. Concrete blocks must be dry before they are used. If they are built into the wall wet they will shrink slightly as they dry and cracks may occur. On site they must be covered in such a way that air can circulate freely around them.

Bedding. Blocks may be laid on a full bed of mortar; or they may be ' shell ' bedded, i.e. no mortar in the centre of the block. This latter method reduces the ingress of moisture at the joints (it breaks any potential capillary path) and is more suitable for 9 in. wide blocks; for thinner blocks normal bedding should be employed. ' Weak ' mortar should be used (see p. 49).

Shrinkage. Shrinkage is a key factor in the use of concrete blocks for building. Lightweight blocks, especially those manufactured by foaming or air-entraining methods are liable to excessive shrinkage unless they are specially cured. B.S. 2028 lays down the following:

Type of block	Maximum average drying shrinkage (per cent)	Maximum average moisture movement (per cent)
'A'	0·04	0·03
'B'	0·06	0·05
'C'	0·08	—

Note.—' Drying shrinkage ' is a movement obtained when a saturated block is dried under specified conditions, and ' moisture movement ' is the increase in length of a block when resaturated.

Walls over 50 ft long should be provided with expansion joints running vertically. This may be in the form of a butt joint (filled with mastic ⅜ in. thick). It is usually best to express this joint in a straightforward way; to try to hide the mastic joint with pointing will merely cause trouble later on. This vertical joint can sometimes be masked by a rainwater pipe.

Surface Treatment. For external work, blockwork may be exposed so long as it is established that the particular mix used is frost-proof. Some kinds of block are more liable than others to develop patches of algae, moss, etc. (This is also true of natural stone and other materials in some instances.) Colour can be introduced by selecting suitable aggregates or by using white or coloured cements. Very dense concrete blocks are liable to staining.

Finer texture blocks can be used very satisfactorily exposed for internal work, and are also more suitable for painting.

Rendering is a satisfactory way of dealing with concrete blocks externally, especially when the blocks are not too smooth; particularly good for rendering are blocks of no-fines concrete (see p. 90).

HOLLOW CLAY BLOCKS

These are made of selected clay which is dried and burned. Even though the walls of the blocks are relatively thin, they are strong and light. They have the important advantage that their movement due to variations in moisture content is negligible.

Sizes

Building Blocks (inner linings, party walls, cladding and load-bearing partition work):

Length	.	.	.	.	12 in.
Height	.	.	.	.	$8\frac{5}{8}$ in.
Width	.	.	.	.	3 in., 4 in.

This type is usually made keyed to receive rendering (i.e. the surface is grooved $1'' \times \frac{1}{4}''$).

Rug faced building blocks are available $8\frac{3}{4}'' \times 5\frac{5}{8}'' \times 6''$ wide; they are suitable for non-cavity construction (see p. 94).

Partition Blocks—Standard keyed blocks:

Length	.	.	.	.	9 in.
Height	.	.	.	.	$8\frac{5}{8}$ in.
Width	.	.	.	.	2 in., $2\frac{1}{2}$ in., 3 in.

Smooth-faced blocks are made in similar sizes, with a 4 in. wide block available in addition.

Special bonding, conduit, closure, and fixing blocks are available (see p. 94).

Although chases can be cut in these blocks after they have been erected, this is not advisable as they tend to get severely damaged. It is much better to plan the runs of services, so that special conduit blocks can be built in the right places.

Thermal Insulation. Because of the large amount of air within the cells of the blocks, the insulation value is good; for example, an 11 in. cavity wall with $4\frac{1}{2}$ in. brick outer leaf and a 4 in. block inner leaf has a ' U ' value of 0·25.

Maximum Unsupported Lengths. Either the length or the height should not be greater than the following:

2 in. blocks	.	.	8 ft	$4\frac{3}{4}$ in. blocks	.	.	15 ft
$2\frac{1}{2}$ in. ,,	.	.	10 ft	6 in. ,,	.	.	20 ft
3 in. ,,	.	.	12 ft	$8\frac{3}{4}$ in. ,,	.	.	25 ft

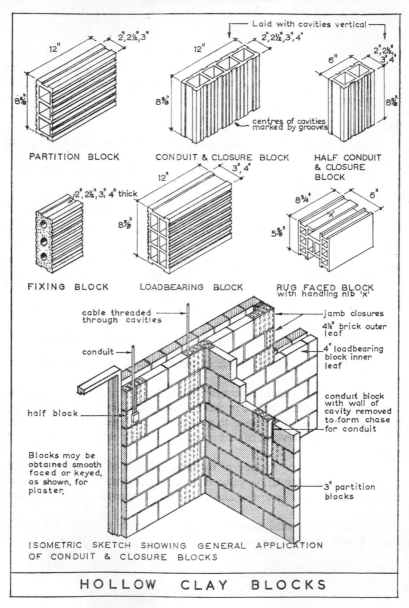

Laid with cavities vertical

PARTITION BLOCK

CONDUIT & CLOSURE BLOCK

HALF CONDUIT & CLOSURE BLOCK

centres of cavities marked by grooves

FIXING BLOCK

LOADBEARING BLOCK

RUG FACED BLOCK
with handling nib 'x'

cable threaded through cavities

jamb closures

4½" brick outer leaf

conduit

4" loadbearing block inner leaf

conduit block with wall of cavity removed to form chase for conduit

half block

Blocks may be obtained smooth faced or keyed, as shown, for plaster.

3" partition blocks

ISOMETRIC SKETCH SHOWING GENERAL APPLICATION OF CONDUIT & CLOSURE BLOCKS

HOLLOW CLAY BLOCKS

If bigger walls than this are required then they must be split up into panels of the maximum size indicated. The edges of the block-work should be firmly joined to the supports or piers.

Mortar. As with other block-work normal load-bearing walls and partitions should be bedded in 1 : 1 : 6 (cement, lime, sand), and non-load-bearing walls and partitions $2\frac{1}{2}$ in. thick and over in a 1 : 2 : 9 mix. A 1 : 9 cement sand mortar with a plasticiser is satisfactory for most applications.

8

Masonry—Stonework

NATURAL STONES

Classification

THERE are three main types of stone:

1. *Igneous rock:* a rock that has been subject to a high temperature way back in geological time and has a fused crystalline structure.
2. *Sedimentary rock,* which may have been formed from an older rock and redeposited with a different matrix by the action of air or water.
3. *Metamorphic rock,* which may be basically either sedimentary or igneous and which has been affected by earth movement or heat and/or pressure to give it a new structure.

Igneous Rocks. The main building stones in this classification are the Plutonic ones which have a coarse, crystalline structure, having been formed deep in the earth's crust and having cooled slowly. They are commonly known as granites, e.g.:

Corrennie. Salmon to red colour, used for engineering, building and decorative purposes, small pockets tend to form in the surface, from Aberdeenshire.

Cretown. Light grey, even grain, used for engineering and building, from Scotland.

De Lank. Mainly white with a little pink, with a tendency to brown if not carefully chosen, from Bodmin, Cornwall.

Lamorna. Grey colour, large crystals of felspar, used for engineering, from Penzance, Cornwall.

Mountsorrel. Dark grey colour, with some felspar, or may be dark reddish-brown, from Sileby, Leicestershire.

Shap. Two varieties, one pink and brown and the other red-brown with black and grey speckles, from Westmorland.

Sedimentary Rocks. Limestones and sandstones. Limestones vary a great deal and vary in form from biological precipitation (i.e. the deposition of minute shell creatures) or the recementing of older calcareous rocks.

Sandstone usually consists of consolidated or cemented sand. The older geologically sandstone is, the more satisfactory it is likely to be for building. The following is a list of examples:

Ancaster.   An oolitic limestone. Not satisfactory in industrial atmospheres, buff-coloured, easy to work, suitable for interior use, from Lincolnshire.

Bath.   An oolitic limestone. Light cream with pale grey flecks, should not be used in very exposed or polluted conditions, from quarries near Bath, Somerset.

Bolsover Moor.   Yellow-brown, a magnesium limestone having been formed in shallow water, weathers well except in London, very good for carving, not available in large sizes, from Derbyshire.

Bristol Pennant.   Fine-grained, blue-grey, hard and able to take carving.

Chillmark.   Yellow-brown, used for mouldings and carvings, poor in industrial atmospheres, from Chillmark, Wiltshire.

Clipsham.   Pale cream or buff, for general building and plain ashlar work, from Lincolnshire.

Darleydale.   A millstone grit, from buff to grey, fairly smooth with good weathering properties, from Derbyshire.

Hornton.   Greeny-blue to brown, takes a fine polish, and weathers well in industrial atmospheres, rather inconsistent texture, from Edgehill, Warwickshire.

Hopton Wood.   Has a trace of fossil remains and takes a good polish, interior work and ornamental carving, from Middleton, Derbyshire.

Kentish Rag.   Green and grey, suitable for rough rubble work.

Mansfield.   Yellow and red, suitable for decorative work, or external work away from towns, from Nottinghamshire.

Portland Stone.   A fine oolitic stone with an indiscernible bed, ivory, suitable for industrial atmospheres, from south Dorset.

Marbles. These are metamorphic rocks, another class of which is slate. These are useful for decorative work such as shop fronts and facings, and for interior linings. It is an expensive material and may be polished to achieve the maximum decorative effect. Facings and linings are usually about $\frac{3}{4}$ in. thick, pavings are about $1\frac{1}{2}$ in. thick, i.e. Purbeck, reddish-brown and grey, takes a polish and is not very lasting, from Swanage, Dorset. There are many varieties of Italian marble capable of taking polishes and suitable for interior work.

QUARRY STRUCTURE

Most building stone has ' lamena ' structure. This is especially true of sedimentary rocks.

Bedding. This is the plane in which the stone is most easily split and it is
vital that, in walling, the stones are laid with their natural bed horizontally.
The bed is not always easy to see, as in the case of Portland stone, but it
is still important to lay the stone correctly, as stone laid with the bed running
in the same direction as the surface of the wall is liable to be damaged by
frost shaling off the surface. Exceptions to this rule are in the case of projections where the bed should be parallel to the perpends, and in arches where
the bed should be at right angles to the thrust. At the time the rocks were
being laid down, many millions of years ago, the bed was truly horizontal in
both directions. Since that time, the earth's crust has invariably moved and
folded, so that in the quarry the bedding planes 'dip', and often tilt sideways
—which is called the ' strike ' of the rocks.

Grain. This is the second direction of easy splitting and is usually only
discernible by a mason when the stone is cut.

STONEWORK

Definition. The term ' masonry ' refers to walls and structures built in
natural stone or cast stone. It includes walls built of other blocks which
have to be bonded together. This chapter deals chiefly with masonry in
natural stone, but reference is made at the end to the properties and uses of
cast stone.

Characteristics of Stonework. The principle is the same as brickwork
but the units are larger and can vary in size. Large blocks of stone are cut
from the quarry and sawn into blocks of handleable size. Harder stones are
split or cut into smaller sizes in the quarry and are used in irregular shapes
with the minimum of ' dressing ', that is, cutting to rectangular or other
desired shape. Stones in most regular masonry walling are about 1 to 2 ft
cube content and weigh 1½ to 3 cwt. This possible variation in size and shape
gives the architect much more opportunity to make the proportions of the
stones conform to the general scale and proportions of the building, i.e.
the stones in the base of a large monumental building should be large. Some
stones such as the quoin stone of a large cornice will have to be very large.
Lifting apparatus such as a block and tackle has to be used for all stones
larger than the normal ashlar walling block. The amount of variation can
be seen from the example on p. 100.

Natural stones vary considerably in hardness, so the harder stones tend to be used in irregular walling, e.g. random rubble. The softer, which can be cut easily with mechanical saws, will be cut into precise blocks for building into ashlar walling (p. 100), or for dressings. Thick mortar joints, to accommodate the irregular surfaces have to be used for rubble work, thin joints typify ashlar work. Of course, local building, i.e. garden walls, cottages, etc., are usually built in random walling to save labour, irrespective of the nature of the stone.

For economy, masonry walls are now usually faced with stone only, the backing being brickwork or concrete block, as labour costs now make stonework always more expensive than brickwork.*

Most stonework is very strong, granite is immensely strong, being used for docks, lighthouses, etc.

Principles of Use. Building stones, except granites and slate, will absorb water, some more than others. Moisture may also penetrate the joints. Therefore precautions should be taken in the design of stonework to prevent moisture penetrating the structure, particularly through horizontal ledges, cornices, string courses, parapets, etc. This may disfigure and damage the stone or affect the structure behind. Precautions depend on the nature of the stone and the exposure of the building, but it is common practice to protect all wide projections, cornices, etc., to put damp-proof courses in parapets and under copings, and, in the case of not so durable stones, to cover small projections with metal flashings.

Defects in stones are dealt with in *Advanced Building Construction (Structures)*.

TECHNICAL TERMS

The following is a list of technical terms frequently met with in mason's work.

Bed Surface. The surfaces of a stone perpendicular to the pressure, which surfaces must be worked in one plane surface. Masons, to form thin joints, often make the beds hollow. This is bad, as all the pressure will be thrown on the outer part, which is liable to spall the edge of the stone.

Bonders. Long stones placed through from front to back of a wall, as shown on p. 104 A, to tie the wall transversely. These may be either headers or through stones (see Headers).

Copings. The highest and covering course of masonry, forming a waterproof top, to preserve the interior of wall from wet, which in frosty weather might burst the wall. Copings must have D.P.C. (see p. 76). Page 100

* *Code of Practice C.P. 121.201 deals with ' Walls Ashlared with Natural or Cast Stone '.*

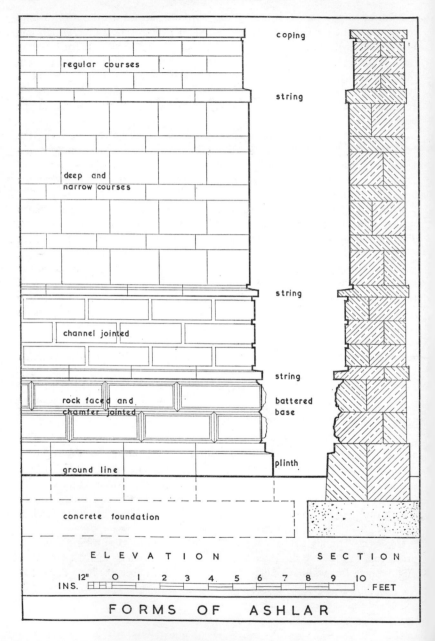

coping

regular courses

string

deep and
narrow courses

string

channel jointed

string

rock faced and
chamfer jointed

battered
base

plinth

ground line

concrete foundation

ELEVATION   SECTION

12"   O   1   2   3   4   5   6   7   8   9   10
INS.   .FEET

FORMS   OF   ASHLAR

shows flat copings on the top surface, which should be used only for inclined surfaces, as on a gable or in sheltered positions. Feather-edged copings are also used on gable ends, however, to throw the water inwards on to the roof. Page 104 B gives section and elevation of feather-edged copings, the upper surface of which is inclined to throw water off on one side of the walls; these are necessary for parapet walls of crowded thoroughfares. Saddle-back is the name applied when the upper surface is inclined or weathered both ways, as on p. 104 G, and segmental when the section of coping shows the upper surface to be a part of a circle, as in F.

Corbel. A piece of stone projecting from a wall to support a projecting feature.

Skew Corbel. A projecting stone at the lowest part of the triangular portion of the gable end of a wall supporting the starting piece of coping, and resisting its sliding tendency. The skew corbels are often tied into the wall by long bronze cramps.

Cramp. Slate or metal connections used in stonework, as slate and bronze cramps, shown on p. 115 A, B and E.

Dressings. Stones are said to be dressed when their faces are brought to a fair surface; but any stones which are cut or prepared and are used as finishings to quoins, window and door openings, stones applied as an ornamental feature, such as quoin stones, window and door jambs, are described as dressings.

Drip-stone. A projecting stone moulding, having a throated under-surface, to throw water off clear of walls, and usually placed over arches of doors, windows, etc. If the moulding is returned square, it is termed a label moulding.

Grout. This is a thin mortar which is poured over the stones when brought up to a level surface, to fill up any interstices between the stones in the hearting of walls or other positions as necessity requires.

Headers. These are bonding stones, which extend across not more than three-fourths of the thickness of the walls, as shown on p. 104 A; if the stones extend the whole thickness they are usually termed *through stones* (see Bonders).

Jambs, Window and Door. For purposes of strength these should be of cut stone and attention given that each course is securely bonded. For that reason it would not be advisable to build them in rubble. Page 113 shows alternate courses, one showing the stones forming the window jambs acting as stretchers—these are termed outbands, as shown on p. 113 A and B; and the other a through stone or header forming the face of reveal and the face of rebated jamb, and is termed an inband.

Parapet. The top section of a wall where it conceals the gutter of the roof (see p. 237).

Pillar. A vertical support, square or rectangular in section and always independent of walls.

Plinth. A horizontal projecting course or courses built at the base of a wall, as shown on p. 100.

Quoins. The angle stones of buildings. In rubble and inferior stone walls, quoins are built of good blocks of ashlar stone to give strength to the wall. These are sometimes worked to give a pleasing effect, and where hammer-dressed and chamfered, are said to be rusticated. They are, at times, merely built with a rough or quarry face, as on p. 104 H, only having the four face edges of each stone laying in one plane.

Sills. These are the lower horizontal members of openings, and those in stone up to 4 ft 6 in. long are usually of one length, being pinned in cement to both sides of the opening. They should be fixed after the carcase of a building has been finished, and any settlement that was likely to occur through a number of wet mortar joints has taken place. Where it is inconvenient for sills to be fixed *after* the carcase of a building is completed, they may be built in as the work proceeds, provided they are bedded only under the jambs with the section of the sills between the jambs left clear of mortar until the building has settled. If this is not done and the sills are bedded solid throughout their lengths, then they may fracture due to the unequal stresses produced by the pressures transmitted by the jambs being concentrated at the ends only, and not being evenly distributed through the entire lengths of the sills. They may be plain and square, as for door-sills or thresholds, or sunk, weathered, moulded with drip and with properly formed stools and grooved for metal water-bar, or sunk, weathered, throated and grooved for metal water-bar, or moulded, grooved and weathered.

Spalls or Shivers. These are broken chips of stone, worked off in the dressing. Stone whose face is damaged by the action of frost or fire is said to have spalled.

String Courses. Horizontal projecting bands of stone, as on p. 100, often carried below windows, of architectural importance, imparting a feature to the building. On p. 113 B the sill forms an integral part of the string course.

Tailing Irons. These are formed of H, L or T sections for holding down the ends of projecting members. They should be in bronze.

Templates. Pieces of stone placed under the end of a beam or girder to distribute the weight over a greater area, usually Blue York Stone but concrete ' padstones ' are now in general use.

Throatings. Grooves on the under surfaces of copings, sills, string courses, etc., as in section, p. 104 F, forming a drip to prevent the water that would otherwise trickle down and disfigure the walls.

This disfiguration also occurs where metal lettering has been fixed to and proud of a stone fascia. Even if the dowels are bronze or galvanised, disfiguration will still occur when they are fixed horizontally since the impurities in the air will settle upon them and will be dissolved by condensation and rain water.

If, however, they are fixed to slope down from the stone face to the lettering they support, the trouble will be avoided.

Through Stones. Stones which extend through the entire thickness of wall, to tie or bond it, as shown on p. 104 B. These are considered objectionable, for the reason that if any projection has to be taken off at the back, to present a fair face, it would disturb the setting of the adjoining masonry, also damp is more likely to show on the interior of walls where the continuity of the material is uninterrupted.

In the Lake District stone walling is often built with each stone sloping outwards in section, while each through stone is covered by another on plan, thus providing an efficient D.P.C. throughout the whole height of the wall.

Vaulting. The arched stone ceiling of any space (see *Advanced Building Construction (Structures)*).

Weathering. The top face of a stone worked to a plane surface inclined to the horizontal for the purpose of throwing off the water is said to be weathered, as in sills, cornices, etc., but carefully distinguish the expression ' weathered ' as applied to the effect of the weather on stonework or paintwork, etc.

FOUNDATIONS AND FOOTINGS

Stone walls may be provided with concrete foundations. Where built on rocky sites, the concrete is dispensed with or used only to level up irregularities. Stone footings usually consist of two courses of long stones, rectangular in section, the least dimension being about 9 in.; on these the walls are erected, as shown on p. 104.

STONE WALLING

This is classified as follows:

(1) *Rubble:* Flint; random rubble set dry; random rubble set in mortar; Kentish Rag; random rubble built in courses; uncoursed, squared or snecked rubble; squared rubble built up to courses; regular coursed rubble.

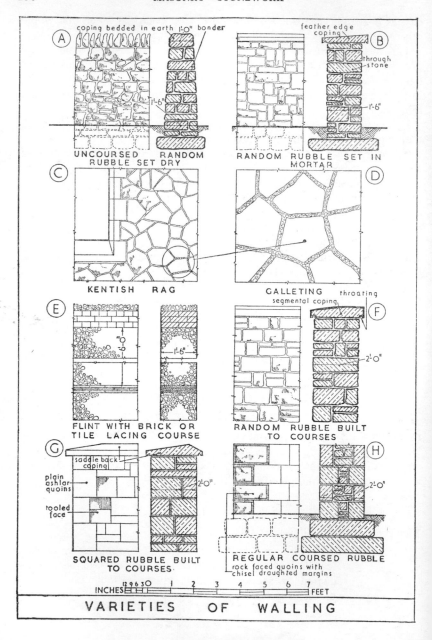

A — UNCOURSED RUBBLE SET DRY — coping bedded in earth 1'-0" bonder — 1'-6"

B — RANDOM RUBBLE SET IN MORTAR — feather edge coping — through stone — 1'-6"

C — KENTISH RAG

D — GALLETING

E — FLINT WITH BRICK OR TILE LACING COURSE — 6'-0" — 1'-6"

F — RANDOM RUBBLE BUILT TO COURSES — throating — segmental coping — 2'-0"

G — SQUARED RUBBLE BUILT TO COURSES — saddle back coping — plain ashlar quoins — tooled face — 2'-0"

H — REGULAR COURSED RUBBLE — rock faced quoins with chisel draughted margins — 2'-0"

INCHES 12 9 6 3 0   1   2   3   4   5   6   7 FEET

VARIETIES   OF   WALLING

(2) Block-in-course.

(3) *Ashlar:* Ashlar facing with brick backing; ashlar facing with rubble backing.

Rubble walls are those built of thinly-bedded stone, generally under 9 in. in depth, of irregular shapes as in common or random rubble, or squared as in coursed rubble.

Block-in-course is composed of squared stones usually larger than coursed rubble, and under 12 in. in depth.

Ashlar is the name given to stones, from 12 to 18 in. deep, dressed with a scabbling hammer, or sawn to blocks of given dimensions and carefully worked to obtain fine joints.

The length of a soft stone for resisting pressure should not exceed three times its depth; the breadth from one-and-a-half to twice its depth; the length in harder stones four to five times its depth, and breadth three times its depth.

Considering these in detail:

Flint Walls. These are largely employed in the chalk districts, where large quantities of flints are found beneath the beds of chalk. The flints are small and of irregular form. The larger stones are selected for the facing, the exposed surface being chipped to present the silica face. For the best work they are squared up to form small briquettes; they are laid in regular courses, as at St. Saviour's Cathedral, Southwark. The quoins, windows and door dressings are always built with squared stone or brick to give strength and obtain regularity in these parts. The facing flints are then laid, being separately and carefully bedded in mortar; the hearting is then inserted from every 6 to 9 in. in height, and bedded either by grouting or by a process similar to larrying in brickwork. Owing to the smallness of the material, flint walls are liable to be deficient in longitudinal and transverse strength. To remedy this, lacing courses, consisting of large, long flat stones, or of three courses of plain tiles or bricks, are built in at intervals of about every 6 ft in height, as shown on p. 104 E.

Random Rubble. The name given to walling built of stones that are not squared (see p. 104).

Random Rubble Set Dry. In the stone districts boundary walls are built of rubble set without mortar in courses about 12 in. high, provided with a rough coping as shown on p. 104 A, bedded in mortar, to form a water-resisting top, to keep water from getting into the body of the work.

Uncoursed Random Rubble Set in Mortar. The stones are used as they come from the quarry, the bond being obtained by fitting in the inequalities of the stone, and by using one bond stone every super yard on face; any openings between stones to be pinned in with spalls, as shown on p. 104 B. Walls built of random rubble should be made one-third thicker than the thickness necessary for brick walls.

Kentish Rag. Walls of this type, as shown on p. 104 C, are built of a compact, heavy, unstratified limestone largely found in Kent in beds from 6 in. to 3 ft in thickness alternating with quartzose sand. It absorbs very little water and resists the weather well. It is not suitable for internal work, as moisture condenses upon its surface. The blocks are roughly dressed to a polygonal form, being fitted with a hammer as they are bedded in the wall. In this work all quoins and dressings are built with properly squared stones. The face stones are first carefully bedded in mortar, the hearting being afterwards filled in partly by bedding and partly by grouting in mortar.

Spalling often occurs in Kentish Rag as it is almost impossible to lay each stone on its natural bed. Restoration of spalled and defective stones is very difficult owing to the fact that there are no through stones or bond. Each stone is brought to a level face in the wall by inserting a small piece of stone under it at the back. Cutting out defective stones could quite easily result in a fall of the stones above it. Bronze dowels could be inserted in the remaining stonework and the missing stone could be replaced with Portland cement and stone dust mixed to match the surrounding stonework.

Random Rubble Built to Courses. This usually consists of roughly bedded or easily cleft stones, of irregular shapes, with only the acutest angles knocked off; they are arranged to form horizontal beds at intervals of 12 to 18 in. height, every stone being bedded in mortar. The object is to ensure that there shall be no continuous vertical joints (see p. 104 F).

Uncoursed, Squared or Snecked Rubble. This type of work is built in districts where a highly stratified stone is abundant; such stones lend themselves to be easily squared. With these stones, horizontal bed joints are readily obtained, but as the stones are of irregular depths there is a great tendency to obtain long vertical joints; to prevent this, small stones, termed snecks, are inserted where required. For good work not more than four side-faces should form any continuous vertical face joint. To limit the length of vertical joints, no stone for house walls should be more than 8 in. in depth. One bonder should be inserted in every superficial yard of wall face.

Squared Rubble Built to Courses. The stones are roughly squared and built up to courses to prevent long vertical joints and to ensure a good bond. Page 104 G shows squared rubble brought up to level beds with plain ashlar quoins.

Regular Coursed Rubble. In this kind of work all stones in one course are

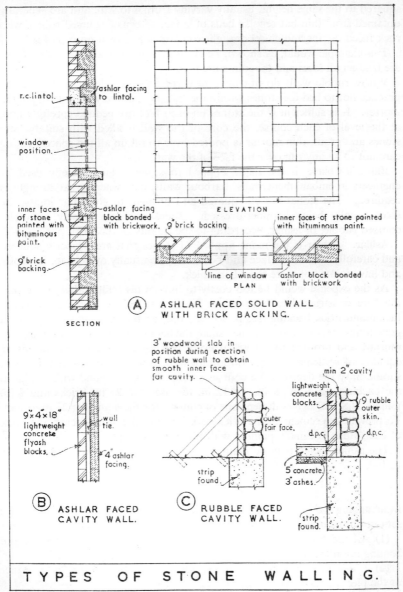

r.c.lintol.

ashlar facing to lintol.

window position.

ashlar facing

inner faces of stone painted with bituminous paint.

ashlar facing block bonded with brickwork. 9" brick backing.

ELEVATION

inner faces of stone painted with bituminous paint.

9" brick backing.

line of window
PLAN

9" brick backing.

ashlar block bonded with brickwork

SECTION

(A) ASHLAR FACED SOLID WALL WITH BRICK BACKING.

3" woodwool slab in position during erection of rubble wall to obtain smooth inner face for cavity.

min 2" cavity

9"×4"×18" lightweight concrete flyash blocks.

wall tie.

4" ashlar facing.

lightweight concrete blocks.

outer fair face.

9" rubble outer skin.

d.p.c.

d.p.c.

strip found.

5" concrete. 3" ashes.

(B) ASHLAR FACED CAVITY WALL.

(C) RUBBLE FACED CAVITY WALL.

strip found.

TYPES OF STONE WALLING.

H 2

squared to the same height, usually varying from 4 to 9 in. and are generally obtained from thin but regular beds of stone. Regular coursed rubble with rock faced quoins and chisel draughted margins is shown on p. 104 H.

This example would, as shown, be classed as ashlar walling, as the stones are true on all faces and the joints are fine.

Where rubble walls do not have to carry any great loads it is common practice not to bed the stones within the thickness of the wall individually in mortar. It is sufficient if the stones on each face are bedded carefully and, at the level of each course, the core of the wall is filled with suitable size stones and grout, thin mortar is poured over to fill up all the spaces, taking care not to let any run over the face of the wall.

Block-in-Course is the name applied to stone walling, chiefly used by engineers in embankment walls, harbour walls, etc., where great strength is required. The stones are all squared and brought to good fair joints, the faces usually being hammer-dressed. Block-in-course closely resembles coursed rubble, or ashlar, according to the quality of the work put upon it.

Ashlar. Ashlar is the name applied to stones that are properly squared and carefully worked on face and beds, and are usually over 12 in. in depth, and have joints not more than $\frac{1}{8}$ in. thick.

As the expense would be too costly to have walls built entirely of ashlar, they are constructed to have ashlar facing and rubble backing, or ashlar facing and brick backing (see p. 107 A), but, as the backing would have a greater number of joints than the ashlar, the backing should be built in cement mortar, and brought to a level at every bed joint of the ashlar, to ensure equality of settlement. It is important that ashlar backed with brickwork should have the depth of the courses arranged to correspond with a joint in the backing, i.e. 6 in., 9 in., or 12 in. for use with $2\frac{5}{8}$ in. bricks and $\frac{3}{8}$ in. joints. B.S. 1232 gives dimensions of courses for these and for $2\frac{7}{8}$ in. bricks. To prevent the cement in the brickwork staining the stone-facing, the back of each stone is usually painted with bituminous paint.

The ashlar facing may be plain, rebated, or chamfered, as illustrated on p. 100.

JOINTS

In arranging the joints of ashlar masonry, each of the face stones should be set out on the drawings, the following general principles should be observed:

(1) All the bed joints must be arranged at right angles to the pressure coming upon them.

(2) The joint should be arranged so as to leave no acute angles on either of the pieces joined.

(3) The arrangement of the vertical and cross wall joints should be such as to give the maximum bond of one stone over those below and give a pattern satisfying to the eye.

The first condition applies to all kinds of masonry. It is necessary to prevent any sliding tendency taking place between the stones.

The second condition applies chiefly to the joints in tracery work, and any exposed joints in any other work such as gables. Stone being a granular material, anything approaching an acute angle is liable to weather badly; therefore in any tracery work having several bars intersecting, a stone must be arranged to contain the intersections and a short length of each bar, and the joints should be (a) at right angles to the directions of the abutting bars if straight, or (b) perpendicular to any adjacent curved bar. This not only prevents any acute anlges occurring, as would be the case if the joints were made along the line of intersection of the moulding, but also ensures a better finish, as the intersection line can be carved more neatly with the chisel, and is more lasting than would be the case if a mortar joint occurred along the above line. In no case, either in tracery, string courses, or other mouldings, should a joint occur at any mitre line. This is the reverse of a joiner's joint.

Whereas for plain ashlar it is desirable to get most stones approximately the same size, the stones in alternate courses near the quoins cannot be half the length of the other stones. Sometimes for this, stones three-quarters of the usual length are used as the header and closer in brickwork, or the length of stones in both courses may be adjusted as shown in the example on p. 100. In this example is shown the effect of courses alternately deep and narrow, which can relieve the monotony of regular masonry in monumental work. Note that the narrow courses are deep on the bed.

Joints and connections in stone-work may be classified as follows:

1. Joggle joints
2. Cramps
3. Weathered joints

Under the first head are included tabling joints, cement joggles, dowels, and pebble joints.

Joggles. A joggle is a form of joint in which a portion of the side joint of one stone is cut to form a projection, and a corresponding sinking is made in the side of the adjacent stone for the reception of the projection, as shown on p. 112 A and B. It is chiefly used in landings to prevent any movement between the stones joined and so retain a level surface, and also to assist in distributing any weight over every stone in the landing.

Table Joint. It consists of a joggle formed in the bed joints to prevent lateral displacement in the stones of a wall subjected to lateral pressure, such as in a sea-wall, the projection in this case being about 1½ in. in depth and a third of the breadth of the stone in width, as shown on p. 112 c. Slate joggles are often substituted for table joints to reduce expense. They are formed of slate about 12″ × 4″ × 2″ inserted into sinkings made in the bed joint at the junction of the side joints of two stones and top bed joint of another, as shown in D. These were used in the piers of Tower Bridge.

Cement Joggles. These are generally used in the side joints of the top courses of masonry to prevent lateral movement in the same, and consist of a V-shaped sinking in the side joint of each adjacent stone in the same course, as shown on p. 112 c and F.

Dowels. Dowelling is another method of resisting lateral movement. The dowels consist usually of pieces of hard stone, slate or copper about 1 in. square in section and varying from about 2 to 5 in. in length, shown in E, being sunk and set in cement in corresponding mortices in the adjacent stones. They are used in both the side and bed joints. They are generally employed in the top courses of masonry where the weight on or of the individual stones is not great, and also in the dressings, about openings and in the bed joints of the drums of columns, balusters, and in any position where lateral movement is likely to occur. The united mass thus formed from the connected stones renders any movement impossible under normal conditions.

Pebbles. Small pebbles bedded in cement in the joints of stones are used to prevent lateral motion; they are very economical and effective.

Cramps. Metal cramps are used similarly to dowels to bind work together, but are more particularly adapted for positions in which there is a tendency for the stones to come apart, such as in copings covering a gable, or in face stones of no great depth, or cornices and projecting string courses to tie the stones to the body of the wall or to the steel skeleton supports. The cramps are made from thin pieces of metal of varying lengths and sectional area according to the work, bent at right angles about 1½ in. at each end. A chase with a dove-tailed mortice at each end is made in the stones to receive the cramp, the ends of which are made rough and inserted, as shown on p. 115 A and B. The cramps are usually prepared from either wrought iron, copper or bronze. If wrought iron is used, it should be subjected to some preservative process, such as galvanising, to prevent oxidation. Iron is useful on account of its great tensile strength. Copper is valued for non-corrosive properties under ordinary conditions, and its tensile strength, which is not much less than wrought iron; it is, however, comparatively soft. Bronze has properties similar to those of copper, with the exception that it is much harder, which, under most conditions, is to be desired.

The best bedding materials are Portland cement, lead and asphalt. Care should be taken to cover the cramp completely with the bedding material. Lead is at times objected to for external work because it tends to form a galvanic couple with the cramp in the presence of moisture accelerating corrosion.

Lead Plug. Stones may be connected together by means of lead in the following manner, shown on p. 115 c and D.

Dovetail shaped mortices of the form shown are made to correspond in the side joints of two adjacent stones, into which, when placed in position, molten lead is poured, and when cooled is caulked, thus completely filling the mortices and connecting the pieces.

Slate Cramps. These consist of pieces of slate about $7'' \times 2'' \times 1''$ cut to a double dovetail form; they are bedded in Portland cement in sinkings formed to receive them, and are generally used in flat coping stones, as shown on p. 115 E.

Anchor Bolts. Long iron bolts are frequently employed at the backs of cornices that have great projection; in such cases the centre of gravity of the mass is dangerously near the edge of the wall. The bolts are passed through a hole drilled through the back of the cornice, or are inserted into a chase worked along the back face of the stone, and extended a sufficient distance down the back of the wall, being provided at their lower ends with large iron plates or washers; the effect is to bring the centre of gravity of the combined mass a safe distance back from the front of the wall.

In steel framed buildings advantage is usually taken to design the steel members of the roof so that the projecting stone cornices are most effectively tailed down by this steel-work secured to the frame of the building.

In pinnacles at the tops of spires and buttresses, where formed of small stones, it is usual to connect a sufficient number of them together with an iron bolt, which latter usually contains their common axis, thereby increasing the stability.

Rag Bolt. The ends of the bolts are often fixed by having the end that is let into the stone jagged, and run with lead, or Portland cement, the mortice being dovetail shaped, to secure it from any upward pressure, as on p. 115.

Where there is any probability of a great upward stress, the rag bolt is replaced by an anchor bolt and plate. The bolt is passed through a hole drilled through the stone.

Weathered Joints. Under the third head is included all joints or precautions taken to prevent the deterioration of the joints of cornices or other exposed parts of masonry due to the percolation of water into the joints.

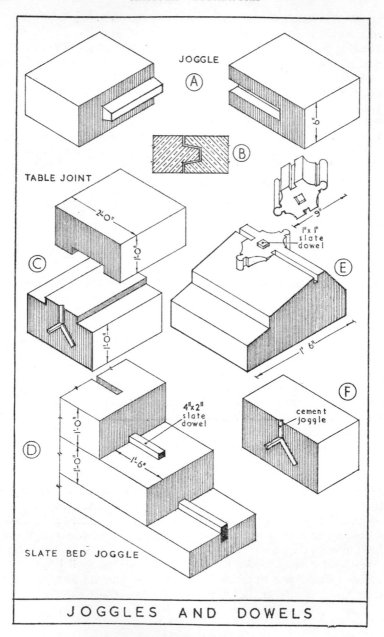

JOGGLE
A

B

TABLE JOINT
C

E

1" x 1"
slate dowel

9"

2'-0"

1'-0"

1'-0"

1'-0"

1' 6"

D

4" x 2"
slate dowel

1'-0"

1'-0"

1'-6"

F

cement joggle

SLATE BED JOGGLE

JOGGLES AND DOWELS

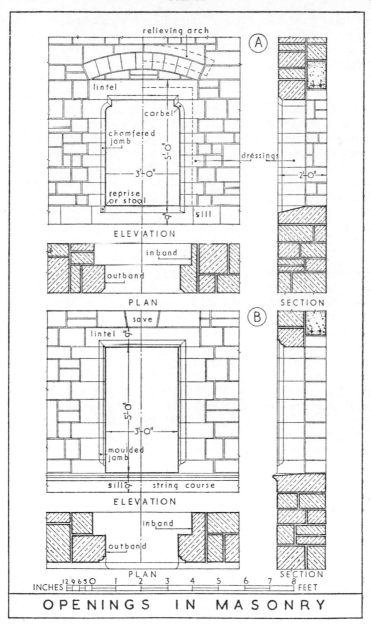

OPENINGS IN MASONRY

Saddled or Water Joint. To protect the joints of cornices and other exposed horizontal surfaces of masonry the sinking is sometimes stopped before the joint and weathered off, as shown on p. 115 F, G and H. Any water passing down the weathered surface is diverted from the joint.

Rebated Joints. These joints are used for stone roofs and copings to obtain weather-tight joints. There are two kinds: (1) when both stones are rebated; (2) when the upper stone only is rebated. In the first case the stones are of the same thickness throughout, their upper surface being level when the joint is made. In the second case the stones are thicker at the bottom edges than at the top, the bottom edge having a rebate taken out equal to the thickness of the upper edge of the stone below it, over which it fits. The part that laps over should not be less than ¾-in. thick. The under surfaces or beds of the stones should be level.

The upper exposed surfaces of all masonry built of soft or porous stones should be protected by a lead covering.

STONE LINTELS

Square openings in buildings are frequently bridged with stone lintels. Stone, owing to its low tensile resistance, is not well adapted to act as a beam, and in wide openings every care must be taken to relieve these members as far as possible of the weight above.

Lintels are of two kinds: (1) where the openings are small, each opening can be bridged in one piece of stone; (2) where the openings are large, each lintel is built up with several stones.

The first class is divided into (a) those bridging narrow openings, or where the lintel is made of great depth, rendering any precautions for relieving the pressure unnecessary ; (b) lintel with a relieving arch over, usually employed in rubble walls, as on p. 113 A; (c) lintels in rubble or ashlar work, where it is inconvenient to use a relieving arch, a flat arch of three stones is constructed above the lintel, as shown in B; the centre stone or key is termed the save. In bedding the save stones no mortar is placed on the lintel, but the stones are supported in their position by means of small wood wedges. After a sufficient mass of the wall has been built to tail down the side saves the wedges are removed. In finishing the wall, the joint between the saves and the lintel is pointed only, thus no weight from the wall above is brought to bear on the lintel.

STONE STAIRS AND STEPS

Stone steps, as used for external terraces, are usually in a harder stone which will resist the frost so that a simple square finish is common and is pleasant.

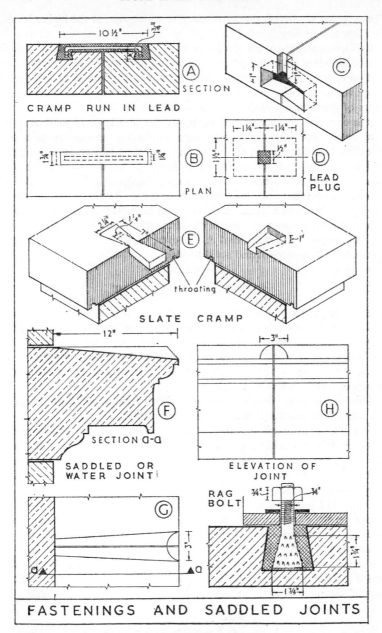

FASTENINGS AND SADDLED JOINTS

These stones are best bedded on concrete which can, at the higher levels, be on a hardcore filling.

Random-on-edge paving gives a very pleasant texture and many variations can be achieved by using cobbles, flints and panels of brick. The stone, if laid on edge, will wear better: if laid on its natural bed, as each lamination wears through, a ring shows and frost will tend to break away the exposed edges of the layer and decay may be accelerated.

It is common practice to bed paving stones in a layer of sand on a hardcore base. For irregular paving such as random stones on edge this is essential, but where areas of flat paving are to be laid to an accurate level and any sinking is to be avoided it is better to lay the slabs in weak lime mortar on a concrete base, as sand bed on hardcore is likely to subside by gradual compaction or by leeching away of the sand when water gets through the joints. This often results in shallow puddles which are very inconvenient.

In a stone staircase each step is one stone jointed to and partly bearing on the step below. The main load is, however, taken by the wall as the end of the stone is built in 6 in. and solid bedded.

STONE SLAB FACINGS

The quality of the finish that natural stone gives to a building can seldom be bettered by any other material. So for important buildings, even where they are tall and framed, stone would be considered as a facing material. Orthodox ashlar work requires thick walls and the large volume of stone would be prohibitive both as to cost of the stone and as to extra cost of structure and foundations to take the weight.

This has led to the development of thin slab facings, which are attached to the face of the structural wall or the panel infilling.

The chief consideration is the method of fixing, and for this non-ferrous metal cramps are usually used. It is advisable, and in most areas the authorities insist, that the main weight of the facing slabs is taken on the structure by some offset or corbel so that the chief function of any metal fastenings is only to hold the slabs back to the wall and not to take their weight.

On p. 117 is shown a wall of a framed building faced with stone slabs, where the slabs are supported every other course on a corbel course which is built into and tailed down by the panel wall which fills in between the structural frame. One corbel course is bedded direct on the beam at floor level, the other comes at half storey height. These slabs are about 2 ft 3 in. square, and if in Portland stone could be 3 in. thick. The size of stone and thickness depend on many circumstances; on the type of stone and how easily it can

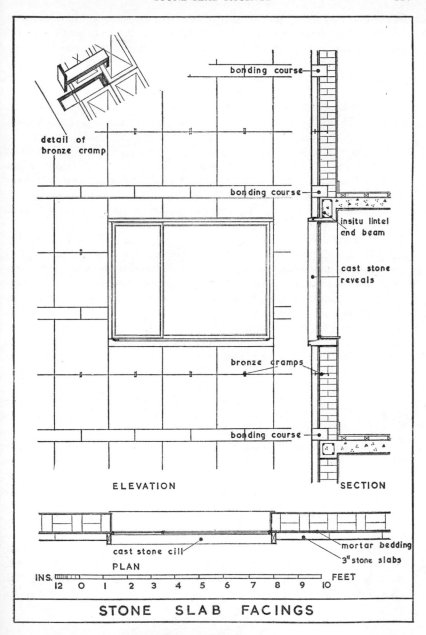

detail of bronze cramp

bonding course

bonding course

insitu lintel and beam

cast stone reveals

bronze cramps

bonding course

ELEVATION

SECTION

cast stone cill

mortar bedding

3" stone slabs

PLAN

INS. 12 0 1 2 3 4 5 6 7 8 9 10 FEET

STONE SLAB FACINGS

be cut into thin slabs; the amount of handling the slabs will have between cutting and fixing on the wall; and the method of fixing. Larger slabs would have to be thicker to avoid fracture in handling and then the saving in weight is reduced; on the other hand, thin small stones need more cramps to fix, and the accommodating of the cramps in the edge of the slab becomes more difficult.

These slabs should be bedded solid, i.e. the whole of the back should be covered with bedding mortar which may be $\frac{1}{2}$ in. to 1 in. thick depending on the accuracy that can be worked to in the stone backing and brickwork.

It is more essential with these slabs than with traditional bonded blocks that the backs should be painted with bituminous paint. This may affect the adhesion of the bedding but, if the back of the slab is serrated or picked, it should have sufficient key.

This detail shows a projecting frame round the window. This is a suitable finish for use with a slab facing as no special quoin stones are necessary. The frame may be in stone to match the slabs, which is simple to detail for the sill and jambs, but the head usually requires supporting by metal cramps and presents difficulties. If the frame is in concrete the sill, jambs and head can be precast ; metal ties are cast in and part left projecting for casting in with the R.C. beam or casing to the R.S.J. Alternatively the head can be cast *in situ* as an integral part of the R.C. beam as shown in the diagram. Sometimes all members of the frame are cast *in situ*, but the casting of the vertical members is a difficult job as a fine finish is essential. Attempts are made sometimes to cast the head *in situ*, using a natural stone aggregate in an attempt to match the sill and jambs which are then in natural stone. It is not easy to get a good match.

LABOURS

The following are the chief labours recognised in the preparation of stonework: scabbling, hammer-dressing, self-faced, half-sawing, chisel-draughting, plain work, which includes a combed or dragged face over a Bath or soft lime-stone, a tooled stroke over the plane faces of a hard limestone and sandstone, such as Portland or York, or a smooth-axed face on granite; sunk work, moulded work, rubbed and polished work. These labours may be put upon straight, circular, or circular circular work.

Scabbling or Scappling. Taking off the irregular angles of stone with the scabbling hammer; is usually done at the quarry, and is then said to be quarry pitched, hammer-faced, or hammer blocked; when used with such faces the stone is called rock or rustic work.

Hammer-dressing. Roughest description of work after scabbling, as shown on p. 122 A, the tool generally used being the waller's hammer.

Self-faced, Quarry-faced or Rock-faced. The term applied to the quarry face, or the surface formed when the stone is detached from the mass in the quarry; also the surfaces formed when a stone is split in two.

Chisel-draughted Margins. To reduce an irregular surface to a plane surface a rebate about an inch in width is worked at two opposite edges of the surface; the parallelism of these rebates is ensured by testing with the winding strips and straight-edge. A similar rebate is worked on the two remaining edges, connecting those first made. A continuous margin or rebate is thus formed about the four edges of the stone, every portion of which lies in the same plane surface. If the stone is small, the irregular excrescence is then removed with the chisel to the level of the rebate. For large surfaces subsidiary draughts are formed traversing the stone between the rebates. In walls, stones which are finished with hammer-dressed or rusticated surfaces have chisel-draughted margins sunk about the four edges to ensure the accuracy of the work. This is shown on p. 122 B.

Plain Work. This is divided, for purposes of valuation, into half plain and plain work. The former term is used when the surface of the stone has been brought to an approximately true surface, either by the saw or with the chisel. This labour is usually placed upon the bed and side joints of stones in walling. Plain work is the term adopted for surfaces that have been taken accurately out of winding with the chisel, and are finished with a labour usually to form an exposed surface.

For sandstone or hard limestone, plain work includes a tooled stroke and chisel-draughted margins, for soft limestones a combed or dragged surface, and for granite a smooth-tooled face.

Boasted or Droved Work. This consists in making a number of parallel chisel marks across the surface of the stone by means of a chisel, termed a boaster, which has an edge about $2\frac{1}{2}$ in. in width. In this labour, the chisel marks are not kept in continuous rows across the whole width of the stone (p. 122 C).

Tooled Work. This labour is a superior form of the above, care being taken to keep the chisel marks in continuous lines across the width of the stone, as shown in p. 122 D. The object of this and the preceding is to increase the effect of large plane surfaces by adding a number of shadows and high lights.

Combed or Dragged Work. This is a labour employed to work off all irregularities on the exposed surfaces of soft stones. The drag or comb is the implement used, and consists of a piece of steel with a number of teeth like those of a saw. This is drawn over the surface of the stone in all directions, after it has been roughly reduced to a plane with the saw or chisel, making it approximately smooth, as shown in p. 122 E.

Furrowed Work. This labour, used to emphasise quoins, consists in sinking a draft about the four sides of the face of a stone, leaving the central portion projecting about $\frac{1}{2}$-in., in which a number of vertical grooves about $\frac{3}{8}$-in. wide are sunk, as shown in p. 122 F.

Reticulated Work. This labour is placed chiefly on quoin stones to give effect. The process is as follows: A margin of about $\frac{3}{4}$-in. is marked about the edge of the stone, and in the surface enclosed by the margin a number of irregularly shaped sinkings are made. The latter have a margin of a constant width of about $\frac{3}{8}$-in. between them. The sinkings are made about $\frac{1}{4}$-in. in depth. The sunk surface is punched with a pointed tool to give it a rough pock-marked appearance, as shown in p. 122 G.

Vermiculated work is similar to reticulated but has a more curved irregular " worm eaten " appearance.

Axed Work. Axed work and tooled work are similar labours. The axe is employed for hard stones, such as granite, but the mallet and chisel for soft stones, because it is quicker.

The method preparing the hard stones after being detached from their beds in the quarry is as follows: the stones are roughly squared with the apall hammer; the beds are then prepared by sinking a chisel draught about the four edges of the bed under operation, the opposite draughts being out of winding, and the four draughts in the same plane surface; the portions projecting beyond the draught are then taken off with the pick. After the pick, the surface is wrought with the axe, the latter being worked vertically downward upon the surface, and taken from one side of the stone to the other, and making a number of parallel incisions or bats, the axe is worked in successive rows across the stone, the incisions made being kept continuous across the surface. In axed work there are about four incisions to the inch. This labour is used for the beds of stones for thresholds and kerb-stones, and in this state the pick marks are easily discernible. Fine-axed work is a finer description of axed work, and is accomplished with a much lighter axe having a finer edge, but is now more often executed by means of the patent axe, which consists of a number of thin blades with 4, 6, 8 or 10 to the inch, and enclosed and fixed by bolting or clamping in a strap-like head. These blades may be taken out of the head and sharpened as required. In fine-axed work the number of incisions to the inch should be specified.

Pointed and Punched Work. The bed and side joints of stones are often worked up to an approximately true surface by means of a pointed tool or punch, the contact surface of the pointed tool being a point, whilst the contact surface of the punch is usually a small rectangle. This labour, as shown in p. 122 H, is often employed to give a bold appearance to quoin and plinth stones, and where so used it usually has a chisel-draughted margin about the perimeter.

Moulded Work. Mouldings of various profiles are worked upon stones for ornamental effect, as shown in p. 122 K. Mouldings are worked by hand as well as by machine. In the former case, the profile of the moulding is marked on the two ends of the stone to be treated by means of a point drawn about the edge of a zinc mould, cut to the shape of the profile. A draught is then sunk in the two ends to the shape of the required profile. The superfluous stuff is then cut away with the chisel, the surface between the two draughts being tested for accuracy by means of straight-edges. The machines for moulded work somewhat resemble the planing machines for wood work (see p. 122 F). The stone is fixed to a moving table. The latter has imparted to it a reciprocating rectilinear motion, pressing against a fixed cutter of the shape of required profile, or some member of it. The cutter is moved nearer to the stone after each journey, thus gradually removing the superfluous stuff till the profile is completed. Moulded work is, strictly speaking, the name given to profiles formed with a change of curvature, and, therefore, should not be applied to cylindrical sections, such as columns.

The weathering properties of stones moulded by hand labour are considered by some far superior to those worked by machinery, as in the latter method the moulding irons, occasionally being driven continuously, become heated and partially calcine the surfaces of the stones, thus rendering them peculiarly susceptible to atmospheric deterioration; but if reasonable care be taken to keep the tools cool by water feed pipes, the method is preferable to hand labour, as it obviates the stress in the stone caused by the jarring of the hand-driven tool.

Sunk Work. This term is applied to the labour of making any surface below that originally formed, such as chamfers, wide grooves, the sloping surfaces of sills, etc., as shown in p. 122 M. If the surface is rough, it is known as half-sunk; if smooth, sunk; and any other labour applied must be added to the same, such as sunk, rubbed, etc.

Circular Work. Labour put upon the surface of any convex prismatic body, such as the parallel shaft of a column or large moulding, is termed circular work, as shown in p. 122 N.

Circular Sunk Work. Labour put upon the surface of any concave prismatic body, such as a large hollow moulding or the soffit of an arch, is termed circular sunk work, as shown in p. 122 M.

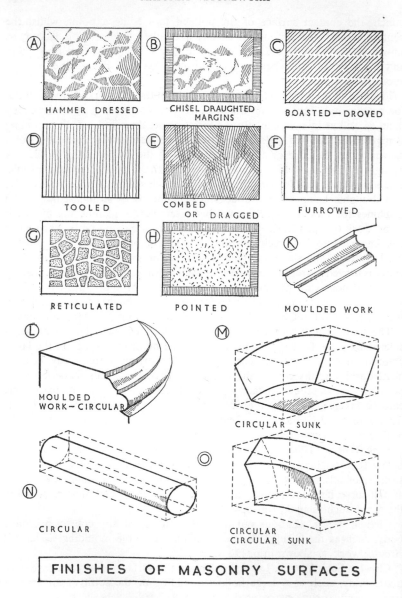

A — HAMMER DRESSED

B — CHISEL DRAUGHTED MARGINS

C — BOASTED—DROVED

D — TOOLED

E — COMBED OR DRAGGED

F — FURROWED

G — RETICULATED

H — POINTED

K — MOULDED WORK

L — MOULDED WORK—CIRCULAR

M — CIRCULAR SUNK

N — CIRCULAR

O — CIRCULAR CIRCULAR SUNK

FINISHES OF MASONRY SURFACES

Circular Circular Work. The labour placed upon columns with entases, spherical or domical work as shown at the extrados of p. 122 o.

Circular Circular Sunk. The labour worked upon the interior concave surfaces of domes, etc., as shown in the intrados of p. 122 o.

Moulded Work, Circular. This term is given to mouldings, as shown in p. 122 L, worked upon circular or curved surfaces in plan or elevation.

Internal Mitres. The intersection of two mouldings, the seen faces making an angle less than 180°.

External Mitres. The name given to the intersection of two mouldings, the seen faces making an angle greater than 180°.

Returned Mitred and Stopped. The name given to a moulding returned in itself, and stopping the same against an intersecting surface.

Long and Short Work. This work is usually employed for quoins and dressings in rubble walls, and is especially noticeable in old Saxon work, cf., Earl's Barton Tower. It consists in placing alternately an approximately square flat slab horizontally which serves as a bonder, and a long stone vertically, also square but comparatively smaller in section. This arrangement in modern practice is sometimes known as *block and start* work.

Rubbed Work. This labour consists in rubbing the surfaces of stones until perfectly regular, and as smooth as possible. The work is accomplished with manual labour by rubbing a piece of stone with a second piece. During the first stages of the process, water and sand are added, gradually reducing the quantity of sand up to the finish. Large quantities of stone are machine-rubbed by means of large horizontal revolving iron discs. The stones are placed on, and kept from revolving with the disc by means of stationary timbers fixed across the table a few inches above the stone. No pressure is applied other than that obtained by the weight of the stone. Water and sand are added to accelerate the process. Only plane surfaces can be rubbed in this way.

Polishing. Marbles, granites and many limestones, after being worked to a smooth surface, are often polished. Polishing by manual labour is an exceedingly tedious operation. Marble polished by hand is carried out by using rubbers and pads, sand and water, pumice, snake stone and putty powder.

STONE CUTTING AND POLISHING MACHINERY *

Polishing Machine. The polishing machine shown on p. 127 A is one of several types manufactured at the present day. It is in three main parts,

* The information relating to stone cutting and polishing machinery has been compiled with the kind assistance of the Anderson-Grice Co. Ltd. of Carnoustie.

i.e. the fixing bracket and the two arms which are connected together by swivel joints thus allowing the vertical rotating polishing disc to be guided freely over the stone. The stone is polished in sections and rests on a movable trolley or bogie, not shown in the illustration.

A smooth surface is imparted to the stone by 12-in. diameter carborundum circular blocks of which there are three grades, coarse, medium and fine, the final polish being obtained by a steel plate faced with felt. The stone or marble block is first squared and prepared for polishing and then placed on the trolley, the coarse surface disc is fitted and the height adjusted. The electric driving motor is started, the water turned on and the rotating disc is guided over the surface of the stone by the operator holding the guide handle. The pressure is hand adjusted by the operator. A shield, not shown in the illustration, may be fixed between the operator and the polishing disc to protect him from the slurry. Upon the surface reaching the required smoothness, the smooth disc is fitted and then the fine disc, the operations described above being repeated for each disc. The stone, after treatment by the fine disc, should be very smooth. Surplus grit and dirt are then cleaned off and the last felt faced disc fitted. Oxide of tin is sprinkled over the stone and the process repeated until the required degree of polish is obtained.

Sawing and Moulding Machine. This machine, illustrated on p. 127 B, may be used for both sawing and moulding. The illustration shows the machine in the process of fluting a column shaft, the process of which is carried out in the following manner. The shaft is prepared for fluting and is then fixed in position between the two brackets which are attached to a movable trolley or bogie as shown. The fluting wheel is lowered on to the shaft by means of either power or the endless cord shown on the right-hand side of the illustration. The water feed, which clears away the slurry at a pressure of 40 lb per sq. in., is then turned on and the main motor which turns the fluting wheel is started. The trolley moves forward under power and thus the stone is ground. The height of the grinding wheel is adjusted by hand after each cut and the column is hand turned as each flute is finished.

When this machine is used for sawing, circular blades, similar to those shown on the cross cut saw, p. 127 C, are fitted in lieu of the grinding wheel. These blades may be either diamond or carborundum. Diamond blades give faster cutting but for finer work or where the work is of a particularly abrasive nature, carborundum blades are used.

Cross Cut Saw. This type of saw, illustrated on p. 127 C, is made in two sizes, one with an 8 ft and the other with a 12 ft traverse.

The saw blades may be either diamond or carborundum but diamond blades are recommended as they have a cutting speed of two to three times that of carborundum. Diamond blades may be obtained in diameters from 32 to 60 in., giving cutting depths up to 25 in. Carborundum blades are generally supplied from 20 to 41 in. diameter and although larger blades can be fitted they require to be specially made. With ordinary use, saw blades last approximately nine months. Diamond saw blades cost approximately £240 each and are roughly twenty times more expensive than carborundum.

Cutting speeds for various materials are as follows:

Portland Stone:	220 sq. in. per minute.
Sicilian Marble:	100 sq. in. per minute.
Medium Hard Slate:	150 sq. in. per minute.

These speeds are based on the use of diamond saw blades powered by a 20 h.p. motor. With carborundum blades the speeds are between a third and a half of the above figures using a motor of similar power.

The machine shown has a fast return motion fitted, which, depending on spindle speed, varies between 15 to 30 ft per minute.

The operation of sawing is carried out as follows:

The material is placed in position on the trolley, which may be operated either by hand or by motor, and is brought up to the saw blade. Final adjustments to the position of the stone are then made and the trolley is locked in position. The water, which clears away the slurry and thereby improves the efficiency of the cutting, is turned on. The saw blade, turning at a speed of 600 r.p.m. is then made to traverse. The traverse speed is adjustable and may be varied to suit the hardness and thickness of the stone. Automatic stopping gear is also fitted to disengage both the ' feed ' and ' return ' movements of the saw at any predetermined point.

Frame Saw. This type of saw, illustrated on p. 128 D, is used for converting large blocks of stone and marble into slabs. These machines are made in various sizes, the smallest take a block of stone 8 ft long, 4 ft wide and 4 ft deep, and the largest a maximum block of 14 ft long, 7 ft wide and 6 ft deep.

The saw blades, which are made of corrugated steel, are fitted longitudinally in the swing frame. The spacing of the blades is varied, depending on the size of slabs required. For the type of machine shown the maximum number of blades which may be fitted is 40. Other models are available, a heavier machine designed for granite working takes a maximum of 20 blades and one designed for marble slabbing takes up to 70.

The operation of sawing is carried out in the following manner: The material is placed in position on a trolley, not shown in the illustration, and is moved under the swing frame. Final adjustment to the position of the material is made and the trolley is then locked in position. The swing frame is then lowered on to the material. The water feed, as may be seen from the illustration, consists of two long tubes with numerous projecting jets. The feed may be swung over the whole area of the material, thus ensuring a plentiful supply of water. Sand or carborundum may be added to the water to assist sawing. The main motor is then started and the swing frame which is suspended on four rods, operates with a forward and backward movement, by means of the steel rod connected to the crankshaft of the flywheel which is in turn connected by a belt to the electric motor. The controls of this machine are centrally placed near the main electric motor.

Sawing and Moulding Machine. This machine, illustrated on p. 128 E, is similar to the machine shown on p. 127 B, although of smaller pattern. It may be obtained in three types as follows: ' Fixed Height ', which is used only for plain sawing; ' Rise and Fall ', used for all bevelling and moulding work. It has a two-speed motor with an independent motor to control the rise and fall movement which, in the case of the standard machine, is 18 in., but movements up to 30 in. are obtainable in the more expensive models; ' Universal ', used for all types of work and has the advantage of a swivel head which allows the machine to cut material at any required angle.

The foregoing machines can be fitted with all the standard grinding wheels, employing either diamond or carborundum circular blades for sawing purposes. Diamond blades give a much faster rate of sawing, but for especially fine quality work carborundum saws are used. The speed of cutting can be gauged from the following examples which are based on the use of carborundum saws:

Portland Stone	.	5 in. deep	7 in. per minute with	5 h.p. motor.
White Marble	.	5 in. deep	4 in. ,, ,, ,,	7 h.p. motor.
Slate	.	3 in. deep	6 in. ,, ,, ,,	5 h.p. motor.

If diamond blades are used the above speeds may be roughly doubled.

The blocks of stone or marble are laid on the table of the trolley or bogie shown. The table is of cast iron and the top is squared to enable the stone to be accurately set. The top is also slotted to allow the blades to pass right through the stone. The table may be either hand or power driven and, apart from the standard type shown in the illustration, a cross traverse table is obtainable allowing the stone to be covered any number of times without the necessity of moving the block itself.

The actual operations of either sawing, fluting, moulding, etc., are carried out in a manner similar to the machine illustrated on p. 127 B.

Planing and Moulding Machine. The machine illustrated on p. 128 F

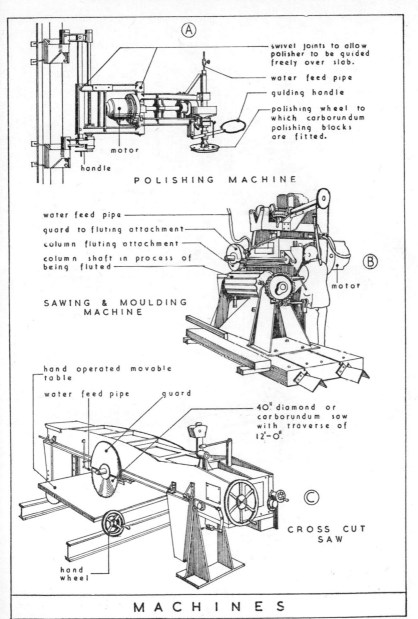

Ⓐ

swivel joints to allow polisher to be guided freely over slab.

water feed pipe

guiding handle

polishing wheel to which carborundum polishing blocks are fitted.

motor

handle

POLISHING   MACHINE

water feed pipe

guard to fluting attachment

column fluting attachment

column shaft in process of being fluted

Ⓑ

motor

SAWING & MOULDING
        MACHINE

hand operated movable table

water feed pipe

guard

40" diamond or carborundum saw with traverse of 12'-0"

Ⓒ

CROSS CUT
      SAW

hand wheel

M A C H I N E S

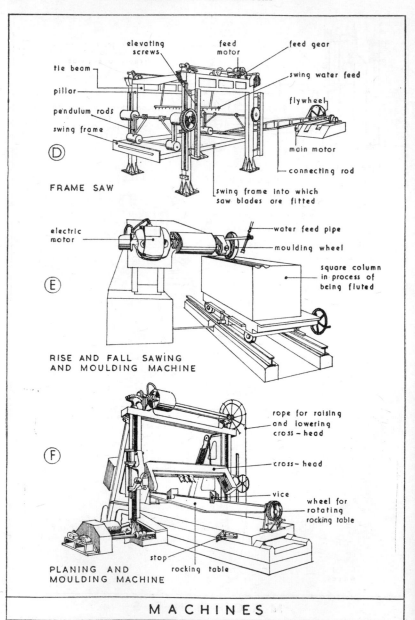

D — FRAME SAW

elevating screws
feed motor
feed gear
tie beam
pillar
pendulum rods
swing frame
swing water feed
flywheel
main motor
connecting rod
swing frame into which saw blades are fitted

E — RISE AND FALL SAWING AND MOULDING MACHINE

electric motor
water feed pipe
moulding wheel
square column in process of being fluted

F — PLANING AND MOULDING MACHINE

rope for raising and lowering cross-head
cross-head
vice
wheel for rotating rocking table
stop
rocking table

MACHINES

may be used for either planing or surfacing and moulding. Two sizes are made, one 12′ × 5′ × 5′, and the other 12′ × 3′ 6″ × 3′ 6″, the main tables being 4′ 2″ and 2′ 7″ respectively. The largest block of stone which may be taken by the largest machine is 12 ft long on the main table and 9 ft long on the rocking table. Average speed of cutting is 10 sq. ft per minute.

The machine is intended mainly for planing or surfacing purposes and this operation is as follows: The stone to be planed is placed in position on the rocking table; those which overhang the table unduly are strutted by wooden struts. The vices are then screwed up at each end of the block, fixing it firmly in position. The necessary planing tool is fitted, as illustrated, to a movable tool box attached to the cross head and is then moved along to the correct position and locked. The cross head is then lowered, either by means of the rope indicated in the illustration or by power, until the cutting blade is just below the surface of the stone. The motor is started and the main table supporting the rocking table moves forward, thus causing the stone to be cut. At the end of the forward movement, the stop, which may be adjusted to the required position depending on the length of the cut required, contacts the ' kicker ' which automatically moves the driving belt to another pulley which reverses the motion. The cutting blade swings over, its fall being broken by pneumatic cushioning and resumes the cutting of the stone on the return movement. Thus the stone is cut in both directions, the cross head being lowered as required.

Many types of moulded work may also be executed on this machine such as circular work, column fluting and cornices. Specially shaped tools are fitted in the manner previously described for these purposes. For fluting, the rocking table is removed and special steel ' centres ' are fitted to the brackets attached to the main table. These ' centres ' are let into the ends of the shaft which is held between the brackets. Column shafts are surfaced before the operation of fluting is commenced. The machine illustrated will take a length of column shaft of a maximum of 8 ft long and maximum diameter of 4 ft 6 in.

CAST STONE

Artificial, reconstructed or cast stone is much used now in external work on buildings. There is no difference in the names: the Code of Practice C.P. 121.201 covers ' Walls Ashlared with Natural and Cast Stone ' and prefers that name. B.S. 1217 is entitled ' Cast Stone ' and covers the material and certain requirements of its manufacture.

Cast stone is dealt with in much greater detail in *Advanced Building Construction*, but short reference here is desirable.

Cast stone is essentially concrete: a good quality concrete, made usually with a natural crushed stone aggregate and white cement and often matching natural stone quite well in the sample. But owing to the cement it will behave like concrete in that cast stone blocks will expand slightly on wetting and contract on drying more than natural stone, hence the tendency for joints to show because they open and close sufficiently to allow slight ingress and retention of moisture. Ashlar blocks should be matured very carefully after cutting so that the initial drying shrinkage should be completed slowly.

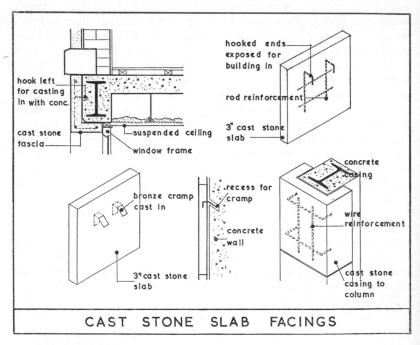

CAST STONE SLAB FACINGS

It is commonly used in exactly the same way as natural ashlar work; it has been made occasionally with a rough face to represent rock faced work, there have recently been examples where concrete blocks have been used with wide joints. These blocks can have a pleasant individual character of their own and need not look like rather poor natural stone.

One great convenience of cast stone is that reinforcements can be cast into the block or slab so that long lintels in one piece can be made and metal anchors or ties cast in which can be used subsequently to secure the block or slab to the structure. Some details are shown on p. 130. Two methods of supporting slabs are shown, one with rods which are built into the backing, the other with plates which can be set in mortices formed in the structure when the facing is to be attached later. L-shaped and U-shaped stones are also easily cast for use as facing and soffit of lintels or for casing stanchions. These would be reinforced to strengthen them for handling, until fixed.

SLATE IN WALLING

Riven Face Slabs. Slate is quarried in several parts of the British Isles, e.g. the Lake District, North Wales, Devonshire, etc. The beds of slate in the quarries often have a slight camber which restricts the maximum size of slate available. For instance, the maximum Lake District slate is $24'' \times 18''$ for $\frac{3}{4}''-1''$ thickness and $18'' \times 12''$ for $\frac{1}{2}''$ thickness.

The slates are split in the quarry with great skill to produce an attractive natural grained surface. Alternatively, the slate can be sanded (matt), rubbed (semi-polished) or frame sawn finished.

Fixing (Wall Facing Slabs). Drillings are made in the edges of the slabs and, into these, thick copper wire or similar non-ferrous cramps are dropped and turned horizontally into the wall, where they are grouted into the brickwork or concrete. The backing may be solid cement mortar or the 'five spot' technique may be used, i.e. a series of dabs which make the plumbing and levelling of the slab easier. The weight of the facing must be taken by a projection from the backing wall of concrete or other material. 'S' hooks are also used of similar copper wire to locate the bottom edges of slabs. Other methods are sometimes used, e.g. robust non-ferrous corbels ($\frac{1}{4}$ in. thick for slabs 1 in. thick) which are let into grooves in the back of the slabs to take their weight, or the weight can be taken on a non-ferrous angle engaging in a rebate at the back of the slab, the angle being rag-bolted to the structure.

The drawing on p. 132 shows the slabs bedded solid on to a cement rendering. The metal cramps are placed every third course, one for each slab.

The drawing on p. 132 also shows the slabs bedded against the concrete or brickwork with the 'five spot' technique, each being fixed with two holes on the top edge for wire cramps, and one hole drilled for the 'S' hook on the bottom edge for location.

Copings. Copings are usually supplied from the quarries in random lengths (not less than 2 ft) and 1 in. thick. They may be weathered twice, throated, and may be frame sawn finished on top. They are drilled to receive anchor cramps every 20 ft or so and are drilled centrally at the end of each slab to

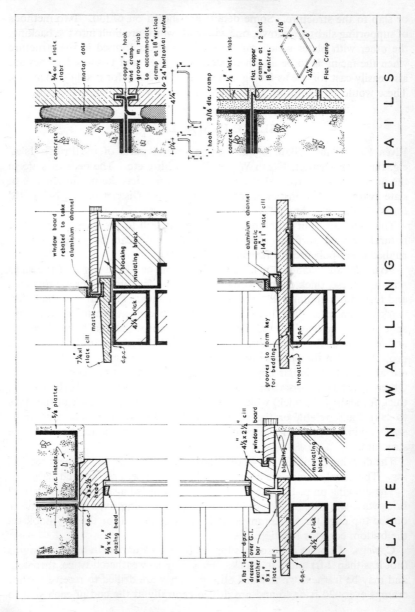

SLATE IN WALLING DETAILS

¾" or 1" slate slabs
mortar dots
copper 's' hook and cramp. groove in slab to accommodate cramp at 18" vertical & 24" horizontal centres
concrete
4¼"
⅛"
1¼"
⅛"
'S' hook 3/16" dia. cramp

½" slate slabs
flat copper cramps at 12" and 18" centres
concrete
5/8"
6"
4½"
4½"
Flat Cramp

window board rebated to take aluminium channel
blocking
insulating block
4½" brick
mastic
7¾" x 1" slate cill
d.p.c.

aluminium channel
1¼" x 1" slate cill
mastic
d.p.c.
grooves to form key for bedding
throating

5/8" plaster
r.c. lintol
4 x 2½" head
d.p.c.
¾" x ½" glazing bead

4½ x 2½" cill
window board
blocking
insulating block
4½" brick
4 lbs lead d.p.c. dressed over G.I. weather bar
6" x 1" slate cill
d.p.c.

receive copper dowls.   It is as well to run a bituminous D.P.C. under the coping so that the joints do not permit moisture to enter the wall.

Sills.   Continuous slate sills in 5 ft lengths can provide a very satisfactory precise solution to the problem of forming sills.   As the material is impervious, the weathering can be made very slight and can taper down to ¾ in.   The sills may be weathered, grooved and throated, and if necessary a rebate can be formed to receive a hardwood fillet or aluminium angle to which the window frames can be fixed.

9

Timber

Composition. The growing tree contains a large amount of moisture which may be 150% of the dry weight of the timber. A large amount of this moisture has to be removed under controlled conditions before it can be used in building. Other components are cellulose and hemi-cellulose; these two materials can be hydrolysed with acids to produce sugars, or they can be used as the raw material for paper pulp, rayon, explosives and glues. Another constituent is lignin which is the only non-carbohydrate present and is the natural cementing material, holding the individual cells to each other. The proportion of lignin (up to 35%), is an index of the compressive strength.

The proportions are roughly as follows:

Cellulose	45–60%
Hemi-cellulose	15–25%
Lignin	25–35%

There are minor constituents—resins, oils, tannins, alkaloids, etc., which are not usually extracted commercially but often give the timber its characteristic odour, i.e. oak, cedar.

Structure. Timbers are divided into two main groups:

Softwoods, i.e. firs, pines—with needle-like leaves: CONIFERAE.

Hardwoods, i.e. oak, beech—broad-leafed: DICOTYLEDONEAE.

The terms hardwoods and softwoods can be misleading as there are some hardwoods, i.e. balsa, which are very soft and some softwoods which are hard, but they give the right idea very generally.

Seasoning. This is the process of removing by drying the excess moisture from the wood in a controlled manner, to prevent the shrinkage which occurs, causing cracks and other defects. The greatest shrinkage will occur in the direction of the annual rings. There is only about half the amount of shrinkage radially; that is why, in order to avoid warping, it is advisable to quarter-saw a log, i.e. cut as far as possible radially.

Logs are cut into boards so that there is a larger surface for drying and so that the outside of the log does not dry and shrink and crack, leaving the interior still wet. The boards are then stacked on ' sticks ' which are 1″ × 1″ bearers put in to facilitate air circulation between each board and left to air season, preferably under cover. This process may be combined with

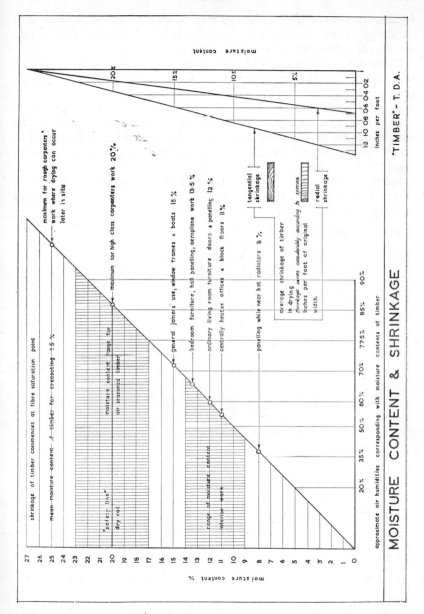

MOISTURE CONTENT & SHRINKAGE

"TIMBER" - T.D.A.

kilning, i.e. oven-drying, or the kiln may be used for the whole process of seasoning. Notice that there is no conflict between the two methods, they are complementary to one another.

Conversion. This consists of sawing up the logs to produce timber of sizes for use. Timber for ordinary carcassing is usually produced by sawing the log ' through and through '. If the timber is high quality then it may be quarter-sawn in many different ways to produce timber for a variety of uses.

Once sawn to size, timber may then be planed with a rotary planer. This reduces the size by $\frac{3}{32}$ in. on each face so that material that is ' planed all round ' is $\frac{3}{16}$ in. smaller on each dimension. This is important to remember when detailing joinery.

Softwood Sizes. Some sizes are readily available and others are not. It is useful to know which are which. The following are normally readily available:

Redwood and whitewood:
$$\left. \begin{array}{l} \frac{5}{8}'' \\ \frac{3}{4}'' \\ \frac{7}{8}'' \\ 1'' \\ 1\frac{1}{4}'' \\ 1\frac{1}{2}'' \\ 2'' \end{array} \right\} \times \left\{ \begin{array}{l} 3'',\ 6\frac{1}{2}'' \\ 3\frac{1}{2}'',\ 7'' \\ 4'',\ 8'' \\ 4\frac{1}{2}'',\ 9'' \\ 5'' \\ 5\frac{1}{2}'' \\ 6'' \end{array} \right.$$

With the exception of: $\frac{5}{8}'' \times 7''$ upwards
$\frac{3}{4}'' \times 8''$ upwards
$\frac{7}{8}'' \times 3\frac{1}{2}''$, $1\frac{1}{2}'' \times 3''$, $1\frac{1}{2}'' \times 4''$
and $2'' \times 3\frac{1}{2}''$

$2\frac{1}{2}''$, $3''$, and $4'' \times 11''$ are also readily available, as are $4'' \times 6''$, $4'' \times 7''$, $4'' \times 8''$, $4'' \times 9''$

Parana Pine: $1'' \times 6''$–$12''$ in $1''$ increments
$1'' \times 6''$–$12''$ in $1\frac{1}{2}''$ „
$1'' \times 6''$–$12''$ in $2''$ „
(with the exception of $10''$ and $11''$)

Eastern Canada mainly Spruce:

$2''$, $2\frac{1}{2}''$, $3'' \times 3''$–$8''$ in $1''$ increments with the exception of $2\frac{1}{2}'' \times 3''$ and $3'' \times 3''$

Douglas Fir and Western Hemlock:

$1'' \times 4'', 6'', 8''$

$1\frac{1}{2}'' \times 4'', 6'', 7'', 8'', 9''$

$2'' \times 3'', 4'', 6'', 7'', 8'', 9''$

$2\frac{1}{2}'' \times 4'', 6'', 7'', 8'', 9''$ (in carcassing qualities only)

$3'' \times 4'', 6'', 7'', 8'', 9'', 11''$ and $12''$

$4'' \times 4'', 6'', 7'', 8'', 9'', 11''$ and $12''$

Lengths. Average lengths may be said to be 12 ft, but vary from 5 ft to 24 ft. Certain species such as Douglas Fir can be obtained up to 60 ft but this increases the price.

Hardwood Sizes. It is interesting to note that hardwoods are imported in random widths where softwoods are imported in parcels of boards of one width. The result of this is that it is inclined to be expensive to order boards in large quantities over 6 in. wide.

' Strips ', i.e. stock $1'' \times 5''$ and less are economical, and ' shorts ', that is, lengths under 6 ft, can be obtained at a reduced rate.

Available sizes of hardwood differ very widely and the following are a few examples.

African Walnut	.	$6''-16'' \times 1''-3''$	Length up to 16'
Agba	. . .	$6''-18'' \times 1''-3''$	Length up to 18'
Beech (European)		Average $7\frac{1}{2}''$ wide	Length up to 10'
Birch (Canadian)	.	$4'' \times 1''-3''$	Lengths about 6'
Camphor Wood (East African)	.	Up to $12'' \times \frac{1}{2}''-2''$	Length up to 18'
Makore	. .	$6'' \times 1''-2''$	Length average 6'
Meranti	. .	$4''-12'' \times 1''-4''$	Length up to 24'
Oak (European)	.	$6'' \times 1''-4''$	Length average 6' and up
Sapele	. .	$1''-24'' \times 1''-4''$	Length up to 20'
Teak	. .	$6''-14'' \times 1''-4''$	Length average 9'

It is always advisable to ask a merchant for his stock lists before ordering material.

Movement. A reduction in the relative humidity of the air by say 10% will produce an equivalent shrinkage or expansion of a piece of timber. For instance, samples of Beech (European), Gurjun, Keruing, Ramin or Tasmanian Oak, 1 ft wide, will move more than $\frac{1}{8}$ in. tangentially and more than $\frac{1}{16}$ in. radially. Joinery must be designed so that this movement can take place without damage. It is impossible to restrain such movement. It is interesting to realise that a table made out of, for example, European beech, of boards glued edge to edge, a total of say 4 ft wide, would shrink 1 in. if the relative humidity of the air (from winter to summer) changed from say 70% to 50%. For this reason, table tops especially are attached to their rails by soffite plates to allow for this movement. Doors with panels made from solid timber, and not ply, are constructed so that the panels move in rebates independently of the frame. Matchboarding used on the exterior of building and on some types of external door are tongued and grooved together so that each board can move independently.

It is important to notice that shrinkage along the length of a piece of timber is less dangerous than radial or tangential movement, but even so this must be taken into consideration.

In carcassing, that is, rough roof or wall framing, with traditional coverings, relative movement is not so significant as in joinery work where the opening of joints is both undesirable and unsightly. In order to reduce the amount of movement the timber is sealed by paint, varnish or oil in order to reduce the moisture absorbed. These surface dressings vary enormously in their effectiveness. Two coats of bituminous paint is the most effective and this is only 70% or so after a month. Compare this with a good oil paint (three coats)—56%; aluminium paint (two coats)—35%; copal varnish—20%; oil and turpentine (two coats brushed)—0%. Some of the new synthetic varnishes in practice appear to be fairly effective.

Distortion is more likely when the difference between radial and tangential movement is greatest. Hardwoods with relatively small movement are Afzelia, East African Camphor wood, Idigbo, Iroko, Muninga (very good). As, in general, softwoods are more often used for carcassing work, the lack of availability of timbers with low movement is not important (see *Advanced Building Construction*).*

DECAY

Fungus. Fungus is a living organism which cannot live unless it has food, moisture, and oxygen. Temperature is not an important factor in this country. The spores (seeds) germinate on the surface of timber pushing out hyphae into the wood. These thread-like minute tubes pierce the cells of the timber branching out into a mat or mycelium. The hyphae secrete

* A good available textbook on joinery and the selection of timbers for this work is *The Design and Practice of Joinery*, by John Eastwick Field and John Stillman published by Architectural Press. See also publications by the Timber Development Association and especially *Empire Timbers* by Forest Products Research published by H.M.S.O. price 4s. 6d. This book not only describes the properties of each available timber, but gives a table showing relative shrinkage and strength.

enzymes which break down the wood and provide food for the fungus. The spores grow often into bracket-like fruit bodies which in turn produce many millions of spores.

A notable exception to this is the infection of some softwoods by *Ceratostomella*, in which case the hyphae feed only on cell contents and not on the cell walls, the holes through the cell walls being so small that they do not affect the strength.

Timber is liable to attack by dry rot and other fungi when the moisture content is over 20%. The most dangerous moisture content being 30–40%.

Dry Rot (*Merulius Lacrymans*). Once this fungus has established itself it is much less dependent upon external moisture supply. It will even moisten dry wood before it attacks it. The mycelium will develop into thick greyish cords which can penetrate brickwork to find fresh wood to attack. The spores are rust-coloured.

Wet Rot (*Coniophora Cerabella, or Cellar Fungus*). This fungus requires wet conditions in which to exist. The sheet-like fruit bodies may vary from green to brown, the spores being produced in little pimples. Whereas *Merulius* produces a charred effect, *Coniophora* produces darkened tracts across the grain.

Prevention. Keep the timber dry, at least drier than 20%, and this may be done by providing thorough ventilation and of course, proper damp-courses.

Frequent causes of the trouble are broken rain water pipes and drains.

Cure. Affected wood must be removed and burned. All surrounding construction should then be treated (if uninflammable) with a blow-lamp, but otherwise with a proprietary antiseptic. The remaining woodwork should be treated with a preservative as should any new work.

BEETLE ATTACK

It is unusual for timber to be attacked until it has been cut for seven or eight years.

Furniture Beetle (*Anobium Punctatum*). This is a very common beetle about $\frac{1}{8}$ in. long, which flies to timber in the late summer, and lays small white eggs in minute cracks and crevices. The eggs hatch into larvae (worms) which bore into the wood. These develop to about $\frac{1}{4}$-in. long, and continue to bore through the wood for one or two years. They finish near the surface of the wood, pupate, and from this the beetles develop to repeat the life-cycle.

Death Watch Beetle (*Xestobium Rufovillosum*). This is similar to *Anobium*

Punctatum, being of the same family, but it only attacks hardwoods. The larvae are bigger and are covered with long, yellowish hairs. The other chief characteristic is the dust left in the holes which in this case consists of large bun-shaped pellets. The beetle makes a ticking sound during the mating period May or June, by tapping its head on the side of the holes.

Powder Post Beetles (*Lyctus*). There are several varieties of this beetle, which are usually about ⅛ in. long and red, brown or black in colour. It attacks sapwood of certain hardwoods, i.e. oak, ash and elm. It produces a fine, flower-like dust which is pushed out of the holes on to the surface.

Control and Preservation. Best time to apply preservative is in the early summer so that the beetles are killed on emerging from their flight-holes. Liquids should be brushed well into cracks and fissures. Death Watch Beetle will not attack dry timber, free from rot; and Powder Post Beetle will not attack timber other than the sapwood in hardwoods.

The function of a preservative is to poison the food matter in the timber, but this poison must not be dangerous to the carpenter and it must not wash out in the rain. Its effectiveness will depend upon the degree of penetration that can be achieved.

Creosote. This is a cheap and effective method of preservation which may be brush-applied or applied by pressure impregnation in tanks.

Wolman Salts. These may be brush applied also. The proprietary system can be carried out by specialists. This preservative has the advantage of being practically colourless and has no bad effect upon paints and other finishes unless water gets into the timber behind the paint film.

Water-soluble Preservatives. Examples of these are Sodium Fluoride, Zinc Chloride, Mecuric Chloride and Copper Sulphate. Most common of these being Zinc Chloride. The main difficulty with this type being that they are only suitable for interior use.

DESIGN

Carpentry. Here, the principal problem is usually the spanning of space, e.g. roof of a house, suspended upper floors, lintels, etc. The chief technique is that of making the joints between the various members, as in a roof truss. Techniques have developed considerably recently so that instead of timber being cut away to form a joint, metal fastenings can be used which do not necessitate this and therefore more economical timber sizes can be employed.

Joinery. Joinery is mainly concerned with the craft work involved with fully finished timber which is exposed to the view. The problem of relative movement looms very large. Very many types of joints have been developed in the course of time which are both strong and show any shrinkage as little as possible.

Several new, very efficient glues have been produced in the last decade or so which are making some of the traditional joints obsolescent.

Another important problem in joinery is that of producing plain surfaces. At first the problem seems very simple, but when it is realised that supporting framework and the timber forming the plain surface or panel move in different directions and have different coefficients of movement, it can be seen how difficult it can be.

Joinery work includes both hardwoods and softwoods, but timber being both planed and sanded is $\frac{3}{32}$ in. smaller on each face when finished than its ' nominal ' size, that is the size when it has been sawn only.

STRESS GRADING OF SOFTWOODS

When designing in timber structure, it is vital to know the maximum stress each member can take. Timber without defects is obviously stronger than timber with defects (e.g. knots, shakes, badly sloping grain, etc.).

In practice, it would be highly uneconomical to specify absolutely ' clear ' (defect-free) timber. Certain limited defects have to be accepted.

As a result of much research and testing the effect on the strength of timber, of the various types and sizes of defects, is now known.

Group	Standard name	Minimum weight per cu. ft at 22% moisture content— lb	Basic stresses in lb per sq. in.				
			Flexure and compression parallel to grain	Compression perpendicular to grain	Tension	Shear parallel to grain	Modulus of elasticity minimum
1	Douglas Fir (coast) Longleaf Pitch Pine Shortleaf Pitch Pine	27 32 27	1,000	350	1,500	100	1,000,000
2	Canadian Spruce European Larch Redwood Whitewood Western Hemlock	22 27 26 21 23	800	250	1,200	100	750,000

The architect can thus design a structure and know that the supplier can select for him timber which will stand up to the stress he requires.

Softwood for structural uses is now divided into two groups. The table gives the recommended stresses for two strength groups of the softwoods commonly available.

Slope of Grain. This may be determined by a scribe, which consists of a cranked rod with a swivelled handle, with a gramophone needle set at a slight angle in one end; the needle by means of the handle is drawn along the wood in the apparent direction of the grain producing a scribed line. The angle which this line makes with the edge of the piece of timber is called the inclination of the grain, or slope.

Beams and compression members not more than 4 in. thick		Compression members over 4 in. thick	
Slope of grain on any surface	Maximum permitted slope on an adjacent surface	Slope of grain on any surface	Maximum permitted slope on an adjacent surface
1 in 8	nil	1 in 11	nil
1 in 9	1 in 18	1 in 12	1 in 27
1 in 10	1 in 14	1 in 13	1 in 21
1 in 11	1 in 12	1 in 14	1 in 18
		1 in 15	1 in 17

The two important figures you will notice are that 1 in 8 is the maximum slope for beams and compression members under 4 in. thick, and 1 in 11 is the maximum for compression members over this size.

Wane. This is the rugged ' chamfer ' produced by the timber being cut from too close to the outside of the tree. The total reduction due to wane in the width of any surface (at any point) should not be more than a quarter for beams and compression members up to 4 in. thick, and should not be more than one-sixth for compression members over 4 in. thick.

Rate of Growth. Group 1 timbers not less than six rings (annual) per inch. Group 2 timbers not less than four rings per inch.

Knots. Knots on the edge of a piece of timber are measured at right angles to the edges. Those on the face and within the middle half of the depth of the face are taken as the average of its maximum and minimum diameters. Those in the top or bottom quarters, or that are cut into by the arris, are measured at right angles to the arris. Where knots extend more than a quarter of the depth of the face the measurement is taken on the edge as for margin knots; otherwise these are known as arris knots, for which both exposed dimensions are taken at right angles to the edge.

Knot clusters are measured in the same way as those mentioned above, and expressed as the sum of the averages of the diameters of the several knots. Knot holes are measured in the same way as knots.

Shakes, Splits, and Checks. These are measured with a feeler gauge 0·005 in. thick or less. They are measured in respect of either face or edge of the piece of timber.

Nominal width of surface in.	Knots on edge or at centre line of face of beam or on any surface of a tension member in.	* Margin knots or knots on any surface of compression member or member subject to combined flexure and compression in.	Shakes, checks and splits in.
1	½	¼	½
1½	¾	¼	¾
2	1	½	1
2½	1¼	¾	1¼
3	1½	1	1½
4	2	1¼	2
5	2½	1¼	2
6	3	1½	2¼
7	3¼	1½	2½
8	3½	1¾	3
9	3¾	2	3¼
10	4	2¼	3¾
11	4¼	2½	4
12	4½	2¾	4½

* Margin Knot: A knot appearing on the face outside the middle half of the depth of the face, near to or breaking through an edge.

The stress grading of timber in the yard is a specialist job, but it is well to know the principles involved in order that supplies may be checked, and so that below-standard timber can be eliminated.

Relatively few firms are able to supply stress graded material. It is a great disadvantage to a designer if he cannot call for properly stress-graded material. However, the number of firms who are able to grade is increasing.*

* These rules for stress grading are set out in a booklet published by the Timber Development Association called *Structural Grading of Softwoods*.

10

Roofs and Floors

TIMBER FLAT ROOFS

ONE of the most straightforward ways of providing a roof is to span from wall to wall with timber joists. The spacing of the joists depends upon what has been chosen to carry the bituminous felt, asphalt, or metal waterproofing, not forgetting the insulation.

Material	Joist Spacing
¾ in. Boarding	16 in.
½ in. Chip Board	16 in.
¾ in. Chip Board, Compressed Straw Board (2 in.)	2 ft or 4 ft
2 in. Wood Wool	2 ft
Proprietary Metal Decking	Average 8 ft

The joists must be wide enough to provide adequate fixing where sheet materials butt, e.g. 2 in. for compressed strawboard (Stramit) joists need to be at least 2½ in. wide.

The joists must be deep enough to carry the weight of the roof plus the weight of snow and of people on the roof doing maintenance work without deflecting unduly. The wider apart the joists are spaced, the more load they will have to carry and therefore the deeper they will have to be.

The joist sizes may be calculated by the old rule of thumb method which is rather inaccurate, i.e. half the span in feet plus two equals the depth in inches,* e.g. $\frac{16'}{2} + 2 = 10''$ depth.

* It is more satisfactory to calculate the joists as follows:

Example: To calculate the depth of joists required to carry a boarded flat roof from which traffic is excluded. Assume that the joists will be 2 in. wide and that it is proposed to use 1 in. nominal boarding carrying a three-layer bitumen felt roof. The joists span 16 ft on to brick walls and are spaced 1 ft 6 in., apart.

Felt	. 2 lb	per sq. ft		
Insulation, say . .	. 1 lb	” ” ”		
Boarding 1 in. thick .	. 3 lb	” ” ”		
Joists at 1 ft 6 in. centres, say	9 lb	” ” ”		
	15 lb	” ” ”	Dead load	
	add 15 lb	” ” ”	Live load	
	30 lb	” ” ”	Total load	

Imposed Loads (Live Loads). The Code of Practice 3 : Chapter 5 1952, states that an allowance of 30 lb a sq. ft or 15 lb a sq. ft if the roof is inaccessible to traffic should be allowed for live loads for flat roofs or roofs sloping up to 10°. This is subject to a minimum load of 240 lb uniformly distributed per ft width of roof slab or roof covering.

In the case of sloping roofs, on slopes between 10° and 30°, allow 15 lb per sq. ft measured on plan. On slopes between 30° and 75°, interpolate value between 15 and nil.

This imposed load or live load allowance takes into account maintenance traffic only.

Wall Plates. The joists must be adequately fixed at their ends. The usual method of doing this is to seat them on wall plates usually of 4″ × 3″ material to which the joists are spiked. This wall plate is in turn fixed to the top courses of the brickwork or blockwork with galvanised straps.

Where openings occur in the supporting walls the roof joists are carried on lintels over the openings. These lintels may be calculated in much the same way as the roof joists are, except that instead of uniformly distributed loads coming on to the lintels the loads will be point loads, e.g. central point load will be calculated with a bending moment of $\dfrac{WL}{4}$.

PITCHED ROOFS

Trusses. Where spans are larger, the roof may be carried on triangulated trusses. This in effect increases the depth of the spanning element towards the centre where the greatest bending moment occurs.

Single Raftered Roofs. Drawings on p. 147 indicate simple forms of roofs without trusses. It will be noticed in types A and B the lateral thrust

---

Total weight carried by each joist (W) = 1 ft 6 in. × 16 ft × 30 lb = 720 lb

Bending moment = $\dfrac{WL}{8}$ i.e. $\dfrac{720 \times 16 \times 12}{8}$ = 14,400 lb in.

$$BM = \frac{fbd^2}{6} \text{ assuming Group 1 Timber and}$$
$$f = 1{,}000 \text{ lb./sq. in. (extreme fibre stress)}$$
$$b = 2 \text{ in. (breadth)}$$

$$14{,}400 = \frac{1{,}000 \times 2 \times d^2}{6}$$

Therefore d^2 = 43 in.
d = say 7 in.

Therefore use 7 in. × 2 in. Group 1 timber

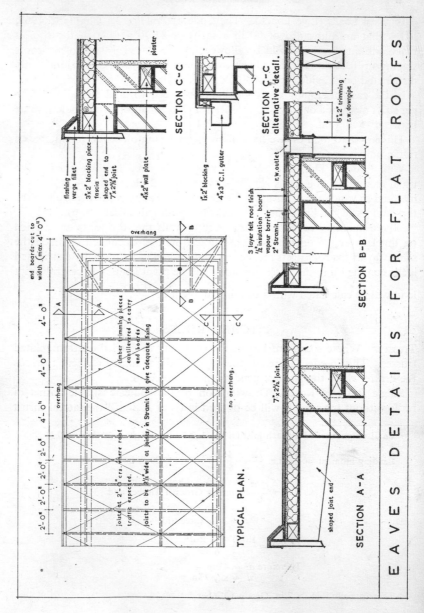

SECTION C-C

flashing
verge fillet
3"x2" blocking piece
fascia
shaped end to
7"x2½"joist
4"x2" wall plate

plaster

SECTION C-C alternative detail.

1"x2" blocking
4"x3" C.I. gutter

5"x2" trimming
r.w. downpipe

r.w. outlet

3 layer felt roof finish
½" insulation board
vapour barrier
2" Stramit

SECTION B-B

TYPICAL PLAN.

end boards cut to width (max. 4'-0")

overhang

2'-0" 2'-0" 2'-0" 2'-0"   4'-0"   4'-0"   4'-0"

overhang

no overhang.

timber trimming pieces
cantilevered to carry
end boards

joists at 2'-0" crs. where roof
traffic expected.

joists to be 2½" wide at joints in Stramit to give adequate fixing

7"x2½" joist.

shaped joist end

SECTION A-A

EAVES DETAILS FOR FLAT ROOFS

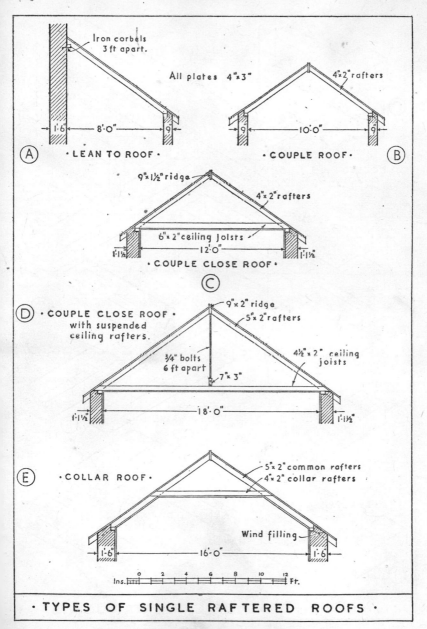

Iron corbels 3 ft apart.

All plates 4"x3"

4"x2" rafters

1·6"   8'·0"   9"

(A) · LEAN TO ROOF ·

9"   10'·0"   9"

· COUPLE ROOF ·   (B)

9"x1½"ridge

4"x2"rafters

6"x2"ceiling joists

1'·1½"   12'·0"   1'·1½"

· COUPLE CLOSE ROOF ·

(C)

(D) · COUPLE CLOSE ROOF ·
with suspended
ceiling rafters.

9"x2"ridge

5"x2"rafters

4½"x2" ceiling joists

¾" bolts
6 ft apart

7"x3"

1'·1½"   18'·0"   1'·1½"

(E) · COLLAR ROOF ·

5"x2"common rafters
4"x2"collar rafters

Wind filling

1·6"   16'·0"   1·6"

Ins. |0 2 4 6 8 10 12| Ft.

· TYPES OF SINGLE RAFTERED ROOFS ·

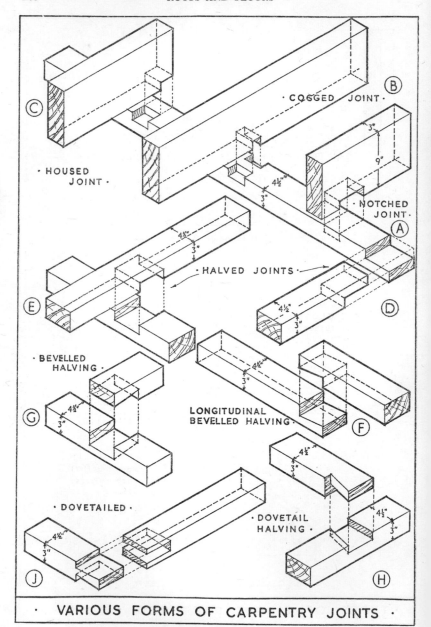

VARIOUS FORMS OF CARPENTRY JOINTS

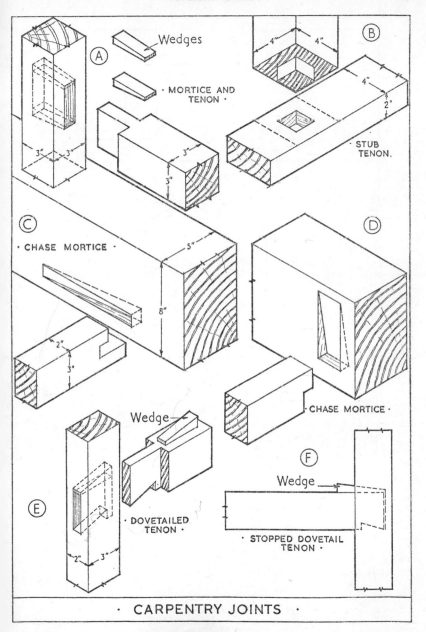

Wedges

(A) · MORTICE AND TENON ·

(B) 4" 4" 4" 2" STUB TENON.

3" 3" 3" 3"

(C) · CHASE MORTICE · 5" 8" 2" 3"

(D) · CHASE MORTICE ·

Wedge

(E) · DOVETAILED TENON · 2" 3"

(F) Wedge · STOPPED DOVETAIL TENON ·

· CARPENTRY JOINTS ·

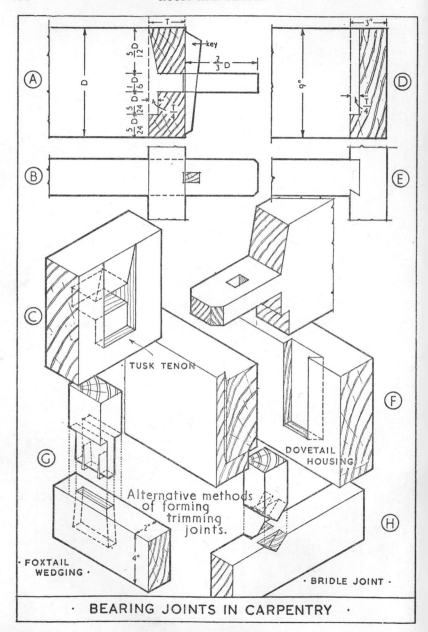

TUSK TENON

DOVETAIL HOUSING

Alternative methods of forming trimming joints.

· FOXTAIL WEDGING ·

· BRIDLE JOINT ·

· BEARING JOINTS IN CARPENTRY ·

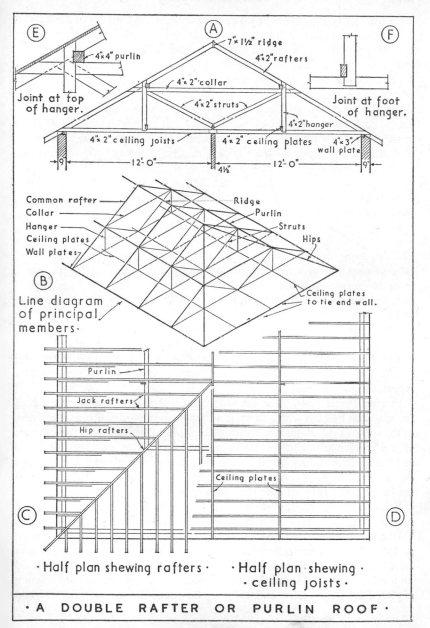

E — 4"x4" purlin — Joint at top of hanger.

A — 7"x1½" ridge — 4"x2" rafters — 4"x2" collar — 4"x2" struts — 4"x2" hanger — 4"x2" ceiling joists — 4"x2" ceiling plates — 4"x3" wall plate — 9" — 12'-0" — 4½" — 12'-0" — 9"

F — Joint at foot of hanger.

Common rafter — Collar — Hanger — Ceiling plates — Wall plates — Ridge — Purlin — Struts — Hips — Ceiling plates to tie end wall.

B — Line diagram of principal members.

C — Purlin — Jack rafters — Hip rafters — Ceiling plates — D

· Half plan shewing rafters · — · Half plan shewing · ceiling joists ·

· A DOUBLE RAFTER OR PURLIN ROOF ·

from the feet of the rafters is taken by the walls, and the walls have to be made strong enough to withstand these horizontal forces. It is always more satisfactory to tie the feet of the rafters together with, if possible, ceiling joists as in Example C. Example D shows a form which is now obsolescent where a ¾ in. bolt is used from ridge to ceiling joist. Example E shows a collar roof where the tie is placed higher up to give additional headroom. This means that in, for example, dwellings, the walls need not be taken up so high. (It should be noted that Model By-laws require that in habitable rooms situated in the roof of a building the minimum height of 7 ft 6 in. must be extended over at least half the area of the room measured at a level of 5 ft above the floor. Another by-law (73) also requires that the top of every window opening provided for ventilation must be not less than 5 ft 9 in. above the floor.) The tie in the collar roof (or collar rafters) should be attached to the common rafters by timber connectors.

Purlins. Where the span of the rafters by themselves would be excessive, a beam or purlin is placed under them to provide support, and thus reduce the effective span; one or more may be provided depending upon the length of rafters (see p. 153). A rough and ready method of calculating purlin depth from its supports on gable wall or between struts is to take half the span in feet, add 2 and the result is the depth in inches, i.e. for a span between struts of 10 ft

$$\frac{10}{2} + 2 = 7 \text{ in. depth.}$$

The Fifth Schedule in most Building By-laws gives purlin spans and spacings for plain tiles and single lap (interlocking) tiles, and for slates (see Appendix, p. 359).

Strutted Purlin Roof. The drawing on p. 153 shows an economical roof for spans up to 22 ft where there is a load-bearing partition near the centre of the span. Typical joints are shown on p. 154. The battens in this case are 1″ × 1″, which are slightly more economical than 1½″ × ¾″. The rafters are at 18 in. centres and are ' birdsmouthed ' over the wall plates. The felt runs down over the rafters (sagging slightly so that water does not collect against the battens) and is taken over the edge of the gutter.

Where the ' beamfilling ' brickwork surrounds the rafters, a felt D.P.C. must be wrapped round the timber, to protect it from rot.

Dormer Window and Eaves. Details of a dormer window are shown on p. 155. The common rafters are trimmed for the opening with timbers at least half an inch thicker than the common rafters. Studding is then erected on the floor joists and forms the side or cheek of the dormer. On this framing is placed the ceiling joists and rafters. Boarding is fixed to the gable and

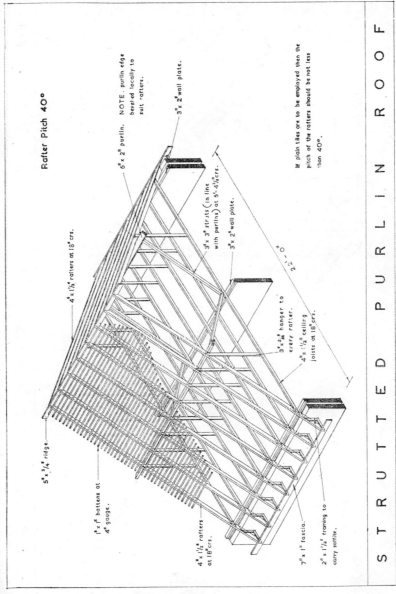

Rafter Pitch 40°

NOTE: purlin edge beveled locally to suit rafters.

6" x 2" purlin.

3" x 2" wall plate.

4" x 1½" rafters at 18" crs.

3" x 3" struts (in line with purlins) at 5'-4½" crs.

3" x 2" wall plate.

3" x 2" hanger to every rafter.

4" x 1½" ceiling joists at 16" crs.

2'-2" - 0"

Y

If plain tiles are to be employed then the pitch of the rafters should be not less than 40°.

5" x ¾" ridge.

1" x 1" battens at 4" gauge.

4" x 1½" rafters at 18" crs.

7" x 1" fascia.

2" x 1½" framing to carry soffite.

STRUTTED PURLIN ROOF

E.B.C.

L

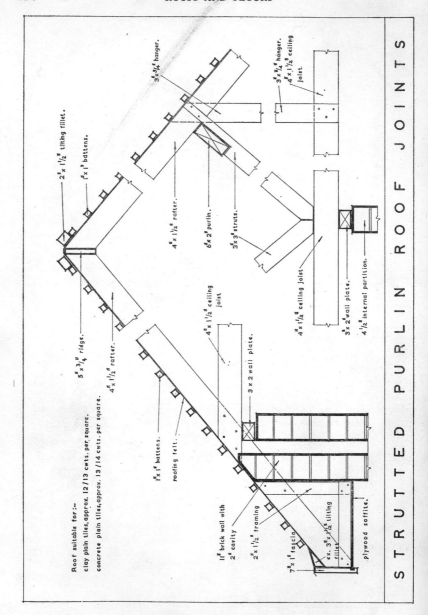

Roof suitable for :—
clay plain tiles, approx. 12/13 cwts. per square.
concrete plain tiles, approx. 13/14 cwts. per square.

5" x 3/4" ridge.

4" x 1½" rafter.

2" x 1½" tilting fillet.

1" x 1" battens.

4" x 1½" rafter.

3" x 3/4" hanger.

6" x 2" purlin.

3" x 3" struts.

4" x 1½" ceiling joist.

4" x 1½" ceiling joist.

3" x 3/4" hanger.
4" x 1½" ceiling joist.

3" x 2" wall plate.
4½" internal partition.

3 x 2 wall plate.

1" x 1" battens.
roofing felt.

11" brick wall with 2" cavity

2" x 1½" framing

7" x 1" fascia

ex. 3" x 1½" tilting fillet

plywood soffite.

STRUTTED PURLIN ROOF JOINTS

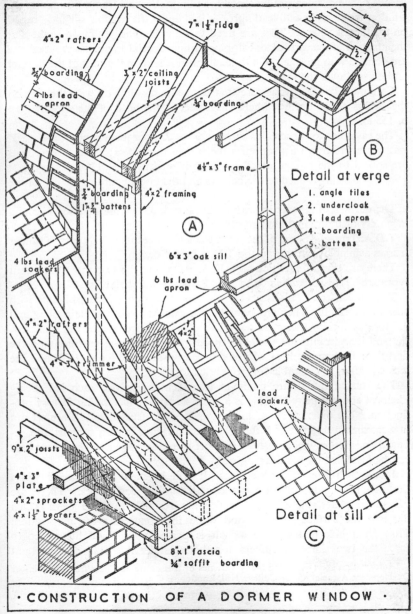

4"x2" rafters

7"x 1½" ridge

¾" boarding

3"x 2" ceiling joists

4 lbs lead apron

¾" boarding

4½"x 3" frame

¾" boarding
1"x ¾" battens

4"x 2" framing

Ⓐ

6"x 3" oak sill

6 lbs lead apron

4"x 2"

4 lbs lead soakers

4"x 2" rafters

4"x 3" trimmer

9"x 2" joists

4"x 3" plate

4"x 2" sprockets

4"x 1½" bearers

lead soakers

8"x 1" fascia
¾" soffit boarding

Detail at verge

1. angle tiles
2. undercloak
3. lead apron
4. boarding
5. battens

Ⓑ

Detail at sill

Ⓒ

· CONSTRUCTION OF A DORMER WINDOW ·

L 2

cheeks of the dormer and battened for tiling. Vertical framing supports the window frame and a 6 lb lead apron is laid under the window sill and dressed on the tiles as shown. Tiles are fixed to tiling battens, with lead soakers at the junction of the vertical and sloping tiling. Special angle tiles are used and are pointed with mortar. A 4 lb lead apron is laid on the roof of the dormer and dressed over the top row of tiles.

Care must be taken to ensure that the gable tiles line up with the tiles on the cheeks of the dormer where they meet at the head of the window (see p. 155 B).

The eaves are constructed as shown; 9″ × 2″ floor joists support a 4″ × 3″ wall plate which in turn supports the feet of the rafters; 4″ × 2″ sprockets are spiked to the rafters and these are stiffened by 4″ × 1½″ soffit bearers; ¾″ soffit boarding is fixed to the bearers and the fascia board to the feet of the sprockets.

The dormer window is interesting because it shows the potentialities and ingenuity of traditional construction.

T.D.A. Trusses. Some of the most efficient and economical types of timber trusses available are those to the T.D.A.* roof design.

There are several varieties of T.D.A. truss, but the two most important types are ' Trussed Rafters ' and the ' Standard Industrial Truss '.

Trussed Rafters. This is a very economical system which will cope with spans up to 26 ft. They are available for pitches of 40° for plain tiling and 35° for interlocking tiles or slates. The advantages are, apart from economy, that no long lengths are used, the need for load bearing partitions on the first floor is eliminated (as with a strutted purlin roof, see p. 153), and the trussed rafters are suitable for prefabrication.

The trussed rafters are made in two identical halves, each half being identical and not paired. This is a great advantage facilitating factory production. The diagram on p. 158 shows how the trussed rafters are set out at a maximum distance of 6 ft. The trussed rafters in turn support a ridge-board and purlins which in turn support common rafters. (These members can be identified on the drawing on p. 159.)

Joints with Timber Connections. It will be seen from the drawings that the principal joints are made with timber connectors. These are galvanised plates, the edges of which are serrated to form teeth which dig into the surface of the wood when the connectors are in position. Through a hole in the plate a bolt is passed which is tightened up to force the two timber members together. Under the head and the nut

* Information sheets showing many varieties of trusses are available from the Timber Development Association, 21 College Hill, London, E C.4.

T.D.A. 40° ROOF, 'Type A', for spans up to 26 ft 0 in
35° ROOF, 'Type B', for spans up to 26 ft 0 in.

T.D.A. 22 ½° STANDARD INDUSTRIAL TRUSSES
'Type A', for spans up to 57 feet 6 ins.
'Type B', to take suspended ceilings,
for spans up to 45 feet 0 ins.

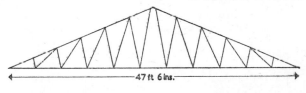

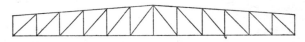

HOWE TRUSS   4° pitch   to span 60 feet
MacAndrews & Forbes

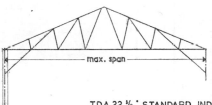

T.D.A. 22 ½° STANDARD INDUSTRIAL KNEE-
BRACED TRUSS, 'Type C'.
for spans up to 32 feet 10 1/2 ins.

ROOFS AND TRUSSES   types and spans

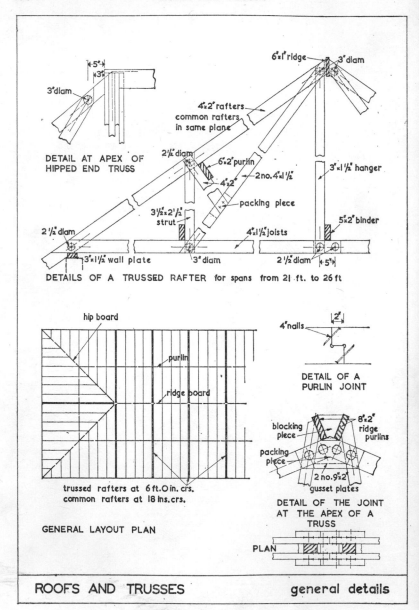

DETAIL AT APEX OF
HIPPED END TRUSS

3″diam

5″
3″

6″x1″ ridge

3″diam

4″x2″ rafters
common rafters
in same plane

2½″ diam

6″x2″ purlin

2 no. 4″x1½″

4″x2″

packing piece

3½″x2½″
strut

4″x1½″ joists

3″x1½″ hanger

5″x2″ binder

2½″ diam

3″x1½″ wall plate

3″ diam

2½″ diam

5″

DETAILS OF A TRUSSED RAFTER for spans from 21 ft. to 26 ft

hip board

purlin

ridge board

trussed rafters at 6 ft. 0 in. crs.
common rafters at 18 ins. crs.

GENERAL LAYOUT PLAN

4″ nails

2″

DETAIL OF A
PURLIN JOINT

blocking
piece

8″x2″
ridge
purlins

packing
piece

2 no.9″x2″
gusset plates

DETAIL OF THE JOINT
AT THE APEX OF A
TRUSS

PLAN

ROOFS AND TRUSSES   general details

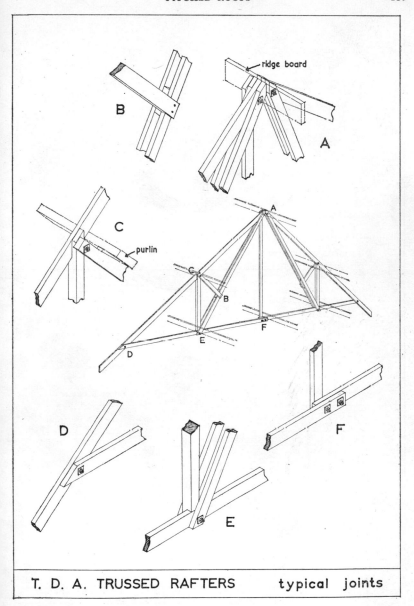

T. D. A. TRUSSED RAFTERS   typical joints

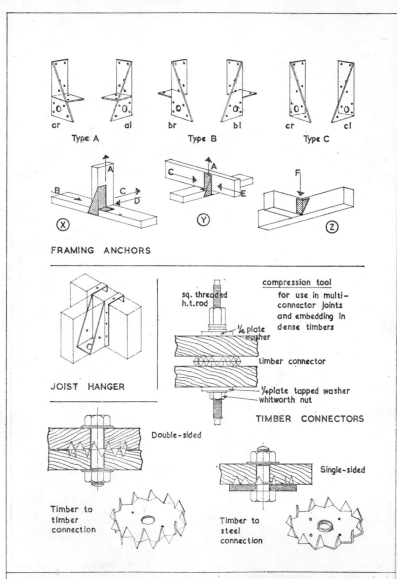

ar   al   br   bl   cr   cl

Type A   Type B   Type C

FRAMING ANCHORS

JOIST HANGER

compression tool

for use in multi-connector joints and embedding in dense timbers

sq. threaded h.t.rod

⅛ plate washer

timber connector

¼ plate tapped washer
whitworth nut

TIMBER CONNECTORS

Double-sided

Single-sided

Timber to timber connection

Timber to steel connection

TIMBER CONNECTIONS

SAFE WORKING LOADS FOR ONE 'BAT' CONNECTOR AND BOLT (IN SINGLE SHEAR)

Allowable LOAD in pounds per CONNECTOR and BOLT at angle of load to grain (According to Group)

Connector size	Bolt Dia.	Timber thickness — In one face only	Timber thickness — Opposite in two faces	Group I Timber: Douglas Fir (Coast), Longleaf Pitch Pine, Shortleaf Pitch Pine							Group II Timber: Canadian Spruce, Most European Timbers, Western Hemlock						
				0°	15°	30°	45°	60°	75°	90°	0°	15°	30°	45°	60°	75°	90°
2" sq.	½"	1"	2"	1,280	1,235	1,155	1,075	1,015	985	980	950	915	840	780	740	720	715
		1¼"	2½"	1,330	1,295	1,235	1,155	1,075	1,075	1,065	1,035	995	915	845	795	775	765
		1½"	3"	1,335	1,315	1,255	1,205	1,155	1,125	1,120	1,055	1,015	945	875	825	800	795
		1¾" & over	3½" & over	1,335	1,320	1,285	1,245	1,215	1,195	1,185	1,055	1,030	975	915	875	845	840
2¼" sq.	½"	1"	2"	1,540	1,595	1,515	1,435	1,375	1,345	1,340	1,240	1,205	1,130	1,070	1,030	1,010	1,005
		1¼"	2½"	1,590	1,655	1,595	1,515	1,465	1,435	1,425	1,325	1,285	1,205	1,135	1,085	1,065	1,055
		1½"	3"	1,595	1,675	1,615	1,565	1,515	1,485	1,430	1,345	1,305	1,235	1,165	1,115	1,090	1,085
		1¾" & over	3½" & over	1,695	1,680	1,645	1,605	1,575	1,555	1,545	1,345	1,320	1,265	1,205	1,165	1,135	1,130
3" sq.	½"	1"	2"	2,095	2,050	1,970	1,890	1,830	1,800	1,795	1,600	1,565	1,490	1,430	1,390	1,370	1,365
		1½"	3"	2,150	2,130	2,070	2,020	1,970	1,940	1,935	1,705	1,665	1,595	1,525	1,475	1,450	1,445
		1¾" & over	3½" & over	2,150	2,135	2,100	2,060	2,030	2,010	2,000	1,705	1,680	1,625	1,565	1,525	1,495	1,490
3" sq.	⅝"	1"	2"	2,245	2,175	2,035	1,915	1,835	1,795	1,785	1,660	1,610	1,510	1,430	1,380	1,360	1,350
		1½"	3"	2,441	2,375	2,235	2,105	2,015	1,955	1,945	1,875	1,810	1,670	1,560	1,490	1,455	1,440
		1¾" & over	3½" & over	2,460	2,415	2,305	2,195	2,110	2,065	2,045	1,950	1,880	1,740	1,620	1,540	1,500	1,490
3½" sq.	¾"	1"	2"	3,050	2,960	2,770	2,630	2,530	2,480	2,470	2,275	2,210	2,080	1,980	1,930	1,900	1,890
		1½"	3"	3,415	3,300	3,070	2,870	2,750	2,670	2,655	2,560	2,460	2,270	2,130	2,045	2,000	1,990
		1¾" & over	3½" & over	3,525	3,420	3,190	2,980	2,840	2,770	2,755	2,710	2,600	2,390	2,220	2,110	2,060	2,050

The values given above may be increased when the effects of wind and snow are considered.
Dead load + superimposed load + snow load   Add 12½% to given values.
Dead load − superimposed load + wind load   Add 25% to given values.

The loads given in the above table are based on tests carried out at the Forest Products Research Laboratory in co-operation with the Timber Development Association and may be subject to slight modification in view of further research.

are placed two square washers so that the head and the nut do not sink into the wood when the bolts are tightened up. Timber connectors can be obtained in various sizes for various loads. Most of those used in T.D.A. trusses are $2\frac{1}{2}$ in. in diameter for use with $\frac{1}{2}$ in. diameter bolts. The washers used with these trusses are $\frac{1}{8}$ in. mild steel, 2 in. square.

The advantage of a joint made with timber connectors is that the shear and tension stresses are transferred most efficiently, practically up to the maximum stress that the appropriate timber section can itself withstand. This is because of the load-spreading effect of the teeth over a wide area of the interface of the joint, and because only a very small amount of wood, i.e. the hole for the bolt, is removed to make the joint.

Single-sided timber connectors are available where it is necessary to join timber to steel, as in rigid framed construction.

TIMBER DIMENSIONS, SPACING AND END DISTANCES

Connector size		2″ sq.	2½″ sq.	3″ sq.	3½″ sq.
Minimum washer size		2″ sq. × ⅛″	2¼″ sq. × ⅛″	3″ sq. × ⅛″	3½″ sq. × 3⁄16″
Minimum timber size connector in one face only		¾″ × 2½″	⅞″ × 3″	1″ × 3½″	1″ × 4″
Minimum timber size connector in both faces		1½″ × 2½″	1¾″ × 3″	2″ × 3½″	2″ × 4″
Spacing of connectors	0°	3″	3¾″	4½″	5″
	90°	3″	3½″	3¾″	4″
End distance	Min.	1½″	1¾″	2″	2¼″
	Std.	3″	3″	3½″	4″

With reference to the Table on p. 161:—

Single Connector Joint. The loads given are for two member joint assembly with one connector, a bolt and nut and two square washers.

Loads and Standard Distances and Spacing. The loads given are for standard end distances and spacings. If it is necessary to depart from these standard dimensions the allowable load must be reduced.

Loads at Angle to Grain. When loads at angles to grain are different from those given in the table the safe load may be determined by interpolation.

Multiple Connector Loads. For a multiple joint assembly in which more than one connector of the same or different sizes are used on the same bolt, or with separate bolts, the safe load is the sum of the loads given for each connector unit.

Moisture Content. The loads given are for timber with a moisture content of 20%; this is approximately the percentage reached by timber in this country from air drying. If there is any risk of decay a suitable preservative treatment should be given.

Assembly of Connector Joints. All bolt holes should permit the bolt to be driven easily. Generally, the bolt holes should be $\frac{1}{16}$ in. larger than bolt diameter.

Care should be taken to ensure that the drill or bit is always at right angles to the timber member.

It is most important that the bolts are properly spaced, i.e. at distances not less than the table above; and that the minimum end distance from the centre of the bolt to the end of the member is adhered to, otherwise failures may result.

A threaded tool with a large nut and ballrace washer is available for initially tightening up joints. When the joints are first assembled, a bolt sufficiently long for the completed joint will not be long enough till the teeth of the connector have been driven into the interfaces of the joint, so this tool is practically indispensable.

Variety. A wide variety of trusses and frames are possible using the timber connector technique. See drawing on p. 157 for some examples.

Framing Anchors. These are galvanised metal angle plates drilled for nail fixing which are quick and efficient for light framing. They can be used to take shear, compression, and tension stresses so long as care is taken to see that the nails are loaded in shear. Diagram on p. 160 indicates their uses and types. It will be noticed that they are handed, which means that ordering must be undertaken with care.

It is important to specify that the anchors must be galvanised or sherardised, and it is advisable to paint the framing anchors when fixed with two coats of high quality bituminous paint. It is vital to use nails (galvanised) of the right size and gauge, so that there is a drive fit. In making a joint with a framing anchor no material is cut away so that the maximum economy of timber is achieved.

Safe Working Values. (For use with softwood.) In general when two or more anchors are used in combinations the allowable load will be the sum of the individual loads (see Drawings X, Y and Z, p. 160).

FRAMING ANCHORS (see p. 160)

Load direction (Drawings X, Y and Z)	A	B	C	D	E	F
Short-term loading (wind, snow, earthquake)	450	825	420	300	510	790
Long-term loading (live loads, dead loads)	300	530	290	200	340	525

Values given are for one anchor in pounds.
(By courtesy of McAndrews and Forbes Ltd.)

CONCRETE ROOFS AND FLOORS

Flat Roofs *in situ.* In its simplest form timber shuttering, i.e. a timber platform, is erected at ceiling level, and propped frequently to support the load of the wet concrete. The top surface of the timber is then painted with mould oil to prevent the set concrete from adhering to the timber so that the timber cannot be removed easily. Small 'tiles' of high grade concrete are then cast, 1 in. thick. These are placed at frequent centres over the timber shuttering. These tiles support the steel reinforcing mesh and ensure that the underside of the mesh will have a cover of at least 1 in. of concrete. The concrete is then cast to the required thickness, and vibrated or punned so that it is properly consolidated around the reinforcement and so that all the voids are eliminated. At this point care must be taken that vibration or punning is not overdone so that a cement rich skin or laitance is not brought to the surface—reducing strength of the mix. As soon as the concrete has set sufficiently the shuttering is removed for re-use elsewhere.

It should be noted that although high-grade concrete may in itself be waterproof it is not impermeable to water vapour. In any heated building insulation must be provided, but it should be provided in such a way that condensation cannot occur. It has been found that one of the best ways of applying the insulation is to stick 1 in. insulation board to the top surface of the concrete with a continuous layer of hot bitumen, the felt or asbestos roofing being fixed to the top of the insulation. This arrangement ensures that the hot bitumen layer, being the vapour barrier, is kept at a temperature above the 'dew point' or 'condensation point' of the air within the building, because the insulation is above it. The mistake is frequently made that either no vapour barrier is placed in the roof or that it is placed above the insulation where it can be chilled below the condensation or dew point of the air within the building, causing large quantities of moisture to condense out within the insulation and concrete structure.

Where the humidity of the air is expected to be relatively low, i.e. in

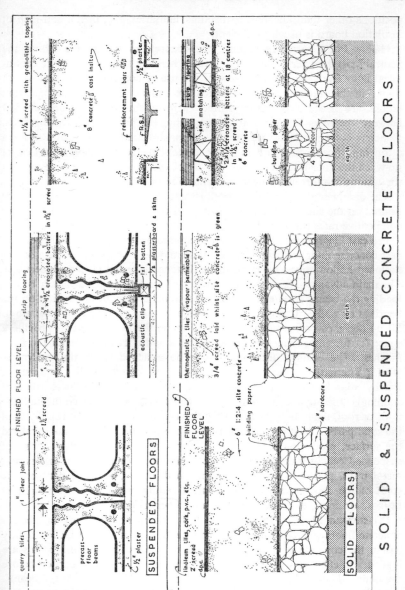

SOLID & SUSPENDED CONCRETE FLOORS

positions other than kitchens, bathrooms, laundries, etc., then a half-inch of insulation board is usually sufficient.

Hollow Pot Floors. In section, the concrete in the middle (about the neutral axis) does very little work to resist bending stresses. A more economical floor from the point of view of the use of concrete is the hollow pot floor; in this, hollow clay tiles, which are similar to hollow clay partition blocks, are placed direct on the timber or metal shuttering. Spaces are left between the rows of blocks at frequent intervals for the reinforcing rods. Concrete is then poured to fill these spaces, surround the rods, and to form a topping of concrete 2 or 3 in. thick to resist the compressional stresses set up when the floor is loaded. Stirrups are placed in to tie up the topping with the tension reinforcement near the underside of the floor.

The disadvantage with *in situ* work is that so much wet concrete has to be poured on the site. In spite of this a good contractor can often quote very competitive rates for an *in situ* concrete floor.

Pre-cast Floors (see p. 165). There are numerous proprietary makes of pre-cast concrete floor and roof beams; these may be T-shaped in section or like flattened hollow tubes, or again like a flattened inverted U (trough section). The main advantage here is that the work of erection is just a matter of off-loading the beams from a lorry and placing them straight in position on the bearings or walls. It is often then necessary to cast a screed of concrete to fill up the gaps between the beams and to tie the floor together, provide a space for the embedding of electric conduits and a true surface for the floor finishes. The ceilings underneath may be attached to a timber framework ; alternatively beams may be plastered direct on the undersides. Patchy discoloration of the ceiling may occur in this case (pattern staining) caused by the different rates at which heat is transferred through the floor or roof, the hollow parts of the floor transmitting heat less rapidly than the solid parts. Dust particles carried on the resulting air currents bombard the surface, producing the staining. There are many proprietary forms of suspended ceiling involving the use of aluminium or mild steel angles and metal trays, plaster board, insulation board, etc. The space between the soffit of the concrete and the suspended ceiling may be used for lighting fittings, air ducts, electrical conduits and other services.

Pre-stressed Floors. Pre-stressing is a refinement in the use of steel in concrete floors whereby wires of much smaller diameter are stretched tightly within the concrete tending to arch the beam upwards till the beams are loaded. In effect this means that much heavier loads can be carried before the underside of the concrete starts to crack with the sagging of the beams. Proprietary makes are available. The main difficulty is that the amount of

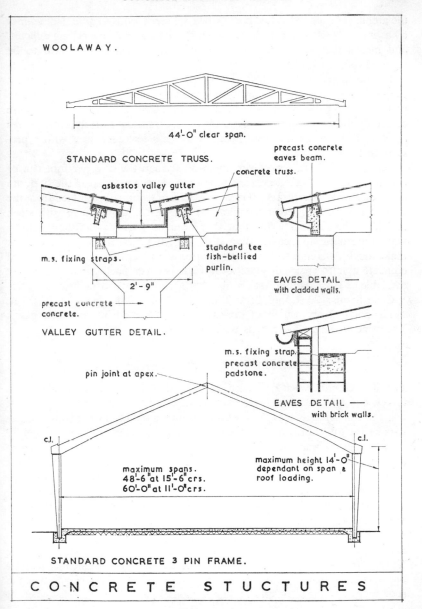

WOOLAWAY.

44'-0" clear span.

STANDARD CONCRETE TRUSS.

asbestos valley gutter

concrete truss.

precast concrete
eaves beam.

m.s. fixing straps.

standard tee
fish-bellied
purlin.

2'-9"

EAVES DETAIL —
with cladded walls.

precast concrete
concrete.

VALLEY GUTTER DETAIL.

m.s. fixing strap.
precast concrete
padstone.

pin joint at apex.

EAVES DETAIL —
with brick walls.

c.l.   c.l.

maximum spans.
48'-6" at 15'-6" crs.
60'-0" at 11'-0" crs.

maximum height 14'-0"
dependant on span &
roof loading.

STANDARD CONCRETE 3 PIN FRAME.

CONCRETE   STUCTURES

the arching of each individual beam when delivered tends to differ (sometimes by as much as two inches). This makes the plastering of the ceiling difficult, and means that the more expensive suspended ceilings may have to be resorted to.

The positions of any holes in either pre-cast or pre-stressed floors must be worked out beforehand, and cardboard tubes or other formers placed in position when the concrete is poured. If, as is frequently the case, holes are drilled or chiselled in the floor after the concrete has set the reinforcing wires are very likely to be damaged, which may be a serious matter with a pre-stressed floor.

Concrete Roof Trusses. Over about 50 ft span the cost per foot run of concrete truss tends to decrease as the span increases, whereas the opposite is the case with a steel truss. Trusses are cast in sections, assembled from the ground and then raised in position. Their cost is competitive with steel, and have the singular virtue that they need no painting. Although these trusses are naturally heavier than steel ones, the increase is not such as to make much difference to base sizes. Purlins can be provided in pre-stressed concrete able to span adequately the 15 ft between each truss. Spans are available ex stock as follows:

Clear Spans: 20 ft 4 in., 26 ft 2 in., 32 ft 2 in., 38 ft., 44 ft., 49 ft., 54 ft.

The columns are usually of pre-cast concrete slotted into concrete bases. The principal advantage here is the fire resistance.

FRAMES FOR PITCHED ROOFS

The distinction between these and trusses is that there is no triangulation of forces, e.g. a Woolaway single-span frame consists of columns up to 50 ft apart to which are attached (by a post tensioning method) what would otherwise be the top chords of the trusses (see p. 167). The apex joint is slightly thicker than the remainder of the chords which are in fact *in situ* jointed at their centre points. The joint between columns and chords at the eaves is also thicker (as at the apex) because there the bending moment is greatest.

The concrete three-pin frame is similar in some respects except that most of the moments are taken up at eaves level, the chords getting slenderer towards the apex where there is a pin joint formed with steel hinge plates. The other two pin positions are theoretically at the base of the columns. Spans are available up to 60 ft at 11 ft centres.

These frames for pitched roofs are more expensive than concrete trusses, but have the advantage that there are no bottom ties. This means that the roof space can be completely utilised. This is useful in factories where a fork-lift truck type of transport is employed, and in churches and halls. This ' arched ' framed construction described above can be carried out in other materials.

OTHER ROOF AND FLOOR SYSTEMS

Laminated Timber Arches. The development of new efficient waterproof glues has made the development of laminated arches possible which can achieve great spans, up to 150 ft. One technique of construction of such arches is first to make a rigid formwork of timber to the profile of half of the arch, i.e. from foot to apex; planks are clamped to this shape and one by one glued together to form a multi-layer sandwich of the required thickness. When the glueing process has been completed the halves are then cut, cleaned and planed, and delivered to the site where they are erected and bolted together at the apex; the feet of the arches fit into metal plates grouted into the foundation concrete. (See drawings on p. 170.)

Steel Frames. Great strides have been made recently in structural theory the plastic method of design—enabling arches of R.S.J. section to be formed in which bending stresses are distributed throughout the frame. This results in much saving of steel and a delicate-looking form.

A point to be borne in mind is that in order to make steel fire resisting it has to be surrounded in concrete or some other protective material (brick-work, sprayed asbestos, gypsum or Portland cement, plaster on metal lathing, etc.).

Steel Tubular Trusses. *Efficiency.* For compression members the tube is a very efficient section, the material being evenly distributed and an equal distance from the neutral axis. Welding techniques are now reliable and make the jointing of tubes a straightforward proposition.

From this has developed a technique of making welded tubular trusses.

Standardisation. Tubular trusses are available from stock in the following sizes:

	Approximately*			Approximately*
30 ft 0 in.	. £14 0s. 0d. 1961		50 ft 0 in.	. £37 0s. 0d. 1961
35 ft 0 in.	. £17 0s. 0d. ,,		60 ft 0 in.	. £49 0s. 0d. ,,
40 ft 0 in.	. £22 0s. 0d. ,,		70 ft 0 in.	. £70 0s. 0d. ,,
45 ft 0 in.	. £27 0s. 0d. ,,		80 ft 0 in.	. £82 0s. 0d. ,,

The trusses are placed at 15 ft centres and usually stand on tubular columns. Purlins (£2 15s. 0d. (1961)) are spaced about 4 ft apart and are 3 in. in

* These prices are by courtesy of Clarke, Nicholls & Marcel, Consulting Engineers.

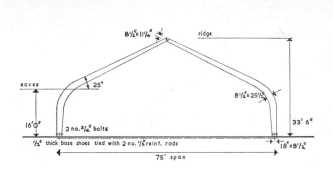

8½" x 11¼"   ridge

25°

eaves

8½" x 25½"

16'0"   33'6"
2 no. ¾" bolts
½" thick base shoes tied with 2 no. ½" reinf. rods
18" x 8½"
75' span

GLUED LAMINATED ARCH   spaced at 15'0" centres

apex halved and fixed with a ½" bolt and 2½" split ring
connector.

manufactured in Grade I timber with waterproof glue
of ¾" lamina

LOADING: dead 10 lbs/sq.ft.
live and snow 15 lbs/sq ft
wind 16 lbs/sq ft on roof only

sheeted roof finish
2"x 8" purlins

3'

weld

24° pitch

36"

SPAN 30 ft 0 in.

21"

2 no. 2"x 9"
rafters ¼" apart.

8"   12"   ½"

¼" shaped m.s. apex
gusset inset between rafters.

2 no. shaped timber blocks
encasing steel gusset.

eaves gusset of 2 no. 2½" m.s. plates welded together and connectored
to rafter and column as shown inset between timber members
2 no. shaped timber blocks encasing
steel gusset.

2 no. timber columns, ¼" apart

connectors and bolts

end of timber column
top of conc. foundation

5"x ½" flange welded to
5/16"x 9" m.s. plate
15"x 9" m.s. base plate

⅜" gussets

15'   20'

span 24'0"   pitch 22½"

RIGID FRAME   CONSTRUCTION

RIGID FRAME AND   GLUED LAMINATED ARCHES.

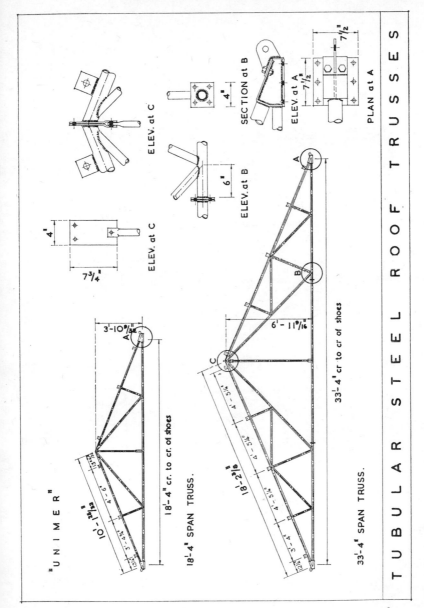

ELEV. at C

ELEV. at B

SECTION at B

ELEV. at A
7½"

PLAN at A
7½"

4"

6"

ELEV. at C
4"
7¾"

"UNIMER"

3'-10⁵⁄₃₂"

A

18'-4" cr. to cr. of shoes

10'-1²⁵⁄₃₂"
4'-6"
3'-4¾"

18'-4" SPAN TRUSS.

A

B

6'-11⁹⁄₁₆"

C

33'-4" cr to cr of shoes

18'-2¹⁄₈"
4'-5¾"
4'-5¾"
4'-5⅜"
3'-4⅜"

33'-4" SPAN TRUSS.

T U B U L A R   S T E E L   R O O F   T R U S S E S

M 2

"UNIMER."

purlin cleat to be omitted when
eaves purlin is not required.

ragbolt.

tubular column.

conc. infill.

concrete pad.

DETAIL OF TRUSS FIXING
TO PADSTONE.

DETAIL OF STANDARD
COLUMN BASE FIXING.

nut welded to plate at
end of purlin.

1" dia. stud.

eaves gutter brackets
fixed to eaves purlin.

column base.

foundation bolts
& plate set in
concrete pad.

DETAIL OF CONNECTIONS OF
TRUSS TO COLUMN CAP &
PURLIN TO TRUSS.

DETAIL OF ALTERNATIVE
COLUMN BASE FIXING.

DETAILS OF TUBULAR STEEL TRUSSES

diameter. Sheeting rails for asbestos cement or other wall sheeting are the same diameter and are placed at about the same space.

Columns. The feet of the trusses may be carried on tubular columns. For a truss up to 30 ft in span a $4\frac{1}{2}'' \times 9''$ gauge column is usually used and would cost approximately £4 10s. 0d. delivered. For a truss of 80 ft span a $8\frac{5}{8}$ in. diameter column would be used with a wall thickness of $\frac{1}{4}$ in. It would cost approximately £25 0s. 0d. These figures give some idea of the range of cost involved. As a rough guide, the following table gives an indication of column sizes for differing heights and spans.

Column Sizes (diameter and wall thickness)

Height to Eaves (ft)	Truss Spans					
	30	40	50	60	70	80
8	$4\frac{1}{2}'' \times 9G$	$4\frac{1}{2}'' \times 7G$	$4\frac{1}{2}'' \times 5G$	$5\frac{1}{2}'' \times 6G$	$5\frac{1}{2}'' \times 6G$	$6\frac{5}{8}'' \times 7G$
12	$5\frac{1}{2}'' \times 6G$	$5\frac{1}{2}'' \times 6G$	$6\frac{5}{8}'' \times 7G$	$6\frac{5}{8}'' \times 7G$	$6\frac{5}{8}'' \times 6G$	$7\frac{5}{8}'' \times 6G$
16	$7\frac{5}{8}'' \times 6G$	$7\frac{5}{8}'' \times 6G$	$7\frac{5}{8}'' \times 6G$	$7\frac{5}{8}'' \times 6G$	$8\frac{5}{8}'' \times 6G$	$8\frac{5}{8}'' \times 6G$
20	$8\frac{5}{8}'' \times 5G$	$8\frac{5}{8}'' \times 5G$	$8\frac{5}{8}'' \times \frac{1}{4}''$	$8\frac{5}{8}'' \times \frac{1}{4}''$	$8\frac{5}{8}'' \times \frac{1}{4}''$	$8\frac{5}{8}'' \times \frac{1}{4}''$

Information from Tubewrights Limited

Bases. These must be set out accurately with the aid of profiles (see p. 19) and a steel tape using running dimensions. The concrete used is usually 1 : 2 : 4 of good quality (see p. 27). The following table gives an idea of base sizes for various spans:

Truss span	Standard dimensions for concrete bases	Column below floor level	Depth of concrete below column
18 ft 4 in.	$1' \ 6'' \times 1' \ 6'' \times 3'$	2 ft	1 ft
27 ft 6 in.	$2' \quad \times 2' \quad \times 3'$	2 ft	1 ft
33 ft 4 in.	$2' \ 6'' \times 2' \ 6'' \times 3'$	2 ft	1 ft

The bottom of the concrete base (see drawing on p. 172) should always be at least 3 ft below ground level, i.e. to keep the base free from seasonal movement.

Gable End Trusses. Special trusses are available for gable ends which incorporate horizontal rails so that sheeting can be carried up the gable of the roof.

Assembly. The trusses arrive on the site usually in two halves which are then bolted together at the apex and at two points in the bottom tie. The purlin clips are already welded on to the top chord of the truss. The truss is then raised by means of a crane or derrick and lowered on to the column

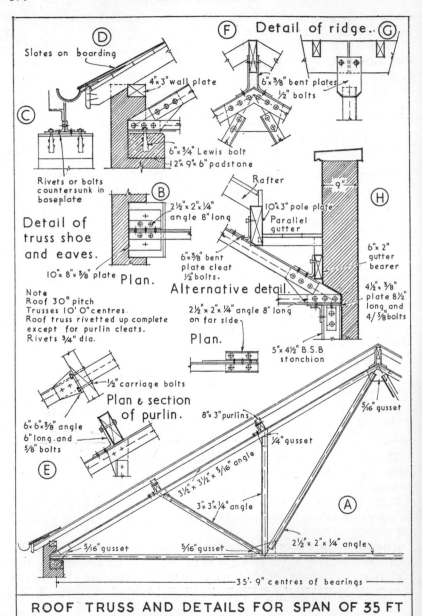

Slates on boarding

(D)

(C)

(F)   Detail of ridge.. (G)

4"x 3" wall plate

6"x 3/8" bent plates
1/2" bolts

Rivets or bolts
countersunk in
baseplate

6"x 3/4" Lewis bolt
12"x 9"x 6" padstone

Detail of
truss shoe
and eaves.

(B)

2 1/2" x 2" x 1/4"
angle 8" long

10"x 8"x 3/8" plate   Plan.

Note
Roof 30° pitch
Trusses 10' 0" centres.
Roof truss rivetted up complete
except for purlin cleats.
Rivets 3/4" dia.

Rafter

10"x 3" pole plate

Parallel
gutter

6"x 3/8" bent
plate cleat
1/2" bolts.

Alternative detail.

2 1/2" x 2" x 1/4" angle 8" long
on far side

Plan.

(H)

9"

6"x 2"
gutter
bearer

4 1/2"x 3/8"
plate 8 1/2"
long and
4/ 5/8" bolts

5"x 4 1/2" B.S.B
stanchion

1/2" carriage bolts

Plan & section
of purlin.

8"x 3" purlins

1/4" gusset

5/16" gusset

6"x 6"x 3/8" angle
6" long and
5/8" bolts

(E)

3 1/2" x 3 1/2" x 5/16" angle

3"x 3"x 1/4" angle

(A)

2 1/2" x 2" x 1/4" angle

5/16" gusset   5/16" gusset

35'. 9" centres of bearings

ROOF TRUSS AND DETAILS FOR SPAN OF 35 FT

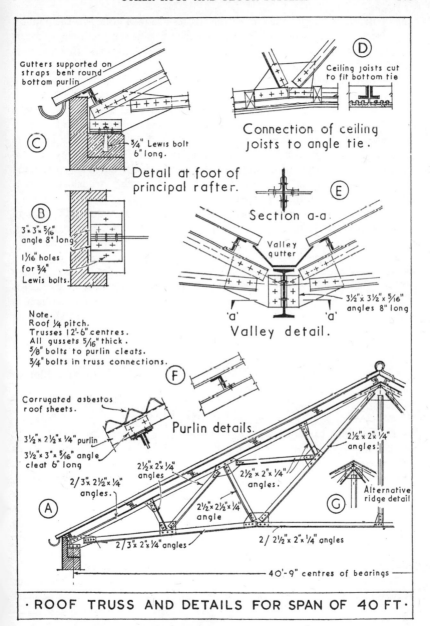

Gutters supported on straps bent round bottom purlin

D

Ceiling joists cut to fit bottom tie

Connection of ceiling joists to angle tie.

C

¾" Lewis bolt 6" long.

Detail at foot of principal rafter.

B

3"× 3"× 5/16" angle 8" long.

1 1/16" holes for ¾" Lewis bolts.

E

Section a-a.

Valley gutter

3½"× 3½"× 5/16" angles 8" long.

'a'   'a'

Valley detail.

Note.
Roof ¼ pitch.
Trusses 12'-6" centres.
All gussets 5/16" thick.
5/8" bolts to purlin cleats.
¾" bolts in truss connections.

F

Corrugated asbestos roof sheets.

Purlin details.

3½"× 2½"× ¼" purlin

3½"× 3"× 5/16" angle cleat 6" long

2/3"× 2½"× ¼" angles.

2½"× 2"× ¼" angles

2½"× 2"× ¼" angles.

2½"× 2½"× ¼" angle

2½"× 2"× ¼" angles.

2½"× 2"× ¼" angles.

Alternative ridge detail

A

G

2/3"× 2"× ¼" angles

2/ 2½"× 2"× ¼" angles

— 40'-9" centres of bearings —

· ROOF TRUSS AND DETAILS FOR SPAN OF 40 FT ·

caps. Bearing plates at the feet of the trusses are then bolted to the column caps (see details on p. 171). Purlins are then positioned; and the asbestos cement, aluminium or other sheeting is fixed to the purlins and sheeting rails (attached to the columns).

For light industrial or storage buildings this type of construction fills a valuable role because of its lightness and efficiency, and its economy derived from the fact that the elements are entirely prefabricated and are drawn from stock. Insulation may be provided by sheeting the building in two layers of, say, asbestos cement with a sandwich of glass fibre insulation. There are several proprietary variations of this on the market. Lighting may be provided by putting patent glazing in the roof, or alternatively corrugated reinforced glass, Acrylic sheet or resinous glass fibre translucent sheet corrugated to match the roof sheeting.

This type of truss has been described in more detail to indicate the general method involved in this category of construction. There are many other similar systems using either welded connections or bolted connections.

Mild Steel Angle Trusses. These may have welded, riveted or bolted connections, and have been standard practice for many years. The principles of construction are similar to the tubular truss, though a little more steel is necessary for the same spans. The surface area of steel to be painted is also slightly greater. Examples of these roof trusses and details are shown on pp. 174–175.

Lattice Beam Construction. There are several proprietary makes of light lattice beams made out of mild steel rod which will span as much as 40 ft and may carry Monitor roof lights or may be arranged saw-tooth fashion to provide north lighting.

TIMBER GROUND FLOORS

A floor similar to the T.D.A. design, which is a modification of North American practice, is shown on p. 177. The size of the joists is 2″ × 3″ (as compared with 4″ or 4½″ × 2″ in normal sleeper wall construction); the 4 in. over-site concrete is spade finished, and receives either engineering bricks, or common bricks with a felt D.P.C., at 1 ft 8 in. centres in one direction and a maximum of 3 ft 10 in. centres parallel to the direction of the joists. Over this is laid 1 in. nominal tongued and grooved boarding.

The space under the boarding should be well ventilated and great care must be taken that no dampness is able to reach the timber either from the oversite concrete or from the surrounding brick or block work.

The hearth in concrete is built up from the oversite concrete; no timber is permitted close to the fireplace (see p. 82).

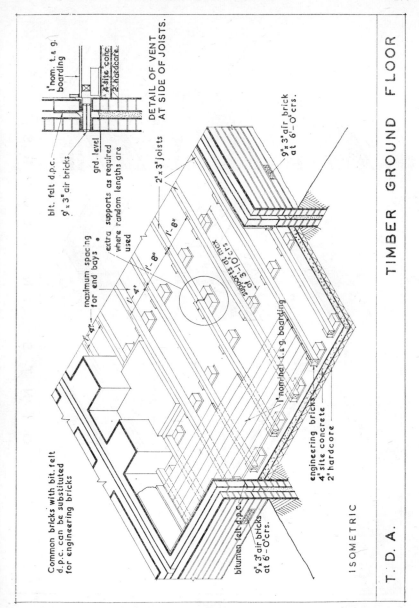

DETAIL OF VENT AT SIDE OF JOISTS.

1" nom. t. & g. boarding

4" site conc.
2" hardcore

bit. felt d.p.c.
9" × 3" air bricks

grd. level

2" × 3" joists

9" × 3" air brick at 6'-0" crs.

maximum spacing for end bays

extra supports as required where random lengths are used

supports at 3'-0" max.

1'-4"

1'-4"

1'-8"

1'-8"

Common bricks with bit. felt d.p.c. can be substituted for engineering bricks

1" nominal t. & g. boarding

engineering bricks
4" site concrete
2" hardcore

bitumen felt d.p.c.

9" × 3" air bricks at 6'-0" crs.

ISOMETRIC

T. D. A.   TIMBER GROUND FLOOR

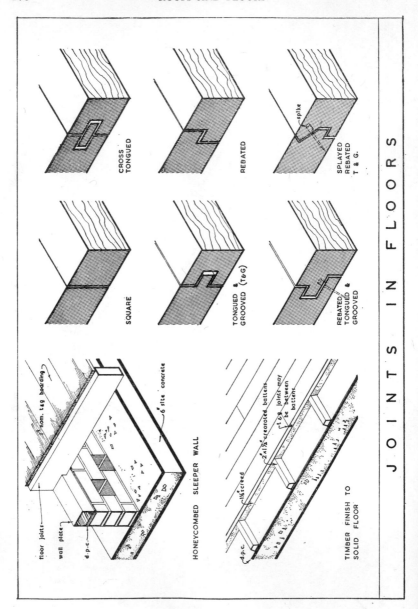

CROSS TONGUED

REBATED

SPLAYED REBATED T & G.
spike

SQUARE

TONGUED & GROOVED (T&G)

REBATED TONGUED & GROOVED

HONEYCOMBED SLEEPER WALL

¾″ hom. t&g boarding
6″ site concrete
floor joists
wall plate
d.p.c.

TIMBER FINISH TO SOLID FLOOR

t&g joints may be between battens
2×1½ creosoted battens
1¼″ screed
d.p.c.

JOINTS IN FLOORS

Joists can be of Group 2 timber (800 lb per sq. in. in bending); these can be drawn from Unsorted and 5ths qualities of European Redwood and Whitewood; and Merchantable qualities of Douglas Fir and Western Hemlock. The design complies with the Code of Practice.

Traditional Timber—Ground Floor. This consists of sleeper walls about 6 ft centres supporting $4\frac{1}{2}'' \times 2''$ or $5'' \times 2''$ joists. The joists are fixed to wall plates running along the tops of sleeper walls by means of spikes skew nailed from each face of the joist. A damp-proof course is placed in the sleeper wall which is usually made with plenty of openings in honeycomb formation to facilitate ventilation. The oversite concrete must be thickened to 5 in., preferably 6 in., under the sleeper walls to take the additional load. It will be seen that this method is not so economical as the T.D.A.-North American variety.

Joints in Floor Boards. It is not satisfactory to butt floor boards with a square joint; they should be either cross-tongued, tongued and grooved, rebated, filleted and grooved, or splayed and rebated (see diagram on p. 178). For these joints the tongued and grooved is perhaps the most popular. The splayed and rebated joint has the advantage that secret fixing is easier. Square or butt joints are bad, because floor boards are almost bound to shrink slightly causing loss of heat through draughts. This air leakage can amount to considerable proportions.

Floor boards must be cramped together as they are laid either by a mechanical floor cramp or by levers, or by folded wedges tightened with a hammer against dogs temporarily driven into the joists. This cramping minimises the effects of shrinkage. Ideally the floor joists should be stacked in the building in order that the timber can adjust itself to the final indoor climate. This practice is most certainly advisable with a hardwood floor.

TIMBER UPPER FLOORS

Joist Bearings. Joist ends should sit on a timber wall plate usually $4''$ or $4\frac{1}{2}'' \times 3''$; this may be supported directly on the brickwork, or on galvanised corbels $4'' \times \frac{3}{8}''$, turned up at the ends to retain the plate (see p. 180).

The joists vary slightly in their depth. In order to make the floor level the joists must be packed up on the plates either by thin slivers of timber or by checking or notching out the joists over the plates to leave a standard neck of joist immediately above the plate. The packing up method is often abused, odd shavings and chips being used; these concentrate the loads and crush the timber, so the packing must be done with even material throughout the whole bearing.

The calculation of joists for floors is the same as for roof joists (see p. 144).

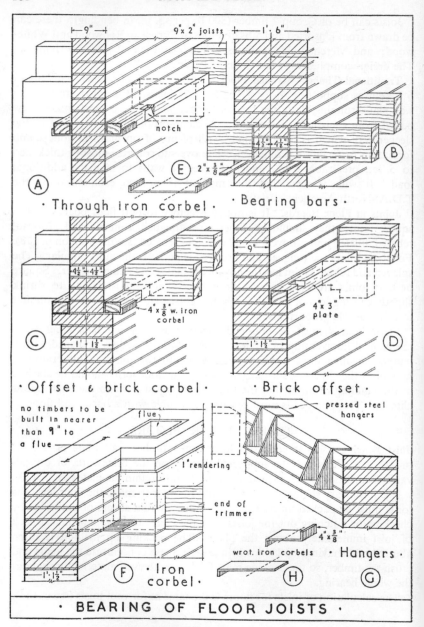

- Through iron corbel ·
9" 9" x 2" joists 1'. 6"
notch
E 2" x 3/8"
· Bearing bars ·
4 1/2" – 4 1/2"
B

· Offset & brick corbel ·
4 1/2" – 4 1/2"
4" x 3/8" w. iron corbel
C
1' 1 1/2"

· Brick offset ·
9"
4" x 3" plate
D
1' 1 1/2"

no timbers to be built in nearer than 9" to a flue
flue
1" rendering
end of trimmer
· Iron corbel ·
F
1' 1 1/2"

pressed steel hangers
4" x 3/8"
wrot. iron corbels
· Hangers ·
G
H

· BEARING OF FLOOR JOISTS ·

In large floors where joints have to be made in joists these should be arranged over plates. If the lining up of the joists is not important the joists may be laid side by side over the bearing and spiked together.

Alternatively the joists may be seated in openings in the inner leaf of, say, a cavity wall. The joists should here be placed on a slip of bitumen felt, so that the bearing area is increased. On no account should the joist end project through and touch the outer leaf of the cavity wall or any wet brickwork.

Trimming. Joists normally bridge from wall to wall. Where fireplaces, staircases or other openings occur some of the joists have to be cut or trimmed to form the opening. These joists in turn have to be supported by a ' trimmer ' running at right angles and bearing into ' trimming ' joists at each side of the opening. These trimming joists, which form two sides of the opening, bear into the walls at either end. The drawing on p. 182 shows a 9″ × 3″ trimmer tusk tenoned into a 9″ × 3″ trimming joist, the remaining joists, both ordinary bridging ones and the trimmed joists, being 9″ × 2″. This joint may also be made with a dovetailed notch, or better still by a joist hanger (see p. 160). Hence:

Bridging Joist: Joist spanning across the room from wall to wall.
Trimmed Joist: Joist cut to form an opening.
Trimmer Joist: Joist running at right angles, thicker, supporting the ends of the trimmed joists, and itself supported by the—
Trimming Joist: A thicker form of bridging joist running past each side of the opening and supporting the trimmer joist.

Some by-laws require the trimming and the trimmer joists to be an inch thicker than the bridging joists, e.g. if bridging joists are 7″ × 2″ then the trimming and trimmer joists should be 7″ × 3″. In this case the trimmer joists should not support more than six trimmed joists. If the loading conditions are worse than this, the members should be calculated (see p. 144).

Joist Hangers. These are available to take joists of the following thicknesses:

1½ in., 2 in., 2½ in., 3 in. and 4½ in. for depths from 6 in. to 9 in. They should be sherardised or galvanised.

Their main use is for carrying transverse timber, in trimming round chimney breasts, fireplaces, staircases, etc. They are fixed by nailing and the straps are bent over the top of the trimming joist (see p. 160).

Double Floors. Where the span exceeds about 16 ft it is usually economical to use a double floor (in timber construction). The usual method is to place rolled steel joists at 12 ft or so centres spanning the shortest distance between walls. The normal timber joists then span on to the steel joists.

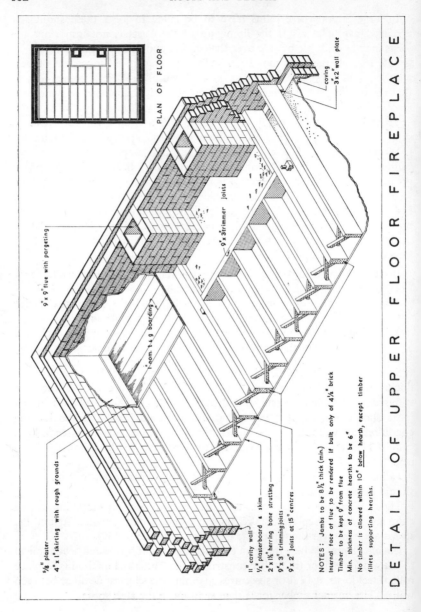

PLAN OF FLOOR

coving
3"×2" wall plate

9"×9" flue with pargeting

9"×3" trimmer joists

1" nom. t.& g. boarding

⁵⁄₈" plaster
4"×1" skirting with rough grounds

11" cavity wall
½" plasterboard & skim
2"×1½" herring bone strutting
9"×3" trimming joists
9"×2" joists at 15" centres

NOTES: Jambs to be 8½" thick (min.)
Internal face of flue to be rendered if built only of 4½" brick
Timber to be kept 9" from flue
Min. thickness of concrete hearths to be 6"
No timber is allowed within 10" below hearth, except timber
fillets supporting hearths.

DETAIL OF UPPER FLOOR FIREPLACE

SOLID FLOORS

There is often little difference in the cost between a T.D.A. type timber ground floor and a solid floor. The design of the solid floor in concrete depends a great deal upon the risk of dampness; if the floor is anywhere in the region of the water table at the worst time of year, i.e. the height at which water will appear in an excavation, then it is necessary to put a damp-proof membrane in the floor. This is good practice. (See p. 165.)

For domestic work the most economical method, if the ground permits, is to put down 4 in. of hardcore, consolidate it well, and blind the surface with ashes or fine material. On this place building paper and over this cast 4 in. minimum 1 : 2 : 4 concrete. This should contain crack control re-inforcement (chicken wire at least). When this has set, various damp-proof membranes may be applied, e.g. bituminous felt, cold bituminous solution, emulsion (two coats), P.V.C. film or asphalt. If there is any danger of positive water pressure then the bituminous felt or asphalt should be laid hot and jointed properly, as for tanking. If there is no danger of water pressure then a screed of at least 1½ in. thickness, preferably 2 in., or 1 : 3 cement and sand is laid over the surface to give a smooth and true finish for the floor layer.* If there is danger of water pressure then a loading layer properly reinforced must be provided. It is necessary to calculate the thickness of this loading layer and the amount of reinforcement required to resist the upwards pressure. The tanking must connect completely with the tanking on the walls and there must be no hole in this whatsoever.

Power Floating. If there is no danger of *water pressure* then the site concrete may be finished with a power float. This consists of a light petrol engine which revolves a flat disc about 3 ft in diameter; this is worked over the surface. The concrete must be a very dry mix and, if properly done, can receive the floor finish direct. The only possible snag here is that subsequent trades may damage this floated finish, which means that much rubbing down has to be done by the floor layer. If the site is properly managed this method can achieve great economies. There are a relatively small number of floor finishes which can be laid on to site concrete treated in this way; however good the concrete, a small amount of *water vapour* is bound to pass through this type of floor, and the finish must be such that this passage of vapour will not be trapped, which would cause the lifting of the floor in bubbles.

Strip Floors. Both hard and softwood strip floors, that is to say floors not exceeding 5 in. wide and 1 in. nominal thickness, usually 3″ × 1″ may be

* See *Laying Screeds as an Underlay for Floor Coverings*, M.o.W. Advisory Leaflet, No. 5.

laid on solid by means of splayed and creosoted (or otherwise rot-proofed) battens let into the screed above the damp-proof membrane. These battens are 3″ × 2½″ or even 2″ × 2″. The technique is to place the damp-proof membrane, set out the battens on top of this at 1 ft 3 in. centres, and then to screed over with cement and sand 1 : 5 to locate the battens permanently and to make the floor quieter. The tongued and grooved boards or strips are then secret nailed to the battens; if the ends of the boards or strips are end matched, that is, the tongue and groove run across the edge, economy is achieved because the boards need not then join immediately over a batten. (See p. 178.)

Wood Blocks and Ply-type Floors. These may be stuck down to the surface of the finishing screed by means of hot bitumen or a proprietary adhesive. It is not a good thing to lay the blocks or strips tightly up to the walls, as slight expansion of the blocks or strips may damage the walls. Strip floors are usually laid with slender wedges against the walls, which must be removed before the skirtings are fixed (except at the ends of the strips). When timber floors have been laid they should be protected with sawdust. One of the last operations should be the sanding and dressing of the surface with wax polish or a proprietary synthetic varnish.

BY-LAWS

Cavity and Damp-proof Course. The cavity in cavity wall construction must be carried down at least 6 in. below the damp-proof course. The ground level should be at least 6 in. below the damp-proof course, so that flowerbeds or other movement of earth will not bridge the damp-proof course and help to transmit moisture into the walling above.

Ventilation. Timber floors (the lowest) must be arranged so that the space below the floor and the over-site concrete is adequately ventilated. Ducts must be provided connecting to air-bricks in outer walls, under solid floors so that adjacent timber floors have through ventilation; this can be done by means of drain-pipes. Sleeper walls must have openings left in them for the same reason.

Minimum Dimensions. The underside of joists in lowest floors must be at 9 in. from excavated ground level if not covered with over-site concrete, or not less than 3 in. from the surface of over-site concrete. No timber must be in contact with wet construction, i.e. must be protected by a damp-proof course.

Tanking must be continuous between floors of basements and walls, up to the main damp-proof course (6 in. above ground level).

11

Joinery

THE difference between carpentry and joinery has been explained on p. 140.

FRAMING

Jointing. There are two main types of joints in frames:

1. Edge to Edge: as in the frame of a panelled door.
2. Face to Face: as in the sides of a drawer.

These joints may be combined as with certain face housing joints.*

Edge to Edge Joints

Plain Mitre. By using a phenol-formaldehyde or other high-grade, pre-ferably gap-filling and waterproof glue,† a plain mitre is theoretically the perfect framing joint. Notice that the grain runs continuously round the joint, and that end grain is glued to end grain (see p. 186). It is very bad to glue end grain to side grain only, as the side grain will then split as soon as the joint is stressed.

The timber may be cut in a mitre box or by a circular or band saw with a suitable bench attachment. The frame is best assembled in a jig while the glue sets so that the joints are kept flat and square. This is perhaps the most difficult part of the operation for ' one off ' work.

The joints can be located or held in position by means of steel pins or a temporarily-pinned batten on the inside of the joint.

Mitre with Tongue and Groove. This is illustrated at p. 186. It has the advantage that it is self-locating and also that the grain still runs continuously round the joint in the proper manner. This joint is sometimes known as a matched mitre.

Mitre with Loose Tongue. This is similar, but instead of a worked tongue and groove, two grooves are worked with a loose tongue glued in position.

---

* Joints are analysed in more detail for the specialist reader in *The Design and Practice of Joinery*, John Eastwick Field and John Stillman, Architectural Press, London.

† The glue ' Aerolite ' fulfils the requirements mentioned, plus the fact that no pressure or heat is needed, and the setting time can be speeded up by the use of a special hardener when required for factory production.

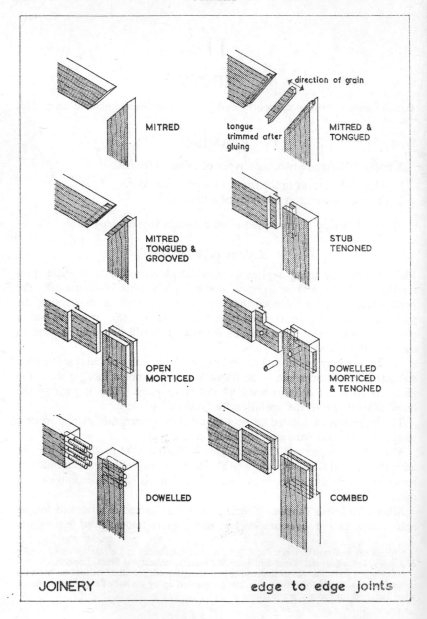

MITRED

direction of grain

tongue trimmed after gluing

MITRED & TONGUED

MITRED TONGUED & GROOVED

STUB TENONED

OPEN MORTICED

DOWELLED MORTICED & TENONED

DOWELLED

COMBED

JOINERY   edge to edge joints

The grain in the cross-tongue should run at right angles to the plane of the joint interface, so that the stresses are carried round the joint. The main function of the cross-tongue is to locate the mitre while the glue is setting.

Open Mortice. This is a very good joint, although theoretically not quite so structurally sound as a mitre, as the tenon is only resisting the stress (diagonal distortion of the frame) for one-third of its total cross-sectional area, the remainder of the joint face being end grain to side grain and therefore ineffective. Nevertheless location from the gluing point of view is very easy, but it is better if the joint is drilled through the face for dowelling (pinning) so that there is no danger of the joint opening out when the glue is setting.

Mortice and Tenon. This is very similar, but the slot is turned into a mortice and a haunch formed. This prevents any tendency of the end-members to twist independently, as sometimes happens across a glued joint. It is usual to drill through the face of the joint and pin with a dowel.

Stub Tenon. This is not a very satisfactory joint and should not be used for framing unless the face of the joint is covered with ply or hardboard, as in the case of a flush door, so that the breaking away of side grain is avoided. In the case of flush door construction, a stub tenon provides a useful locating device while the door is being assembled.

There are many versions of the above joints, e.g. double tenons, twin tenons and double-twin tenons, for jointing thicker material. Double tenons are formed side by side in material $2\frac{1}{2}$ in. thick and over, and twin tenons are used for deep rails and avoid the morticing being so deep as to weaken the frames.

Bare-faced tenon is used where the frame is thicker than the rail so long as no great shear stress is expected on the rail, as half the rail is cut away at the joint.

A variant of the open mortice is the comb joint, which is a useful development because the machining of both members is identical, one of the members being reversed in the course of assembly.

A dowelled joint is used by some firms, but is rather a specialised factory job as the dowel holes have to be very accurately drilled in each member. It is sometimes used in conjunction with a stub tenon.

Face-to-Face Joints

Plain Mitre. Again the main difficulty is clamping or supporting the frame while the glue is setting. This is a fairly straightforward operation for repetition work, and pins or temporary blocks may be used. A cross-tongue can be employed to assist in location, as before.

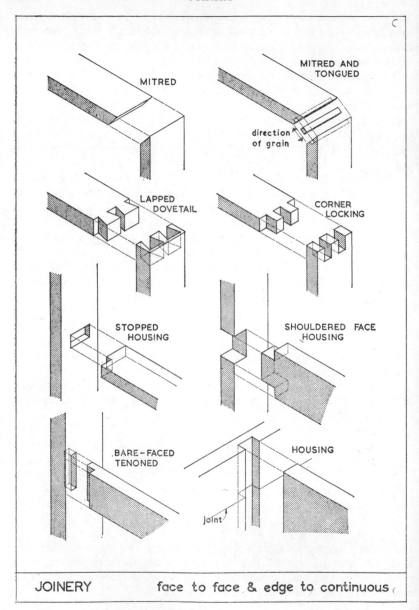

MITRED

MITRED AND
TONGUED

direction
of grain

LAPPED
DOVETAIL

CORNER
LOCKING

STOPPED
HOUSING

SHOULDERED FACE
HOUSING

BARE-FACED
TENONED

HOUSING

joint

JOINERY   face to face & edge to continuous

Dovetail. This is, of course, a traditional joint (see drawing on p. 188) and is looked for as a sign of traditional craftsmanship. It is not suitable for machine production.

Locking Joint. This is the machine-made development of the dovetail. It in fact does not lock in the same way as does the dovetail, but presents a large gluing surface and is therefore mechanically effective.

There are other variations of this type of joint.

Rebated joints, tongued and lapped joints and tongued joints serve to locate members. They are not normally acceptable in good-quality work unless metal or other fastenings are also involved. These joints either involve the gluing of end grain or side grain or expose ' short ' grain to stress.

Longitudinal Joints

These are joints used to provide greater widths of timber, such as in some types of table top or, more generally, in flooring. Owing to moisture movement it is better, when possible, to use laminated boards or plyboards.

Edge to Edge Joint. This is the simplest form, and suffers from the fact that the glue surface is very large indeed and it is therefore necessary to cramp the joint up thoroughly to ensure complete contact. On the other hand, certain gap-filling glues suffer from undue pressure because too much glue is squeezed out of the joint. The joint is also rather difficult to locate.

Tongued and Grooved Joint. This is a very common form in which a small tongue is formed on one half engaging with a groove in the other half of the joint. The tongue must be kept a little shallower than the groove so that the face of the joint closes up tightly, and the sides of the tongue help to eliminate the possible failure, of any part of the glue line. (See p. 191.)

Cross-Tongue. Here, two grooves are cut in each edge, and a cross-tongue with the grain running at right angles to the edges, is glued in. Here again, the cross-tongue should be slightly shorter than the combined depths of the grooves. A double cross-tongue is similar for boards of greater thickness. (See p. 193.)

There are many variants of the treatment of the face of these joints, e.g. V-joint, beaded joint, grooved joint. These all tend to accentuate the position of the joint and hide any shrinkage movement. Another variant enables the boards to be secret nailed rather than glued for flooring (see p. 178).

Metal Fastenings

Slender steel pins are often employed to locate joints when in the process of gluing. The pins are driven slightly below the surface and the surface stopped and finished flush.

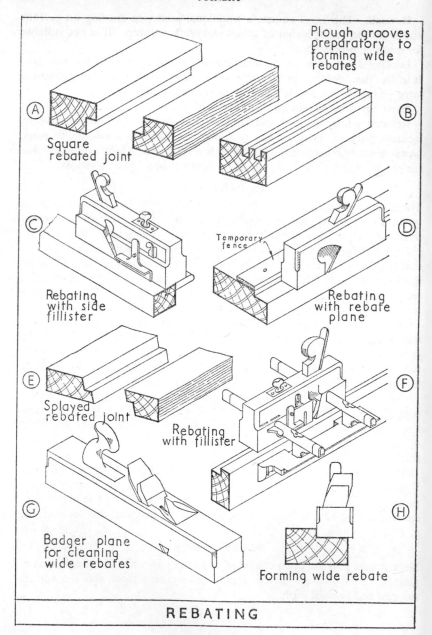

Plough grooves preparatory to forming wide rebates

(A) Square rebated joint

(B)

(C) Rebating with side fillister

(D) Rebating with rebate plane

Temporary fence

(E) Splayed rebated joint

Rebating with fillister

(F)

(G) Badger plane for cleaning wide rebates

(H) Forming wide rebate

REBATING

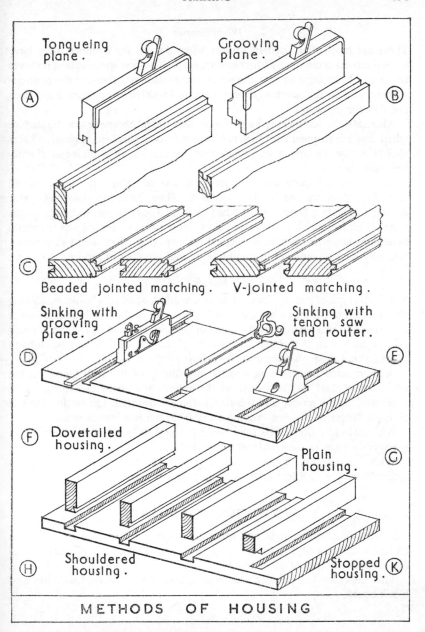

A — Tongueing plane.

B — Grooving plane.

C — Beaded jointed matching. V-jointed matching.

D — Sinking with grooving plane.

E — Sinking with tenon saw and router.

F — Dovetailed housing.

G — Plain housing.

H — Shouldered housing.

K — Stopped housing.

METHODS OF HOUSING

Wood Screws

These are most often used in joinery when panels, for instance, may have to be removed occasionally (duct covers, etc.). The best specification involves the use of brass cups so that the screw driver does not damage the counter-sinking, and so that continual removing and redriving the screw head does not damage the wood.

Alternatively, screws may be driven so that the heads are below the surface when they are stopped with pellets of similar wood glued in. Prepared holes should always be driven in preparation for screws, of a diameter slightly less than the screw.

Scandinavian joinery manufacturers are less coy about the use of metal fastenings than we are in this country. They frequently use metal star dowels to locate a framed joint when gluing. They also use flat angle plates screwed on to reinforce, for example, window frames. So long as the metal fastenings are well made and finished the resulting effect is not displeasing and they have advantages in manufacture and possibly in service.

Housing

This is the type of joint typified by an intermediate shelf of a bookcase joining the side, i.e. a T-joint rather than an L-joint. Here the continuous member is grooved to receive the 'shelf' member (see pp. 188 and 191). The housing may be carried right through to the edge of the boards or it may be stopped short so that the joint appears to be a butt joint.

A shouldered housing involves the machining of the stub tenon on the end of the 'shelf'; the groove in the continuous board can therefore be narrower. If the groove and the stub tenon are dovetailed in section there is then no danger of the shelf pulling away from the continuous member.

Alternatively short dowels may be set in the ends of the shelf member and engaged in holes in the continuous member.

With this category of joint, care must be taken that the shear loading is catered for by a sufficient cross-sectional area of material.

PLYWOODS AND BOARDS

As mentioned before, it is not generally satisfactory to glue or otherwise fix boards edge to edge to form a large timber surface—the tangential shrinkage is almost bound to cause trouble.

This difficulty has induced the production of various forms of ply and block board.

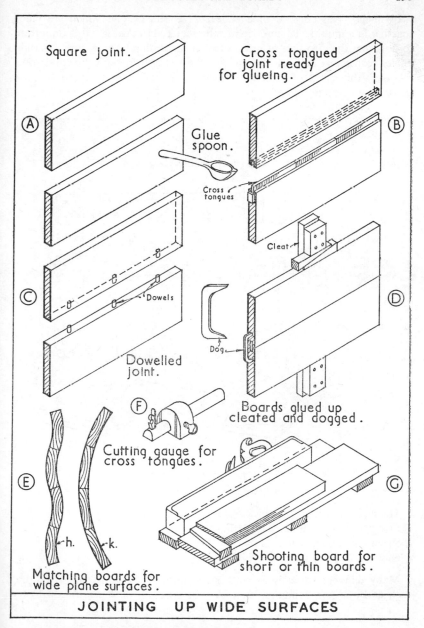

Square joint.

(A)

Cross tongued joint ready for glueing.

(B)

Glue spoon.

Cross tongues

Cleat

(C)

Dowels

Dowelled joint.

(D)

Dog

Boards glued up cleated and dogged.

(F)

Cutting gauge for cross tongues.

(E)

-h.   -k.

Matching boards for wide plane surfaces.

(G)

Shooting board for short or thin boards.

JOINTING UP WIDE SURFACES

Plywood. This consists of a series of veneers or plys which are glued together in a multi-layer sandwich to the required thickness. It is important to note that the direction of grain of each succeeding layer of ply is at right angles to the one below. This makes for strength in both directions of a relatively thin sheet of material. These plys can be built up to produce thicknesses of up to 2 in.

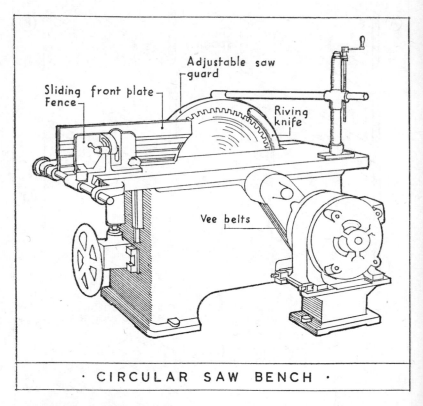

Adjustable saw guard

Sliding front plate

Fence

Riving knife

Vee belts

· CIRCULAR SAW BENCH ·

Three-ply is available in thicknesses $\frac{5}{32}$ in., $\frac{7}{32}$ in., $\frac{1}{4}$ in. or $\frac{5}{16}$ in.
Five-ply in $\frac{5}{16}$ in., $\frac{3}{8}$ in., $\frac{1}{2}$ in., $\frac{5}{8}$ in.
Seven-ply in $\frac{5}{8}$ in., $\frac{3}{4}$ in., $\frac{7}{8}$ in.
Nine-ply in $\frac{7}{8}$ in., 1 in.

Many different varieties of timber are used in the construction of ply, such as Birch and Muhuhu, etc. A vast selection of veneer-finished plywoods are available. Plywood may be specially heat treated to produce various surface patterns. They also may be plastic and metal faced.

The maximum width available is 60 in.; the other standard sizes are 54 in., 48 in., 42 in. and 36 in. The maximum length is 120 in.; others available being 108 in., 96 in., 84 in., 72 in. and 60 in.

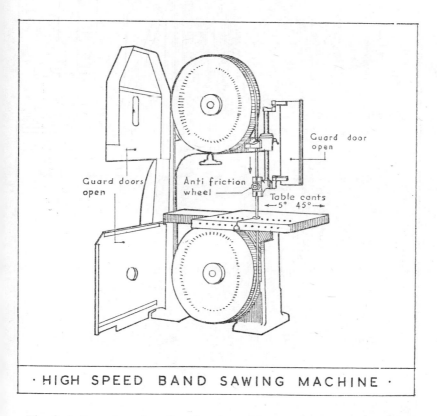

· HIGH SPEED BAND SAWING MACHINE ·

The first dimension gives the direction of long grain on the face of the board, which is useful to note when ordering.

Block Board. These are similar in a way to ply boards except that the core consists of strips of wood about 1 in. wide and preferably quarter-sawn, glued together and sandwiched by two strong veneers usually of hardwood.

Lamin board is very similar indeed, except that the strips are $\frac{1}{4}$ in. wide. Thicknesses available at $\frac{5}{8}$ in., $\frac{3}{4}$ in. and $\frac{7}{8}$ in., ; widths 120 in., 96 in., 84 in.

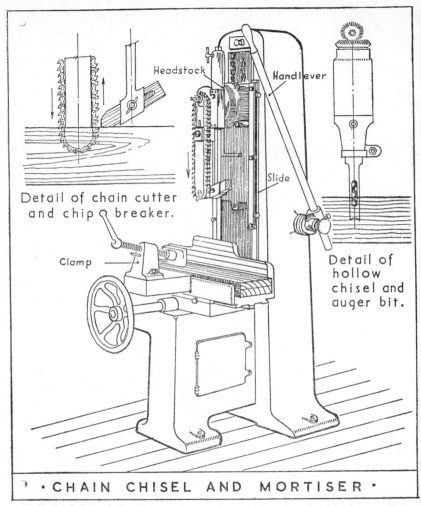

Headstock

Handlever

Slide

Detail of chain cutter
and chip breaker.

Clamp

Detail of
hollow
chisel and
auger bit.

· CHAIN CHISEL AND MORTISER ·

and 72 in.; and lengths 72 in., 60 in. and 48 in. Lamin board is also available up to 2 in. thick.

Glues. This subject is dealt with more fully in *Advanced Building Construction,* but where there is any danger of humid atmosphere or water, or danger of attack from micro-organisms, then the right glue must be specified.*

* British Standard 1455 lays down four main grades varying from weather and boil proof (WBP) down to interior grade ply (INT).

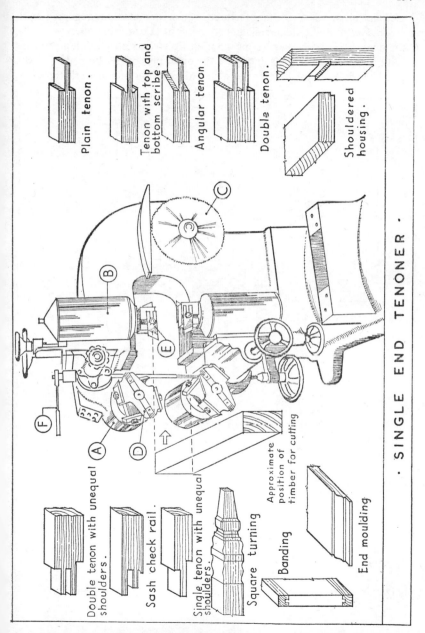

Plain tenon.

Tenon with top and bottom scribe.

Angular tenon.

Double tenon.

Shouldered housing.

Double tenon with unequal shoulders.

Sash check rail.

Single tenon with unequal shoulders.

Square turning

Approximate position of timber for cutting

Banding

End moulding

· SINGLE END TENONER ·

Certain plywoods are manufactured which are also impregnated with preservatives to make them resistant to insect attack and fungus.

Jointing. The main snag about the use of plywood is that unless the glue specification is good there is danger of the outer plys being chipped off at the edges when in use. Generally the higher the quality of the work the more

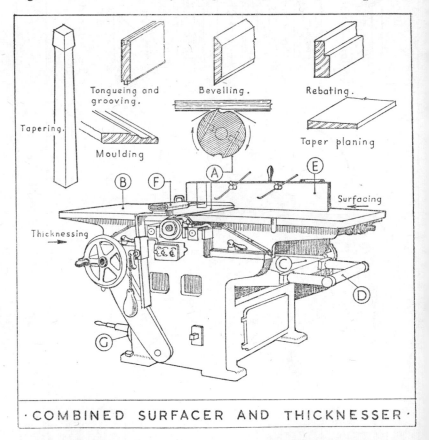

·COMBINED SURFACER AND THICKNESSER·

care is taken to mask the edge of the ply. There are exceptions to this, especially in modern chair construction, where a high-grade synthetic varnish seems adequately to protect the edge of the ply.

Where a frame is involved it may be rebated to receive ply. Otherwise the ply may be mitred; when this job is done carefully it makes a good joint.

For the thicker ply a tongued joint may be formed for glueing.

Secret fixing is possible by rebating the end of one sheet and then grooving the rebate. The adjacent sheet is tongued with one shoulder deeper than the other so that the sheets will engage closely. One sheet can then be screwed down to the ground and the next sheet engaged into the groove.

Various other jointing techniques are available using aluminium trim, battens, etc.

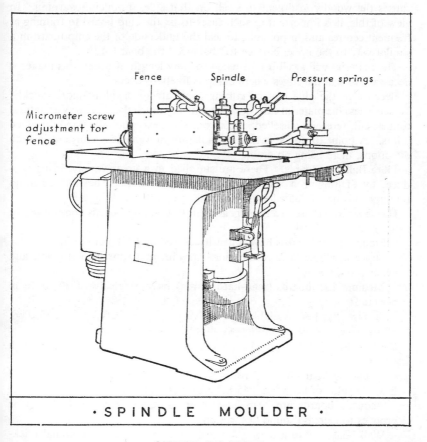

· S P I N D L E   M O U L D E R ·

OTHER BOARDS

Chip Board. This board is available in various thicknesses, those in most common use being in $\frac{1}{2}$ in. and $\frac{3}{4}$ in. The material consists of small chips of wood glued with a synthetic glue to form a ' man-made ' timber. It is available in standard sheets $8' \times 4'$, $10' \times 4'$ and $12' \times 4'$. One manufacturer can produce the board continuously in (theoretically) unlimited lengths.

Whilst it is inexpensive and can take veneers and paint films satisfactorily, it has the same disadvantage as natural timber in that it is liable to warp. This usually occurs when one side only is sealed with paint, varnish, plastic or veneers. This occurs because one side is then exposed to humidity, which causes the wood constituent to swell on that side, producing warping. In view of this, it is important in such cases to fix the chip board to framing at frequent centres and, if possible, to seal the underside of the chip board in a similar way to the upper surface to ' balance ' the board.

The material will swell if moistened for any length of time; this makes it necessary to seal the edges where damp is likely to occur.

Because of the glue matrix, cutting tools are made blunt more quickly. Nevertheless the material can be worked in very much the same way as natural timber, cut, screwed, chiselled, and so on. It is exceptionally good for glued joints. A point to notice is that its moisture movement is constant in both directions, there being no grain.

Fibre Building Boards. These are supplied in a great variety, being produced by a felting process from wood or vegetable fibre. They may be either homogenous or laminated with bituminous or other adhesives.*

Hardboards. These are homogenous fibre building boards compressed to medium or high density.

Standard hardboards have a density exceeding 50 lb per cu. ft.

Super hardboards have additional treatment to increase strength and water resistance.

Medium hardboards (semi-hardboards) have a density of 30 to 50 lb per cu. ft.

Surface finishes available are of very wide variety, e.g. enamelled, plastic faced, veneered, embossed, moulded and perforated.

Softboards. These are made from the same raw materials but are much less dense.

Insulating board has a density of not more than 25 lb per cu. ft, and has a U value of less than 0·45 B.Th.U.'s at half an inch.

Acoustic boards are even less dense and often have perforations or grooves to increase sound absorption.

Wall boards have a density up to 30 lb. per cu. ft and nominal thicknesses from $\frac{5}{16}$ in. to $\frac{3}{8}$ in. and may be either homogenous or laminated.

* British Standard 1142 (1953) applies.

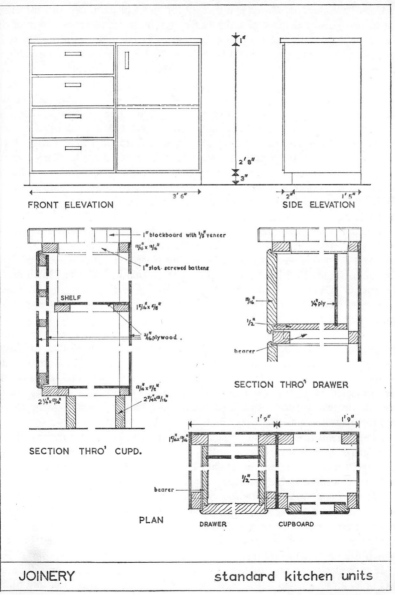

FRONT ELEVATION

1"

2' 8"

3"

SIDE ELEVATION

2"   1' 5"

3' 6"

1" blockboard with 1/8" veneer

13/16" x 13/16"

1" slot-screwed battens

SHELF

1 5/16" x 5/8"

3/16" plywood.

13/16" x 5/8"

2 1/4" x 13/16"

2 1/4" x 13/16"

SECTION THRO' CUPD.

19/16"   1/4" ply

1/2"

bearer

SECTION THRO' DRAWER

1 9/16" x 13/16"

bearer

1/2"

1' 9"   1' 9"

PLAN   DRAWER   CUPBOARD

| JOINERY | standard kitchen units |

Uses. *Standard hardboard* can be used for backs oɪ furniture and fitments, inexpensive doors, facings, bench tops for light industry, temporary shuttering display work, etc. The normal thickness available is ⅛ in., although it is possible to get up to ¼ in. It is not advisable to use it for partitioning in high-class work unless it is practically continuously glued to a stable backing. (If it is fixed to framing in this application it has a tendency to show the framing in certain conditions of light.) *Super hardboards* are more stable, and certain varieties have been used with success as loose-laid flooring in large sheets in Germany. They are more resistant to moisture, but should not be used externally except on temporary buildings (e.g. caravans), when they must be covered with a reliable paint system. They are more suitable than standard hardboards for concrete shuttering; one or two brands are available in several colours, although usually the normal shade is darker than standard hardboard. Sizes range from 4 ft to 6 ft 6 in. wide, and lengths from 4 ft up to 18 ft.

Medium hardboards are normally ¼ in. thick, though some are available up to ½ in. They are therefore stiffer and are better for panelling applications. The texture makes them suitable for pin-up boards in schools, but they are not quite so good in this application as cork which is, however, much more expensive. Other applications include underlays to floorings, display relief carving and ceilings. (They are used as roof linings in London Underground trains.)

Enamelled hardboards are produced in a wide range of colours, types and grades, and can be used for wall and ceiling linings so long as they are fixed properly, both from the point of view of fixing centres and preventing ingress of moisture to joints. It is a useful finishing material provided too much is not expected of it; for instance, it will stand up to use as a draining board for about two years. Cupboard lining and shelving would seem to be appropriate uses.

Plastic laminates are often fixed by manufacturers to hardboard (⅛ in. standard). One new variety of wall board so fixed has been used for railway carriage toilet wall-lining satisfactorily. The material has the advantage that it has a more stable surface.

Moulded and embossed hardboards have a pattern impressed into their surface during manufacture, e.g. reeded, fluted, grooved, etc., and have been used for counter fronts, pelmets, etc. These moulded boards do not show up the pattern of the fixing framework so much as smooth finished boards, which is a definite advantage.

It is bad to use any material which pretends to be another one; for example, an enamelled hardboard which is manufactured to look like tiling (with imitation joints). The joints in genuine ceramic tiling are necessary because of the manufacturing limitations of the material, but are the least satisfactory aspect of this surface finish from the point of view of hygiene and cleanliness. The main advantage of enamelled hardboard over this material is that a continuous surface is available over a much larger area. Unfortunately, the surface quality of enamelled hardboard is not generally as good as the surface quality of ceramic tiles.

Peg boards are available with $\frac{3}{16}$ in. holes at centres of $\frac{1}{2}$ in., $\frac{3}{4}$ in. or 1 in. Metal fittings can be bought which fit into the perforations for various display uses.

Softboards can be used for wall lining so long as they are not subject to impact damage; they are more usually used for ceiling lining and as floor underlays. The standard sizes are 4 × 6, 8, 10 and 12 ft. Bitumen-bonded softboards have better moisture resistance, and can be used for roof insulation or expansion jointing. *Acoustic boards* and tiles with their drilled or slotted surfaces are mostly used on ceilings and high up on walls. They are obtainable in tiles 12″ × 12″ or 12″ × 24″ bevelled and up to $1\frac{1}{4}$ in. thick. They are most usually pinned back to a timber frame or grounds through the grooves or perforations (the perforations do not usually travel through the full thickness of the material).

The major uses of softboard are for roof insulation in the form of linings. This is satisfactory so long as attention is paid to the condensation problem. They are not always a satisfactory lining in factories where wet processes are involved. Insulation board linings suspended under asbestos-cement pitched roofs can be troublesome from the point of view of condensation. A cure for these difficulties can be produced by ventilating the cavity between the insulation board and the asbestos cement, although this increases the heat loss. The material can be used satisfactorily, however, as a lining to the underside of the rafters in pitched roofs in housing.

Fixing. Fibre building board has to be conditioned before use; one way is to brush water on to the backs of the boards 24 to 48 hours before fixing and store them back to back on the site. At the end of this period they should be fixed immediately.

The boards should be cut face side up with ordinary panel saws; the edges can be cleaned with a sandpaper block or plane. Special fibre board cutters and planes are available for grooving, bevelling and cutting.

When nailing to hardboard use 1 in. panel pins; when nailing insulation board use $1\frac{1}{4}$ in. to $1\frac{1}{2}$ in. panel pins. If the boards are not to be exposed to view then clout nails are better. Nails or other fixings should be galvanised or sherardised and spaced 4 in. to 6 in. apart. Nails on adjoining edges

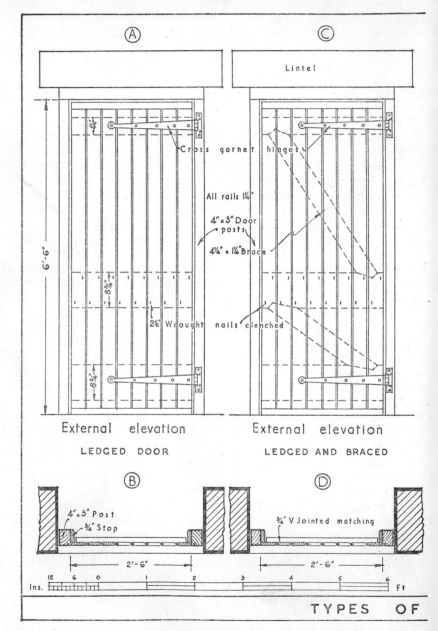

Ⓐ

Ⓒ

Lintel

Cross garnet hinges

All rails 1¼"

4"×3" Door posts

4¼"×1¼" Brace

2½" Wrought nails clenched

6'-6"

8¼"

8¼"

External elevation
LEDGED DOOR

External elevation
LEDGED AND BRACED

Ⓑ

Ⓓ

4"×3" Post
¾" Stop

¾" V Jointed matching

2'-6"

2'-6"

Ins. 12 6 0   1   2   3   4   5   6 Ft

TYPES   OF

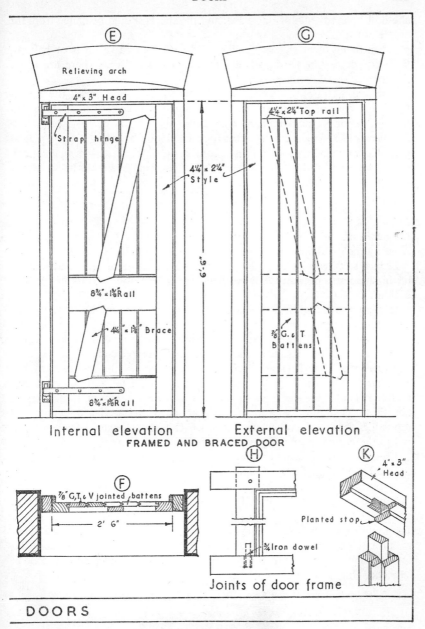

Ⓔ

Relieving arch

4" x 3" Head

Strap hinge

4¼" x 2¼" Style

6'-6"

8¾" x 1⅜" Rail

4¼" x 1⅜" Brace

8¾" x 1⅜" Rail

Internal elevation

Ⓖ

4¼" x 2¼" Top rail

⅞" G. & T Battens

External elevation

FRAMED AND BRACED DOOR

Ⓕ

⅞" G,T, & V jointed battens

2' 6"

Ⓗ

¾ Iron dowel

Joints of door frame

Ⓚ

4" x 3" Head

Planted stop

should be paired and not staggered, and the sheets should be nailed from the centre outwards.

When fixing to plaster or similar solid surfaces and to joists or battens, fibre boards can be fixed with an impact type adhesive. There are many proprietary metal fixing systems.*

Finishing. Unless the boards have already been primed by the manufacturer a coat of priming or petrifying liquid is necessary first; then distemper, oil, or plastic paint can be applied.

It is possible to plaster satisfactorily an insulation board, and many plaster manufacturers make a special plaster for this purpose. The skim coat applied should be $\frac{3}{16}$ in. thick. The joints between the boards should be scrimmed with hessian scrim or wire mesh.

DOORS

Ledged Door. This is the simplest form, only suitable for temporary work. After a time it will have a tendency to distort diagonally (see p. 204).

Ledged and Braced (see p. 204). This is a much more satisfactory door, having braces to prevent the door distorting. This door is suitable for outbuildings.

It is important that the brace is put on to support the top free corner from the bottom hinged corner. This is because braces work in compression, and not in tension; if they are put on the other way round the joints would merely open up after a time as the door drops at its free end.

Framed and Braced Door. This is a refinement of the last type by the addition of stiles which are the same thickness as the top rail. Bottom and middle rails plus the thickness of the battens are the same total thickness as the stiles. The bottom and middle rails are cut with bare-faced tenons; the top rail is fixed with a haunched tenon. The battens extend from the top rail to the ground more effectively to shed water.

These doors are usually fixed with strap hinges with screws or bolts which should be galvanised if used externally. Alternatively, heavy galvanised or alloy butts may be used.

Framed and Panelled Door. The drawing on p. 207 is a traditional form of panelled door showing the application of the various framing joints. The muntins are stub-tenoned into the rails. The principal joints are made with fox-tail wedging, so that the tenons are firmly held in the mortices. To prevent the tendency of the rails to cup, the stiles are grooved and the tenons haunched (haunchion) to resist this tendency.

* See list by Metal Fixing Association, 32 Queen Anne Street, London, W.1.

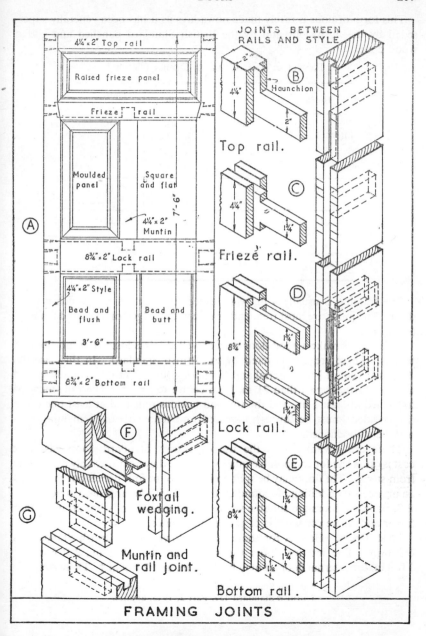

JOINTS BETWEEN
RAILS AND STYLE

Ⓐ

4¼" × 2" Top rail

Raised frieze panel

Frieze rail

Moulded panel

Square and flat

4¼" × 2" Muntin

7'-6"

8¾" × 2" Lock rail

4¼" × 2" Style

Bead and flush

Bead and butt

3'-6"

8¾" × 2" Bottom rail

Ⓑ
2"
4¼"
Haunchion
2"

Top rail.

Ⓒ
4¼"
1¾"

Frieze rail.

Ⓓ
1¾"
8¾"
1¼"

Lock rail.

Ⓔ
1¾"
8¾"
1¾"
1½"

Bottom rail.

Ⓕ

Ⓖ

Foxtail wedging.

Muntin and rail joint.

FRAMING JOINTS

This form of door is rarely made nowadays as it has been generally super-seded by the flush door and by the British Standard panelled and glazed wood door.

PANELLED AND GLAZED DOORS (WOOD)

Doors	Height	Width	Finished thickness
	ft in.	ft in.	in.
Internal　.	6　6	2　0	1⅜
		2　3	
		2　6	
		2　9	
External　.	6　6	2　6	1¾
		2　9	
Glazed　.	6　6	2　6	1¾
		2　9	
		3　10	
Garage　.	6　6	7　0	1¾

The framing is usually 4 in. wide, except the bottom rail, which is 8 in. deep. The joints are most frequently made with wedged mortice and tenons * (see p. 186).

A few firms make a good door with dowelled joints instead of mortice and tenons. These are also covered by the British Standard. In this case the dowels are out of ⅝ in. material and 4⅞ in. long. They must be equally spaced and not further apart than 2¼ in. from centre to centre. The rails must be haunched at least ⅜ in., and the top and bottom rails and at least one other (if provided) must be through-morticed and tenoned; the remaining rails may be stub-tenoned.

There are advantages in the use of British Standard doors, as their cost is often less for comparable quality because they are invariably obtainable from stock. The door may be split up into three or four panels but this seems an unnecessary addition of redundant material without improved appearance. B.S. panelled doors are suitable where sound insulation is not an important factor and where economy is of prime importance.

Flush Doors. Heights for these as laid down in the British Standard is 6 ft 6 in. For interior doors the width may be 2 ft 3 in., 2 ft 6 in., or 2 ft 9 in. for external doors it may be 2 ft 6 in. and 2 ft 9 in.† These sizes are

* British Standard 459, Part 1, 1944, applies.
† British Standard 459, Part 2, 1945, applies.

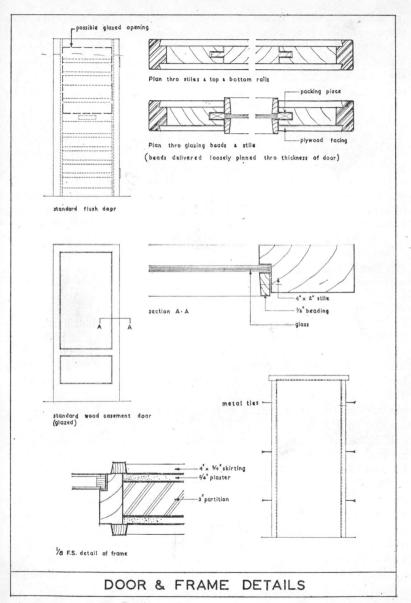

possible glazed opening

Plan thro stiles & top & bottom rails

packing piece

Plan thro glazing beads & stile

plywood facing

(beads delivered loosely pinned thro thickness of door)

standard flush door

section A·A

4" x 2" stile

½" beading

glass

standard wood casement door
(glazed)

metal ties

4" x ¾" skirting

⅝" plaster

3" partition

⅛ F.S. detail of frame

DOOR & FRAME DETAILS

for doors from stock; others of course can be made to any required size or shape, and they are available with glazed panels 18 in., 24 in. and 36 in. deep.

For interior doors moisture-resistant adhesives must be used for the manufacture of the plywood. For external doors a water-insoluble adhesive should be used, for both faces of the door. The plywood should be $\frac{1}{4}$ in. thick for external doors and $\frac{3}{16}$ in. thick for internal ones. Alternatively, hardboard facings may be used.*

These must not project beyond the top and bottom rails and should be flush with the lipping; this lipping must be tongued and glued to both stiles and must be not less than $\frac{7}{16}$ in. wide at any point. Metal fastenings for this lipping should not be used.

The British Standard flush door has a skeleton core consisting of rails stub-tenoned into the stiles, as before. These rails should be at 6 in. centres or closer, otherwise the pattern of this core will be seen reflected on the surface in certain conditions of light.

A better quality of door is the semi-solid one (see *Advanced Building Construction*) and the highest standard is made with a laminated board core (see p. 195).

DOOR FRAMES

Perhaps the simplest and neatest form of door frame is that illustrated in British Standard 1567. For a 3 in. partition with a $\frac{5}{8}$ in. plaster finish on each side the frame is a total of $4\frac{1}{4}$ in. wide by a total of $1\frac{3}{4}$ in. thick. The back is grooved out to a depth of $\frac{1}{4}$ in. to within $\frac{5}{16}$ in. of the edges. This leaves two nibs $\frac{5}{16}" \times \frac{1}{4}"$ behind which the plaster surface can be finished. This fulfils the same function as the architrave and masks the crack the plaster would otherwise make as it slightly shrinks back on setting (see drawing on p. 209).

If, instead of making the frame out of $1\frac{3}{4}$ in. material it is made of $2\frac{1}{4}$ in. material, a stop may be formed by moulding out the remaining width to leave standing a $\frac{1}{2}" \times 1\frac{3}{8}"$.

Assembly. Frames should be supplied assembled (except for garage door frames). Heads, jambs and sills should be scribed and mortice and tenoned with through tenons. Horns should be provided projecting at least $1\frac{1}{2}$ in. beyond the backs of the frames. These horns (continuations of the head) assist in the building in of the frame, and are cut back on the face and masked with brickwork.

Alternatively the joint may be a combed joint which must be dowelled;

* Hardboard to British Standard 1142.

in this case horns cannot be provided. Sills must be made in one piece; if there are no sills then the feet of the jambs must be dowelled with rust-proof dowels for fixing to the floor. It is as well to provide a D.P.C. of felt or, better still, thiokol mastic, to prevent moisture being absorbed into the end grain at the feet of the jambs.

Linings. These are suitable for door openings in partitions 3 in. (plus plaster) and over; their thickness should be not less than $1\frac{1}{16}$ in. finished. For a 3 in. partition with two $\frac{5}{8}$ in. plastered surfaces a frame $4\frac{3}{4}$ in. wide is suitable; this means that it will project $\frac{1}{8}$ in. beyond the plaster face on each side. It is then usual to mask the plaster shrinkage crack (mentioned above) with a neat moulding. Other standard sizes of linings are $5\frac{1}{4}$ in. and $5\frac{3}{4}$ in., depending upon the total thickness of the partition.

Linings are used traditionally the same thickness as the total thickness of the wall. Here the architrave masks the plaster joint; the back of the architrave should be a little thicker than the thickness of the skirting, otherwise the skirting presents end grain to view and a plinth block has to be provided. Skirtings are available ex stock in various standard sections, common ones being $4'' \times \frac{3}{4}''$ with one tumbled (rounded) edge, $6'' \times 1''$ etc. Instead of a tumbled edge various mouldings can be formed on the skirting.

Fixing. Frames and linings may be fitted to timber pallets or wedges between the courses of the blockwork or brickwork. Care must be taken not to drive these in too hard, otherwise the blockwork may be displaced, as considerable force can be exerted in this way. Alternatively, linings may be fixed to timber grounds plugged to the brickwork.

WINDOWS

Double hung windows with cased and solid frames are not used now so much as they used to be, but probably they are still used enough to justify their inclusion in this book. British Standard 6442, 1946, shows a simple form. The outer lining is made an inch larger than the inside lining; a removable window bead retains the inner sash. If both linings were the same size then it would be impossible to remove the windows in case of broken sash-cords, etc. (see p. 212).

Spring-balance Type. This is similar in many ways, but sashes are grooved to suit the tubular spring sash balances.

Standard Wood Casement. These side-hung windows, often coupled with top-hung opening out vents, have been developed by the English Joinery Manufacturers Association for approved firms to supply from stock. These windows are highly competitive in price. Both opening and fixed members

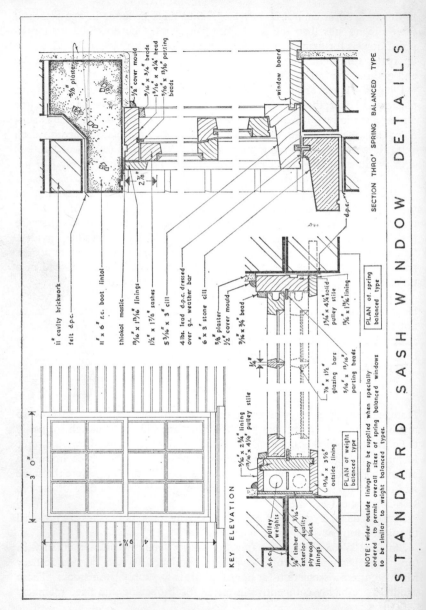

STANDARD SASH WINDOW DETAILS

SECTION THRO' SPRING BALANCED TYPE

PLAN of. spring balanced type

PLAN of weight balanced type

KEY ELEVATION

3' 0"

½" cover mould
⁹⁄₁₆" x ¾" beads
1¹⁵⁄₁₆" x 4¼" head
⁵⁄₁₆" x 1³⁄₁₆" parting beads
window board

11" cavity brickwork
felt d.p.c.
11" x 6" r.c. boot lintol
thiokol mastic
1³⁄₁₆" x 1³⁄₁₆" linings
1½" x 1⅞" sashes
5³⁄₁₆" x 3" cill

4 lbs. lead d.p.c. dressed over g.i. weather bar
6 x 3 stone cill
⅝" plaster
½" cover mould
⁹⁄₁₆" x ¾" bead

1¾" x 4¼" solid pulley stile
³⁄₁₆" x 1³⁄₁₆" lining

⅝" plaster

⅞" x 1½" glazing bars
⁵⁄₁₆" x 1³⁄₁₆" parting beads

⅛"

⁹⁄₁₆" x 2¾" lining
1⅝" x 4¼" pulley stile
1³⁄₁₆" x 3⅝" outside lining

d.p.c.
pulley weights
½" timber or ¾" exterior quality plywood back linings

NOTE: wider outside linings may be supplied when specially ordered to permit overall sizes of spring balanced windows to be similar to weight balanced types.

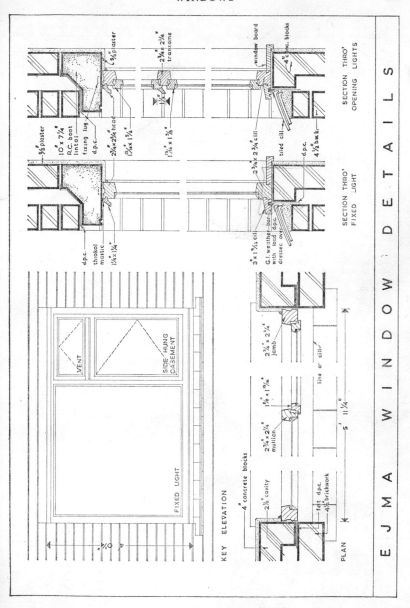

KEY ELEVATION

VENT

SIDE HUNG CASEMENT

FIXED LIGHT

4'0"

SECTION THRO' OPENING LIGHTS

SECTION THRO' FIXED LIGHT

⅝ plaster

2¾ x 2¼ transome

window board

4" conc. blocks

4" c

⅝ plaster

10 x 7¼ R.C. boot lintol

fixing lug

d.p.c.

2¾ x 2¼ head

1¾ x 1¼

1³⁄₁₆ x 1½

1³⁄₁₆ x 1½

2¾ x 2¾ cill

tiled cill

d.p.c.

4½ b.w.k.

d.p.c.

thiokol mastic

1¼ x 1¼

3 x 1⁷⁄₁₆ cill

G.I. weather-bar, with lead d.p.c. dressed over.

1½
1¼

4 concrete blocks

2½ cavity

2¾ x 2¼ mullion

1⅝ x 1³⁄₁₆

2¾ x 2¼ jamb

line o' cill

felt d.p.c.
4½ brickwork

5' 11¼"

PLAN

E J M A   W I N D O W   D E T A I L S

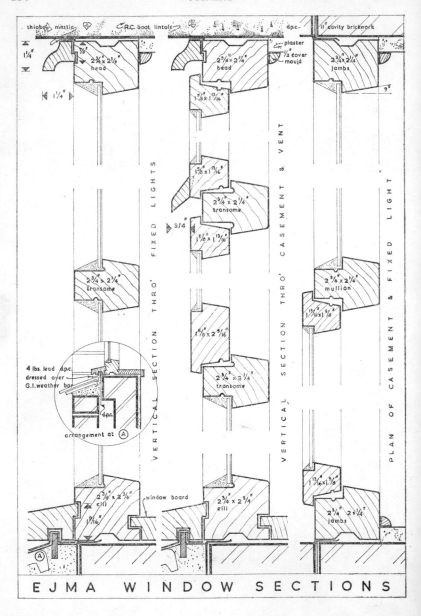

EJMA   WINDOW   SECTIONS

are rebated so that a double draught check is provided (see drawing on p. 214). Notice that a paint groove is provided in the internal angle of the fixed frames. This is done to avoid a build-up of paint at this point in the course of time with successive repaintings which would make the window difficult to shut properly. Half-round anticapillarity grooves are also provided on edges of opening members and in the reveals of the frame. The idea of this is to prevent moisture being drawn in by capillary attraction, though the windows would have to be extremely well-fitting before this could occur.

Windows should be delivered primed by the manufacturer. It is important to specify a high-quality primer. Often this coat becomes chalky before the undercoat and other coats are applied, the vital point being that the life of a paint system depends upon the first coat. The frames should be stored under cover upright before fixing. It is not a good thing to build window frames in as the walling proceeds as it tends to distort the frames. It is better to put the windows in as a ' second fixing '. They can then be screwed or otherwise fixed to plugs in the walling.

Wood windows should always be fixed to the dry leaf of cavity walling or otherwise be protected by a vertical damp proof course. (There should always be a vertical D.P.C. between the wet and the dry leaf in a cavity wall, see p. 213). The gap between the woodwork and the brickwork can then be filled with a suitable mastic, the best type being thiokol mastic.*

Rebates for glazing should be at least $\frac{3}{8}$ in. deep. The glass is usually put in with putty formed to a triangular bead with a putty knife. For a higher class of work, weathered timber beads scribed or mitred at the corners can be pinned in with brass pins or screwed with brass screws. The glass in this case usually has putty ' back and front ' to allow for even support.

The sill must be weathered at a sufficient slope to throw off the water and throated with a groove near the front on its underside so that the water will drip off and not run back to the bed of the sill. Sills are usually bedded in mastic and may have a water bar to act as an additional check to the penetration of moisture at this point, and to locate the sill horizontally. The water bar should have a metal flashing as shown on the drawing on p. 212.

The throating or drip must be able to shed water without obstruction on to a well-sloped tile, stone or metal sill beneath. Alternatively, it may shed the water clear of the wall by the fact that the frame may be close to the outer surface of the wall.

Sills are very subject to defects caused by dampness. Either the weathering

* See *Building Research Station Digest*, No. 105.

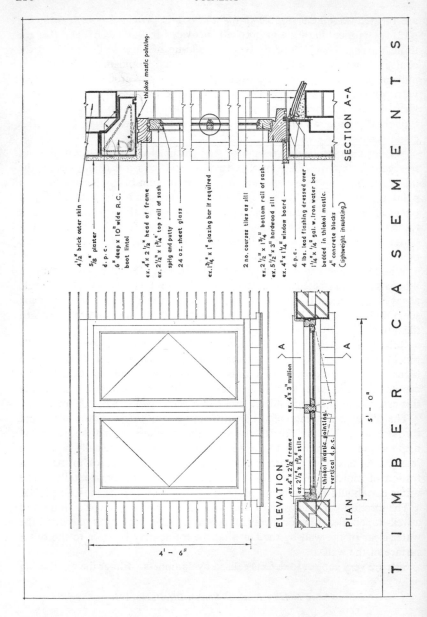

SECTION A-A

thiokol mastic pointing.

4½" brick outer skin
⅝" plaster
d. p. c.
6" deep x 10" wide R.C. boot lintol
ex. 4" x 2½" head of frame
ex. 2½" x 1¾" top rail of sash
sptg and putty
24 oz. sheet glass

ex. 1⅞" x 1" glazing bar if required

2 no. courses tiles as sill
ex. 2½" x 1¾" bottom rail of sash.
ex. 5½" x 3" hardwood sill
ex. 4" x 1¼" window board
d. p. c.
4 lbs. lead flashing dressed over
1¼"x ⅛" gal. w. iron water bar bedded in thiokol mastic.
4" concrete blocks
(lightweight insulating)

ELEVATION
ex. 4" x 2½" frame
ex. 2½" x 1⅝" stile
thiokol mastic pointing.
vertical d.p.c.
ex. 4" x 3" mullion

PLAN

4' - 6"

5' - 0"

A

A

TIMBER CASEMENTS

is not sufficiently steep to shed the water, or water can get back to the bed of the sill because the drip does not function, or because the slope of the tile or stone sill allows the water to run back instead of outwards. These are points to watch carefully.

The head is not so troublesome usually, but the D.P.C. in a cavity above must catch water running down the inside surface of the outside skin and conduct it properly to the outside of the head (see drawing on p. 212).

Standard Double Casement Windows. For this type of window, the fixed frame has a much deeper rebate. There are two lights in each opening instead of one, the inner one being hinged to the outer one and secured by a self-locking catch. The inner window can then be opened independently of the outer one so that all the glass surfaces can be cleaned from the inside of the building. These windows are a standard product and provide good sound and heat insulation.

Standard Casement Windows with Double Glazing Units. In this case, the rebates are slightly deeper than with the single-glazed type to receive double-glazed units provided by the glass manufacturer. The two sheets of glass are $\frac{1}{4}$ in. apart, usually in metal channels and hermetically sealed so that moisture cannot cause condensation within the unit. (Condensation is the main difficulty to overcome in double glazing.) Double-glazed units have to be manufactured to the size required and they are supplied and fixed in an approved mastic.

This technique is more expensive than with the double casement system, but has the advantage that much bigger lights can be provided.

Standard Pivot Windows. Sections are designed in a similar way to sections for the other standard types; (EJMA) metal pivots are provided in the middle of the jambs. The window can be opened through about 170° enabling the outside of the window to be cleaned from the inside. This is a great advantage in tall buildings, both from the point of view of cleaning and reglazing.

Other proprietary pivot windows are available, some being double glazed and fully reversible.

Casement Window. On p. 216 is illustrated a straightforward form of casement window suitable for production in small joiners' shops; notice the weathering, the anticapillarity grooves, the proper use of the water bar, and the small aluminium or lead flashing. A boot lintel is shown recessed slightly from the face of the brickwork; this looks very trim and precise and expresses the concrete satisfactorily.

Folding windows may be made in a similar way to this without the fixed mullion, the meeting stiles being rebated.

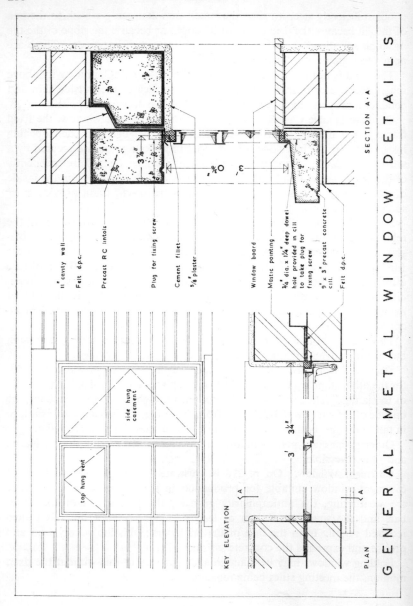

GENERAL METAL WINDOW DETAILS

SECTION A·A

11" cavity wall
Felt d.p.c.
Precast R C lintols
Plug for fixing screw
Cement fillet
⅝" plaster

Window board
Mastic pointing
¾" dia. x 1¼" deep dowel hole provided in cill to take plug for fixing screw
9" x 3" precast concrete cill.
Felt d.p.c.

3' 0¾"

3⅛"

side hung casement

top hung vent

3' 3¾"

KEY ELEVATION

PLAN

The drawing on p. 218 illustrates one of a wide selection of Standard Metal Windows that are available. These are made of galvanised mild steel and are quick and easy to fix. Being made of metal they are not subject to moisture movement. Other sections than those shown are available for larger sizes. These windows are very economical so long as standard sizes are selected from the catalogue. If windows have to be made to special sizes, i.e. purpose made—the price roughly doubles.

For very high class work bronze may be used; the common alternative is aluminium, but in this case the section thicknesses are greater and are slightly different in profile. With the mild steel variety, regular painting is essential to prevent rust spots from spoiling the seal of the opening lights.

Notice the position of the window in relation to the vertical D.P.C. This D.P.C. should be brought out to the front edge of the frame so that the metal is kept relatively dry.

STAIRCASES

On pp. 220 and 221 is shown a simple staircase. A satisfactory width is 2 ft 9 in. The width could be increased if the treads are increased in depth. In this particular instance the treads are ex $1\frac{1}{4}$ in. and the risers 1 in. The strings which carry the weight of the stair are grooved by a router to receive the ends of the treads and risers. This groove should be $\frac{3}{8}$ in. deep and should not run out to the edge of the strings as has been done in the past as this reduces the rigidity of the string in its beam action. It is well to dowel through the string into the edges of the treads and glue to restrain the strings from bowing outwards. The treads and risers should be glued into position with, preferably, a resin gap filling glue. The older type of staircase had tapering grooves so that the treads and risers could be wedged in position, but modern glues make this technique redundant. The newel post at the landing is bolted to the back of the trimmer with coach bolts; alternatively, timber connectors can be used.

In the details the handrail is the same width as the newel and, by placing the newel behind the trimmer, the handrail develops straight into the upper flight without a ' wreath '. Notice that there is a gap of 2 in. between the handrails in plan so that hands are not caught in the awkward angles that would otherwise occur.

In the details illustrated no carriage is shown. Traditionally a 4″ × 3″ carriage runs under the centre of each flight and triangular blocks help to take the weight of the staircase. Once again, if the staircase is glued up with modern glues, this member is redundant.

Other types of staircases are described in *Mitchell's Advanced Building Construction*.* *See also *Building Construction*, Vol. 3, by W. B. McKay (Longmans).

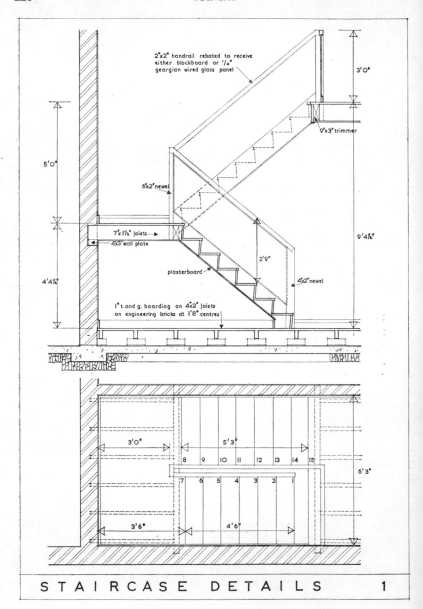

2"x2" handrail rebated to receive
either blockboard or ¹/₄"
georgian wired glass panel

3'0"

9"x3" trimmer

5'0"

6"x2" newel

7"x1½" joists
4"x3" wall plate

plasterboard

2'9"

9'4½"

4"x2" newel

4'4½"

1" t.and g. boarding on 4"x2" joists
on engineering bricks at 1'8" centres

3'0"   5'3"

6'3"

8 9 10 11 12 13 14 15

7 6 5 4 3 2 1

3'6"   4'6"

S T A I R C A S E   D E T A I L S   1

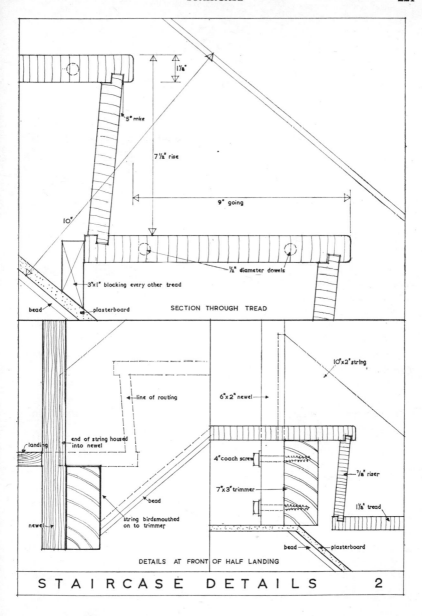

5" mke

1⅛"

7 ½" rise

9" going

10"

½" diameter dowels

3"x1" blocking every other tread

bead   plasterboard

SECTION THROUGH TREAD

line of routing

10"x2" string

6"x 2" newel

end of string housed
into newel

landing

4" coach screw

7/8" riser

string birdsmouthed
on to trimmer

7"x3" trimmer

bead

1⅛" tread

newel

bead   plasterboard

DETAILS AT FRONT OF HALF LANDING

STAIRCASE   DETAILS   2

12

Pitched Roof Coverings

Roof Preparation

THE roof has several functions, some obvious and some not so obvious:

1. Watertight
2. Windtight
3. Heat insulating
4. Deadening to the noise of beating rain
5. Condensation-proof

The roof must fulfil all these functions properly. Overlook any of these points at your peril.

Pitched Roofs. It is the custom to consider any roof below 10° pitch to be a *flat* roof. Between 10° and 22½° only sheet weatherproofings are suitable, e.g. roofing metals, asbestos cement, bituminous felt, etc.

At 22½° the largest (and therefore the most expensive) slate can be used, 24″ × 12″ and over, the best grade of cedarwood shingles and Redland interlocking slates.

At 30° interlocking tiles with adequate head and side locks can be used as can the smaller slates (9 in. and 10 in. wide).

At 35° single lap tiles and slates 8 in. wide can be used.

At 40° plain tiles and slates 7 in. wide can be used.

Underfelting is essential, except in the case of cedar shingles where under-roof ventilation, to prevent rot, is important.

Angle of Creep. Water running down, say, a slate roof will enter the joints between the slates in each course. It will then drop on the slate immediately underneath and fan out as it runs down. The angle of this fanning is known by some as the 'angle of creep'.* This is why there must be at least two thicknesses of slate on a roof, and why it is important that the nail holes are placed in such a way as to avoid the angle of creep from each joint in the slate above. This also explains why the width of a slate is a vital factor in a shallow pitched roof, as the shallower the pitch the wider the angle of creep.

With interlocking and single-lap tiles the side lock and head lock eliminate penetration of water at any particular joint. Variable lap tiles which do not

---

* See *Slating and Tiling*, issued by Messrs. Langley London Ltd.

have a head lock operate in much the same way, except that the head lap must not be reduced below 3 in.

Leakage may be caused by the following:

1. Water may be drawn up by capillary attraction or blown by the wind over the heads of the slates or tiles; alternatively, it may find its way through nail holes.
2. Water may get through side joints between adjacent slates or tiles and creep sideways and downwards to find nail holes; hence the importance of not having too shallow a pitch, and having slates (particularly) of sufficient width.
3. Water may penetrate the slates or tiles directly if they are too porous; this is less likely to occur on a steeply pitched roof.
4. Water may penetrate (and often does unless care is taken) at joints with chimneys, at verges, abutments, ridges, valleys, etc.

Even if the slating or tiling is waterproof it is important that they are fixed properly so that wind cannot blow the slates or tiles off.

Interlocking Slates. This is a very simple form of roof which has been introduced fairly recently (see drawing on p. 224). It is interesting because it is satisfactory down to a minimum roof pitch of $22\frac{1}{2}°$; it appears to be a reconstructed stone product and is usually guaranteed against lamination or decay for fifty years. It is very suitable for T.D.A. trusses (see p. 157).

The slates have both head lock and side lock and measure 15″ wide × 17″ long; $1\frac{1}{2}″ \times \frac{3}{4}″$ battens are recommended laid at a gauge (the distance apart they are laid up the roof) of 14 in.; these are nailed with galvanised nails to the rafter which should be spaced at 18 in. centres. The slates are laid broken bond (the joints between slates in one course above the centre of the slate in the courses below). They are heavy enough not to require nailing; they weigh $9\frac{1}{2}$ cwt per square (i.e. 100 sq. ft).

A very neat angle ridge tile cast to shape is available. The verges must be provided with an undercloak of slates or asbestos cement sheet to avoid the water running back under. Abutments should have a lead, copper or Nura-lite secret gutter (see drawing on p. 224). The outermost slate has a lay batten to support the nib adjacent to the side lock.

This is about the simplest possible form of non-sheet roof.

Natural Slates. Natural slate is obtainable from Wales, Westmorland and Cornwall. As a roofing material it is more expensive than inter-locking slates or tiles, but apart from interlocking slates just dealt with, they are one of the few small-scale roofing materials which can be laid to a shallow pitch (down to $22\frac{1}{2}°$).

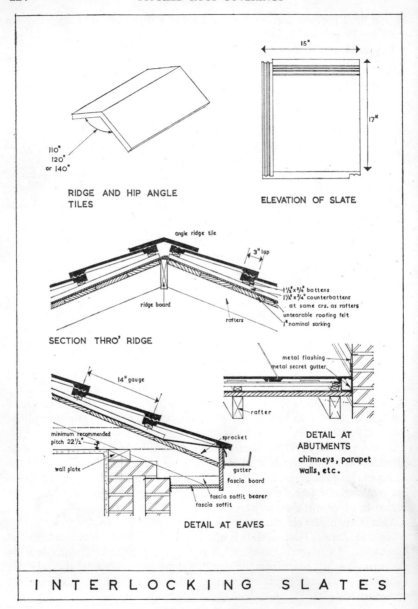

110°
120°
or 140°

RIDGE AND HIP ANGLE TILES

15"

17"

ELEVATION OF SLATE

angle ridge tile

3" lap

ridge board

rafters

1½" x ¾" battens
1½" x ¾" counterbattens
at same crs. as rafters
untearable roofing felt
1" nominal sarking

SECTION THRO' RIDGE

14" gauge

metal flashing
metal secret gutter

rafter

DETAIL AT ABUTMENTS
chimneys, parapet walls, etc.

minimum recommended pitch 22½°

wall plate

sprocket

gutter
fascia board
fascia soffit bearer
fascia soffit

DETAIL AT EAVES

INTERLOCKING SLATES

Slate	Dimensions	Number to cover a square 3 in. lap	1,200 slates, first quality. Weight in cwt approximately
Smalls . .	12″ × 6″	534	14
Doubles . .	13″ × 7″	413	18
Ladies (large) .	16″ × 8″	278	25
Countesses .	20″ × 10″	170	40
Duchesses .	24″ × 12″	115	60
Princesses .	24″ × 14″	99	70
Empresses .	26″ × 16″	79	95

Larger sizes are available, namely Imperials, Rags and Queens, but there is little call for them.

The width of the slate is usually half the length; the following pitches are suitable:

Width of Slate	Minimum Rafter Pitch
6 in. . . .	45°
7 in. . . .	40°
8 in. . . .	35°
9 in. and 10 in. . .	30°
12 in. and 14 in. .	25°

12 in. and 14 in. slates may be used to $22\frac{1}{2}°$ if the exposure is not too severe.

Fixing. Slates may be nailed near the centre or at the head; for the larger sizes of slate centre nailing is the best so as to avoid damage by the wind lifting the slates.

Gauge for Head Nailing. $Gauge = \dfrac{Length\ of\ Slate - 1″ - Lap}{2}$ which for example in Duchess slates would be

$$\frac{24″ - 1″ - 3″}{2} = \frac{20″}{2} = 10″.$$

The battens are therefore fixed 10″ apart at the roof.

Gauge for Centre Nailing. $Gauge = \dfrac{Length\ of\ Slate - Lap}{2}$ which for Duchess slates would be $\dfrac{24″ - 3″}{2} = 10\frac{1}{2}″.$

Lap. The lap varies according to the material and the degree of exposure; for example, $2\frac{1}{2}$ in. for slates and from $2\frac{1}{2}$ in. to 3 in. for plain tiles. It is the

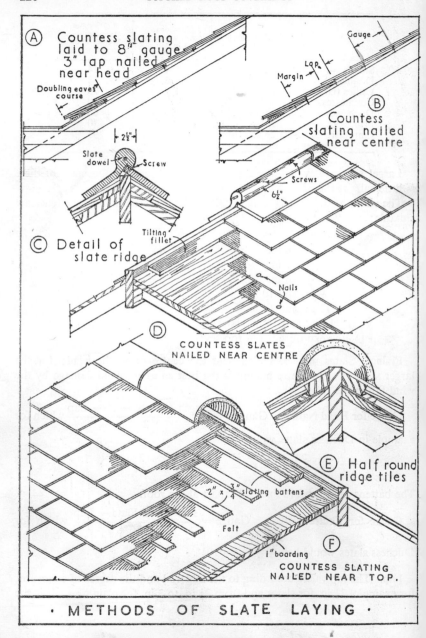

(A) Countess slating laid to 8" gauge 3" lap nailed near head

Doubling eaves course

Gauge

Margin

Lap

(B) Countess slating nailed near centre

Slate dowel — Screw

2½"

(C) Detail of slate ridge

Screws

6½"

Tilting fillet

Nails

(D) COUNTESS SLATES NAILED NEAR CENTRE

(E) Half round ridge tiles

2" x 3" slating battens

Felt

1" boarding

(F) COUNTESS SLATING NAILED NEAR TOP.

· METHODS OF SLATE LAYING ·

distance by which one slate or tile overlaps the head of the slate or tile below but one.

Margin. This is the amount of slate or tile exposed (measured up the slope).

Ridge. The ridge board usually projects 2 in. above the top of the battens or boarding; at the top of the slope against this, a tilting fillet standing $\frac{3}{4}$ in. above the boarding or the top of the battens is fixed to receive the head of the top course of slates. This tilting fillet keeps the top course of slates the same actual pitch as all the rest.

Eaves. A similar tilting fillet is necessary at the eaves in the place of the last batten, the only difference being that it must be triangular (see p. 226), so that a lead or other metal flashing can be laid.

Doubling Eaves Course. This is a course that starts the roof at the eaves, and its length is the gauge plus lap plus 1 in. It is nailed at the head. In Countess slates this would be $8'' + 3'' + 1'' = 12''$; and the nail hole would be 11 in. from the tail.

Verges. This is where the slate or tile roof finishes on a gable wall. It is usual to bed the slates or tiles in cement mortar on the underside; an additional under slate is embedded first upon the wall to protect the wall immediately under the verge. The verge should overhang the wall by at least 2 in.; it should be arranged that the slates or tiles tilt inwards slightly towards the main roof. The pointing must be thoroughly done so that there is no tendency for high winds to strip the verges.

Abutments. Abutments can be dealt with satisfactorily in two ways:

(*a*) With a lead flashing (see p. 241), or
(*b*) With a secret gutter (see p. 241).

A cement fillet in lieu of this is not satisfactory.

Valleys. The valleys are formed with a 9 in. wide valley board running down the internal angle, the battens on either side being stopped against it. In the best practice, the bituminous felt covering to the boarding (or the untearable under slating) is run underneath this board. The valley may be formed by running 'skews' and 'bottoms' alternately up the valley (see drawing on p. 230).

Hips. The neatest form is probably the mitred hip, but it cannot be used on pitches shallower than 40° or 45°. A lead or aluminium soaker has to be placed under each course, as shown on p. 243. The slates are then cut to fit. Alternatively they may be formed (for shallower pitches) with wood rolls and a lead flashing (see drawing on p. 241).

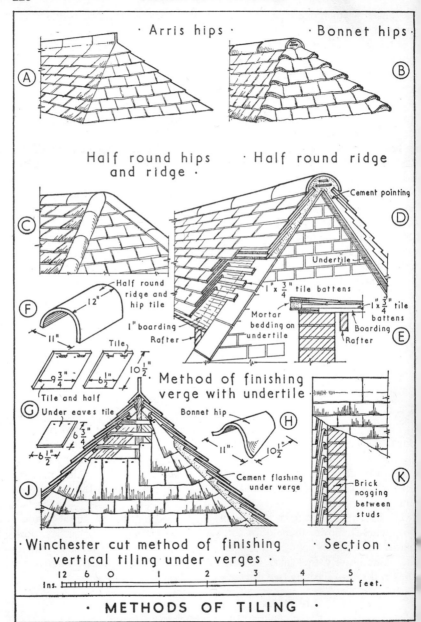

· Arris hips ·

· Bonnet hips ·

Half round hips and ridge ·

· Half round ridge ·

Cement pointing

Undertile

Half round ridge and hip tile

1" x 3/4" tile battens

1 x 3/4" tile battens

12"

11"

1" boarding

Rafter

Mortar bedding on undertile

Boarding

Rafter

Tile

Tile and half

Under eaves tile

9 3/4"   6 1/2"

10 1/2"

Method of finishing verge with undertile

Bonnet hip

6 3/4"

6 1/2"

11"   10 1/2"

Cement flashing under verge

Brick nogging between studs

· Winchester cut method of finishing vertical tiling under verges ·

· Section ·

Ins.   12 6 0   1   2   3   4   5   feet.

· METHODS OF TILING ·

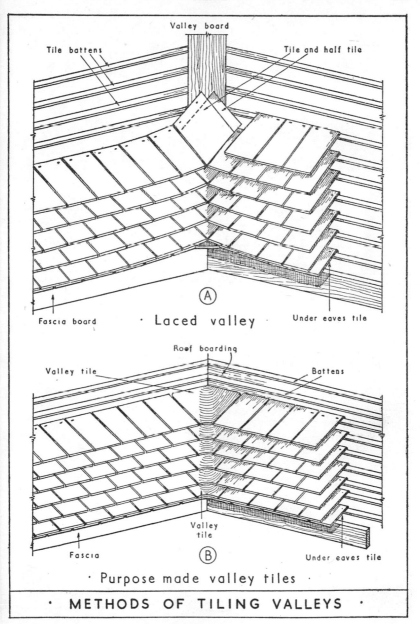

Valley board

Tile battens

Tile and half tile

Fascia board

(A)

· Laced valley ·

Under eaves tile

Roof boarding

Valley tile

Battens

Fascia

Valley tile

(B)

· Purpose made valley tiles ·

Under eaves tile

· METHODS OF TILING VALLEYS ·

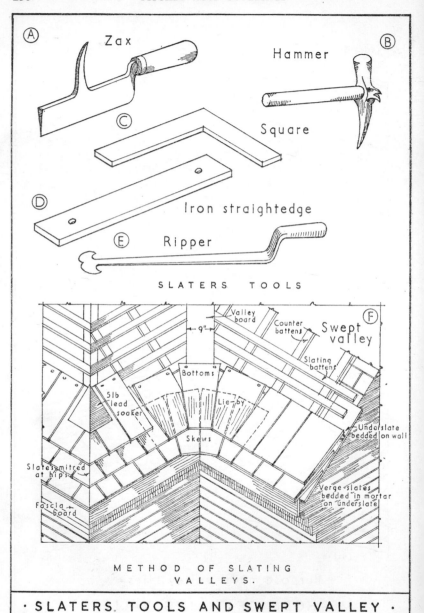

Ⓐ Zax

Ⓑ Hammer

Ⓒ Square

Ⓓ Iron straightedge

Ⓔ Ripper

SLATERS TOOLS

Ⓕ Swept valley

Valley board

Counter battens

9"

Slating battens

Bottoms

5lb lead soaker

Lie by

Underslate bedded on wall

Skews

Slates mitred at hips

Verge slates bedded in mortar on underslate

Fascia board

METHOD OF SLATING VALLEYS.

· SLATERS TOOLS AND SWEPT VALLEY ·

TILING

Plain Tiling. The tile size is usually 10½″ × 6½″ and may vary from ⅜ in. to
½ in. in thickness. Two small nibs are usually moulded on the head to hook
on to the batten. Special tiles or tiles-and-a-half are made 9¾ in. wide for
verges. Various other tiles are made for special application, such as bonnets
for hips, half round tiles for ridges and hips, and short tiles for under eaves,
6½ in. or 7 in. long; ridge tiles 9 in. long.

Tiles are usually laid to a gauge of 4 in., which gives a 2½ in. lap (see above).

The minimum pitch is regarded as 40°, and they should be nailed at this
pitch every fifth course, and the steeper the pitch the more frequently they
should be nailed, so that at over 60° *each* course should be nailed.

Whereas slates weigh about 1 cwt per square, tiles weigh about 12 cwt
per square, i.e. about 22 cwt per thousand. This must be taken into account
when constructing the carcase of the roof. Tiles have a slight camber which
resists capillary attraction under them.

At verges the tiles are first bedded on the walls side by side, not lapping,
to give a flat surface; the general procedure is then as for slating.

Valleys may be laid with purpose-made valley tiles, swept valleys or laced
valleys. Two of these forms are illustrated on p. 229.

Standard Interlocking Tiles. These have side lock, but no head lock, and
can therefore be laid to different gauges, i.e. 12 in. gauge minimum pitch 35°,
11 in. gauge minimum pitch 30°. The usual size for each tile is 15″ × 9″, and
they are usually laid on ¾″ × 1½″ battens. The weight per square is approximately 8 cwt and they may be obtained in several colours and textures.

Roman Pattern Interlocking Tiles. These are wider, being 16½″ × 13″.
Once again they have side lock but no head lock, and can be laid at different
gauges, but the recommended one is 13½ in. when the pitch should be 30°
and not less. The weight per square is also about 8 cwt.

Both these interlocking tile roofs are economical; they should be nailed
each tile in two places (holes are provided), special troughs are made for
valleys, a dentil slip is specially made for filling in the gaps between the rolls
at the ridge under the half-round ridge tile. Plain tiles are used as a doubling
course at the eaves; a sprocket should be placed at the foot of the rafters to
maintain the actual pitch of the eaves tile.

ROOF SUB-STRUCTURE

The ideal form of preparation of a roof to receive slates or tiles is to board
the roof with ¾ in. boarding. It is best to lay this boarding diagonally; this

should be creosoted or otherwise rot-proofed. On top of this felt is laid across the roof starting at the eaves, giving a lap of 2 in. or 3 in. on each horizontal joint. This felt should always be present in a roof. In a roof without boarding, it should be laid immediately on top of the rafters. It should be of the untearable variety (with a stout hessian base).

Over the felt lay counter-battens immediately above each joist. Across these go battens at the correct gauge. The object of the counter-battens is so that the battens do not trap any moisture from condensation or carried in by the wind. The U value of a roof of this construction would be approximately 0·35 (without a ceiling).

Insulation can be improved if, instead of boarding, wood-wool compressed strawboard is used. The counter-battens would still be necessary. Alternatively, insulation can be improved considerably by applying insulation board to the underside of the rafters.

If the counter-battens are left out, the battens are liable to deteriorate by the moisture that they trap running down the roof. If the felt is left out, under bad conditions the boarding will become soaked for long periods (i.e. in snowy weather) which may set up rot.

The cheapest method is to lay the battens straight across the rafters, and this is frequently done. It is a great improvement to include the felt immediately above the rafters. This sags slightly between the rafters avoiding the danger of trapping moisture against each batten. Insulation applied to the underside of the rafters would then provide an excellent roof, safe for pipes and water tanks within the roof. An alternative position for the insulation would be on top of the ceiling joists or between the ceiling joists (loose fill); tanks and pipes in the roof space would then have to be completely lagged against frost.

13

Flat Roof Coverings

LEAD

ROOF coverings comprise various materials: (1) lead; (2) copper; (3) zinc; (4) corrugated steel sheets; (5) asbestos cement sheets; (6) asphalt; (7) glass in the form of patent glazing; and (8) slates and tiles. Rainwater shedding consists also of making watertight with metal those parts of slated or tiled roofs which cannot be made watertight with slates or tiles. For flat roofs, gutters, flashings, etc., lead is an excellent material, and combines lasting and waterproof properties.

Sheet lead, for external work, is obtainable in two forms, cast and milled.

Cast Lead. The lead is melted and run into sand-covered moulds to form sheets of the required size, and may be obtained up to 16 ft long and 7 ft wide. Cast lead is very durable under great changes of temperature, but it is liable to possess flaws and sand holes, and is unsuitable for covering steeply pitched roof slopes.

Milled Lead. Slugs or thick cakes of lead are cast and then passed between rollers to reduce them to the desired thickness. Sheets may be obtained in lengths of 35 ft and widths up to 9 ft. Milled lead is more uniform in thickness than cast lead, and is freer from the sand holes and flaws.

Laying Sheet Lead. The boarding to receive sheet lead should be perfectly smooth. All the joints should be traversed by a plane to take away any projecting arrises which would, sooner or later, show through the lead, especially after wet weather. There should be no sharp angles, and all projections should be rounded off. The grain of the boarding on flats and gutters should be laid in the direction of the current or diagonally in order that any corrugation formed by the casting of the boards should not retain pools of water. Pitch pine or oak or other resinous timbers should not be used directly in contact with lead. A layer of pitch paper or felt is laid on the timber first.

The soles of gutters are recommended to be formed by narrow boards 4½ in. wide, nailed with the heart side upwards, so that the edges will press tightly against the bearers of the boards cast, this is the reverse of boarding used for floors, where the heart side tends to become loose under traffic; the boards should be well nailed, about 1¼ in. from each edge. The width of joints, caused by shrinkage, is obviously much less in narrow than in wide battens.

In fixing lead, the sheets should be free to contract or expand, or pieces used be of such small dimensions that the contraction or expansion will be inappreciable; this is practically satisfied at ordinary temperatures, when the lengths of the pieces do not exceed 7 ft. The joints made between the edges of lead must be arranged so that no water can pass through, nor the covering be blown up by the wind. If the above conditions are not taken into consideration the force of expansion and contraction will cause the sheet lead to slide down if fixed in inclined positions, or buckle and rise in the centre if it be laid on a flat. For steeply pitched roofs it is advisable to use copper, which is lighter and less subject to expansion.

Expansion of Metals. The following table gives the coefficient of expansion for the common metals used in construction, or the ratio of increase in length due to an increase of 1° F.:

Cast Iron	.	.	.	0·0000061	Lead	.	.	.	.	0·000016
Wrought Iron		.	.	0·0000066	Zinc	.	.	.	0·0000155
Steel	.	.	.	0·0000069	Brass	.	.	.	0·0000105
Copper	.	.	.	0·0000094	Gunmetal	.	.	.	0·00001

The difference in temperature to which metals in roofing are exposed in this country between winter and summer is between 90° and 100°F. The increase in length in any sheet of the above metals for any change of temperature, is the product of coefficient of expansion × length × difference in temperature. Therefore, taking a sheet of lead 7 ft long and a difference of temperature of 100° the increase would

$$= 0·000016 \times 84 \times 100 = 0·134 \text{ in.}$$

This amount on a flat roof, experience has shown to be negligible, but on inclinations above 10° the low tensile strength of lead is insufficient to enable it to contract to its original length, and it remains permanently stretched. This results after a few years in the development of cracks in the sheet.

Specification of Lead Coverings. The following are the weights of lead recommended for the various parts of external coverings:

Roofs, Flats, and Main Gutters	.	5 lb to 8 lb lead
Hips, Ridges and Small Gutters	.	5 lb to 7 lb ,,
Aprons and Flashings .	.	.	5 lb lead
Soakers	.	.	.	3 lb to 4 lb ,,
Cisterns, bottom	.	.	7 lb to 8 lb ,,
,, sides	.	.	6 lb to 7 lb ,,
Sinks, bottom	.	.	.	7 lb to 8 lb ,,
,, sides	.	.	.	8 lb to 10 lb ,,
Soil Pipes .	.	.	.	8 lb to 10 lb ,,

Lead is usually described and specified by its weight in lb per superficial foot. The following table gives the thickness of milled lead in common use. The thickness, it may be noticed, is nearly 17/1000ths of an inch for each lb in weight per superficial foot:

Weight in lb per foot super	Thickness in inches	Weight in lb per foot super	Thickness in inches
1	0·017	7	0·118
2	0·034	8	0·135
3	0·051	9	0·152
4	0·068	10	0·169
5	0·085	11	0·186
6	0·101	12	0·203

The lengths of pieces of lead generally used in practice for gutters or flats should not be more than 9 ft, and the fall or inclination of the gutters or flats should not be less than 1 in. in each 9 ft of length. Cover and step flashings should not exceed 6 ft, and ridge pieces not more than 7 ft in length. Dormer cheeks, if very large, should be put on in two or more pieces. Larger dormer tops should have a roll fixed upon them, but for small dormers the lead can expand over the edges. A typical lead flat roof is shown on p. 237.

Nailing. Copper nails should be used, but nailing should not be resorted to unless absolutely necessary. Close nailing is usually under, and open nailing over, 1½ in. spacing.

Bossing, that is, working the lead to the required form with box-wood tools, is preferable to soldering such angles as the returned ends of gutters, drips, or cesspools, or any position where the perpendicular part does not exceed 6 in. in height. Above this it is preferable to solder the angles, to economise in cost. Soldering should, however, be used as little as possible.

Lead Tacks. These are narrow strips of lead, from 2 to 4 in. in width, used for fastening the free edges of flashings, ridge coverings, apron pieces, etc. They are termed *tingles* in the north of England. They are usually placed about one in every 4 ft (see pp. 239 and 241 c).

Laps or Passings are the distances which pieces of lead lap over the adjoining pieces in aprons for gutters, stepped flashings, ridge coverings and other situations where it would be unwise to have the lead in one continuous length. The usual length of passings is 4 in. for upright and 6 in. for horizontal and pitched work (see p. 241 A).

Raglets. The grooves or chases, usually 1 in. deep cut into stone walls to receive the upper edges of the lead flashings.

Fixings for Flashings. Where fixed to brick walls the joints should be raked to a depth of $\frac{3}{4}$ in. and the edge of the flashing turned in, and secured in it by lead wedges varying from 3 to 9 in. apart. The open joints between the wedges should be pointed in cement in brick walls, or with mastic, or be run with lead if in stone walls.

Cover Flashings. The name given to the lead coverings fixed over the turned-up parts of lead gutters or flats; they are usually about 6 in. wide, the object being to keep water from passing between the turned-up lead and the wall, and to allow the covered sheet freedom to contract or expand (see pp. 237 and 239 A).

Apron Flashing. The name applied to the lower horizontal flashing of a chimney shaft, skylight, dormer, or wall penetrating a roof, as shown on p. 243 c.

Tilting Fillets. These are pieces of wood, triangular in section and are used where inclined surfaces abut against walls in order to tilt the slates, and so convey the water away from the walls. Wood fillets are also fixed under the eaves courses of slates, so that they may lie close, and thus prevent the wind getting under them, as shown on p. 226. Two 2″ × 1½″ tilting fillets would be cut from a 2″ × 3″ length.

Cement Fillets. To save the expense of lead flashings, fillets composed of equal portions of Portland cement and sand are run along the junction of lean-to roofs with walls, but the cement sometimes shrinks or breaks away, resulting in an open joint, thus failing to answer the purpose for which it is intended. Zinc soakers, together with cement fillets, are more effectual and are extensively used in cheap buildings, but are not nearly so durable as lead soakers and flashings.

JOINTS

The joints most extensively used for lead coverings for external work may be classified as follows:

Joints Across the Flow or Current. Lap and drip joints.

Joints Parallel with the Flow. Rolls, hollow rolls, and seams or welts.

Lap Joints. These are horizontal joints on inclined surfaces of pitched roofs covered with lead. The boarding should be placed at right angles to the slope. The sheets of lead should be placed between the rolls, the upper ends being close copper nailed, so that the sheets are secured along the top edge. This resists the tendency to crawl down the slope of the roof, and is better than nailing to the face of the boarding. The lower edge being secured by copper clips. If the covering is on a vertical surface, a 4-in. lap would be sufficient; but if the surface has an inclination of not less than 45°, a 6-in.

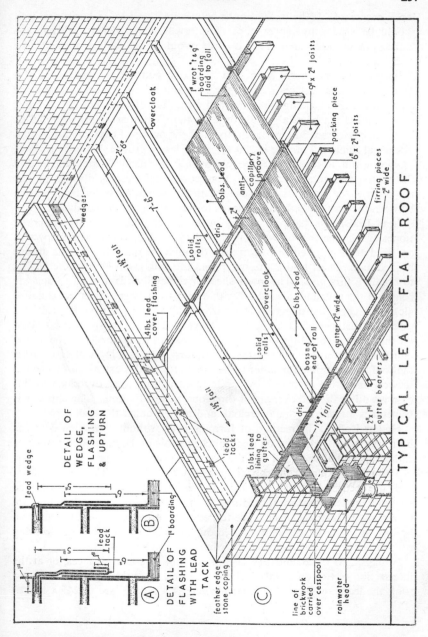

DETAIL OF WEDGE, FLASHING & UPTURN

lead wedge

B

DETAIL OF FLASHING WITH LEAD TACK

lead tack
1" boarding

A

C

line of brickwork carried over cesspool

feather edge stone coping

rainwater head

TYPICAL LEAD FLAT ROOF

1" 'wrot' t&g' boarding laid to fall

9" x 2" joists

packing piece

6" x 2" joists

firring pieces 2" wide

6 lbs. lead

anti capillary groove

drip

solid rolls

overcloak

2'-6"

wedges

4 lbs. lead cover flashing

1 in 1½" fall

1 in 1½" fall

lead tacks

solid rolls

bossed end of roll

6 lbs. lead

gutter 12" wide

drip

1 in 1½" fall

6 lbs. lead lining to gutter

2" x 1" gutter bearers

lap is necessary. If the inclination is between 45° and 15°, a horizontal welt should be used with copper clips at intervals (see p. 239 c). When the inclination is less than 15°, a drip would have to be formed (see p. 237 b).

Lead Drips. Large flat roofs and very long gutters are constructed of a number of plane surfaces slightly inclined and raised a short distance one above the other, forming when finished a number of low steps called drips, which should not be at a greater distance than 7 ft apart. Drips should be made for preference 3 in. in depth, to resist the power of capillary attraction. The usual height is 2 in. (see p. 239 a); when less, a groove should be formed, as shown in b, to resist that force, although it is difficult to dress the lead in the confined space at abutments. For economical reasons, drips in gutters are often made less than 2 in. deep, but this results in water being drawn between the laps of the lead and leads to the rotting of the woodwork.

Lead Rolls. On flats, or at the ridge or junction of the two opposite slopes of a gutter or roof, wooden rolls 1¾ in. or 2 in. diameter and upwards are fixed at the joint either by screwing through the roll or by using a double headed nail. Sheet lead is dressed round the roll, and well into the angles, to obtain a firm grip. The lower sheet or undercloak is dressed to half the height of the roll, and tapered off with a rasp to an edge; the sheet is nailed along the edge, the upper sheet or overcloak is dressed over the roll and extends a distance of 1½ in. on the flat (see p. 239 f). Details e and f show the finish of the roll at the drip. This 1½-in. extension on the flat is sometimes omitted, however, as under certain conditions such as a layer of snow upon the roof, it is possible for water to be drawn under this extension and round the roll under the overcloak by capillary attraction. The overcloak in this case would be dressed over about three-quarters of the roll. The clip at f is sometimes attached to the overcloak and turned under the undercloak.

Hollow Rolls. The method of forming rolls without a wooden core has been very extensively used on steep-pitched roofs on large buildings, such as cathedrals and abbeys, and was the common practice in the mediaeval ages.

To make a hollow roll, copper or lead tacks about 6 in. long and 2 in. wide are secured by two screws each to the boarding, about 2 ft apart; the edges of the lead bay are turned up, as shown in section, p. 239 d, and are then ready to be folded over. The folded edges are then dressed to enclose a hollow, as in the completed roll. Although this is a good method of forming rolls, it is not suitable for positions where any traffic is likely.

Nosings. At the boundaries of flats adjoining vertical surfaces, or at the intersection of two differently inclined surfaces, as at the curb of a mansard roof, the lead covering may be terminated as a nosing (see p. 245 a and b)

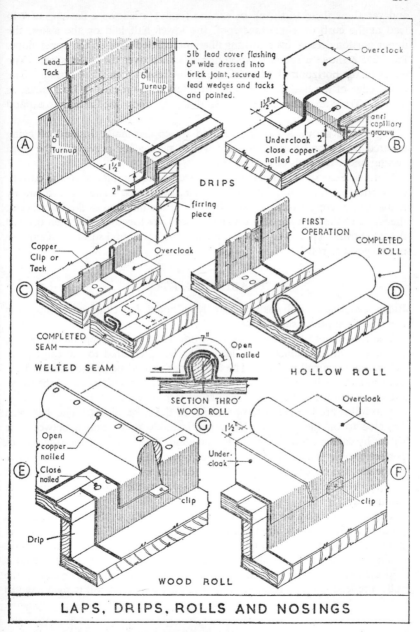

A — 5 lb lead cover flashing 6″ wide dressed into brick joint, secured by lead wedges and tacks and pointed. Lead Tack. 6″ Turnup. 6″ Turnup. 1½″. 2″.

B — Overcloak. 1½″. Undercloak close copper nailed. 2″. anti capillary groove.

DRIPS

firring piece

C — Copper Clip or Tack. Overcloak. COMPLETED SEAM. WELTED SEAM

D — FIRST OPERATION. COMPLETED ROLL. HOLLOW ROLL

SECTION THRO' WOOD ROLL. 7″. Open nailed. G

E — Open copper nailed. Close nailed. Drip. clip.

F — Overcloak. 1½″. Undercloak. clip.

WOOD ROLL

LAPS, DRIPS, ROLLS AND NOSINGS

and yet allow them to shrink or expand freely; c shows a flashing of 7-lb lead at the curb of a mansard roof, the lower half laid on the slates, the upper portion dressed over a tilting fillet and carried 6 in. up the upper slope. Page 245 A shows a rounded wood nosing nailed over the lower sheet. The edges of the horizontal lead work are then dressed round the nosing. The lower edge of the flashing is secured at intervals by means of lead tacks, as shown. These are better than soldered dots, and allow the flashing to expand and contract.

Page 245 B shows a flashing secured by copper nails, instead of being covered by a wood nosing, and flat welted nosing for preventing the wind getting under the ends of the lead bays.

Welts or Seams. The joints for sheet lead when running with the current on vertical surfaces may be the flat welts or seams. These are made by fixing lead or copper tacks about 2 ft apart at the junction of the lead sheets; the edges of the bays are bent up and turned over together, and then dressed flat, as shown on p. 239 c. For flat pitched, or horizontal surfaces, seams are not so good as rolls.

FLASHINGS, ETC.

Ridge Coverings. 6-lb lead is usually adopted for ridge coverings; the lengths of the pieces should not exceed 7 ft.

The lead should be dressed over a wood ridge roll, which should not be less than 2 in. in diameter, the lead tacks being secured to the ridge piece before the ridge roll is fixed. The lead wings should be dressed close to the bottom of the roll, and extend 6 in. down the slope on either side of the ridge, the free edges being secured by lead tacks (see p. 241 A).

Lap joints are formed at the junctions of the ridge pieces. This has been objected to on the grounds that water is liable to be drawn between the sheets by capillarity or driven in by the wind, or drain in, if the ridge is not perfectly level. These objections may be obviated by forming a water groove in the lap, the under piece of lead being dressed into the groove. Any water getting between the laps on the sloping sides would fall on the slates and drain away.

Hips. These may be made watertight in two ways. First by dressing a piece of lead, of the required width and not longer than 7 ft, over a roll, and letting the sides lie 6 in. on the slates similar to a ridge. To prevent the lead sliding down the hip, the lowest piece of roll is fixed, the first piece of lead is laid on with its upper end extending 6 inches beyond the upper end of the roll; the lead is then bossed down. The next length of roll is then fixed in

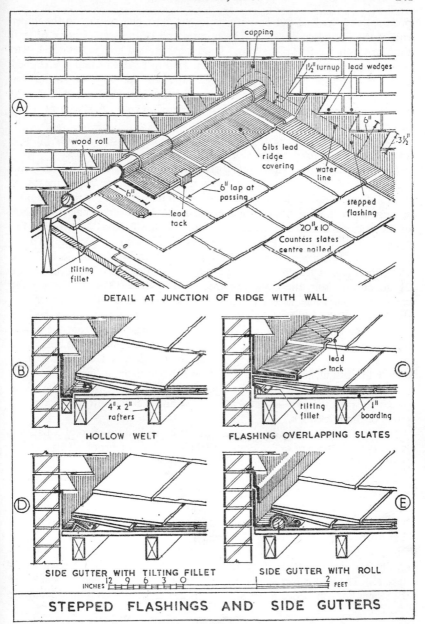

A — capping — 1½" turnup — lead wedges

wood roll — 6 lbs lead ridge covering — water line — 6" — 3½"

6" lap at passing — lead tack — stepped flashing

tilting fillet — 20" x 10" Countess slates centre nailed

DETAIL AT JUNCTION OF RIDGE WITH WALL

B — 4" x 2" rafters

HOLLOW WELT

C — lead tack — tilting fillet — 1" boarding

FLASHING OVERLAPPING SLATES

D — SIDE GUTTER WITH TILTING FILLET

E — SIDE GUTTER WITH ROLL

INCHES 12 9 6 3 0 — 1 — 2 FEET

STEPPED FLASHINGS AND SIDE GUTTERS

position, and the lead put on with its lowest extremity resting on the upper
end of the first piece of lead. The bottom end of the second piece of lead
thus laps over the first piece 6 in. Lead tacks should be fixed about 3 ft to
3 ft 6 in. apart, and the lower piece of the lead to be fixed should be clipped
over the upper at each lap joint. Secondly, the hip may be formed by
soakers. In this case the slates are mitred at the hip. This method should
not be employed on pitches under 45° (see p. 243 B). A sketch of a hip
soaker is also shown.

Valley Gutters. In valleys, the coverings may be arranged to form gutters,
small fillets being fixed on the slopes of the roofs to tilt the slates.

Stepped Flashings. The joints between sloping roof surfaces and end
walls built of brickwork or stone rubble are best protected by means of
pieces of sheet lead, called stepped flashings, 6 in. lying on the roof and 6 in.
against the wall. The upper edges are turned 1 in. into the raglets or joints
of the brickwork prepared to receive them, and are fixed as described in the
paragraph on flashings. Page 244 A refers to this kind of flashing. To set
out stepped flashings, first roll out the piece of lead, which should be 12 in.
wide, then fold it lengthways in the centre, like the letter L. Draw a line
2½ in. distant from the angle, on the stand-up side. This line is usually
called the ' water-line '. The piece of lead should then be laid in position on
the roof, and the horizontal joints in the brickwork transferred to the lead
between the top edge and the water-line. Next draw lines from the points
where the horizontal lines cut the water-line to the point where the horizontal
line immediately above cuts the outer edge of the piece of lead. Draw other
lines 1 in. distant, parallel with and above the horizontal lines. The small
triangular pieces of lead above these last lines are cut out with a knife. The
pieces between the parallel lines are folded and wedged into the raked-out
joints of the brickwork.

Raking Flashing. The name given when the turned-up edge of a flashing
is secured to a chase or raglet, cut parallel to the slope of a roof. This method
is adopted for stone walls adjoining sloping roofs.

Lead Flashings for Chimney Stacks. Page 244 shows the method of preventing any leakage through the joints on the four sides of a chimney stack.
The slating is fixed up to the lower edge of the stack. The lead apron flashing
is then fixed (see p. 244 C) by lead wedges into the brickwork. The slating is
then carried up the sides of the stack. After this, the stepped flashing is
fixed, D, the lead extending 6 in. over the slates; it is prevented from spreading by lead tacks. The back gutter is then fixed, lapping over the side flashings, E. The lead is sometimes dressed into the angle between the stack and
the slope, but it is better to fix a block in this angle slightly sloped from the

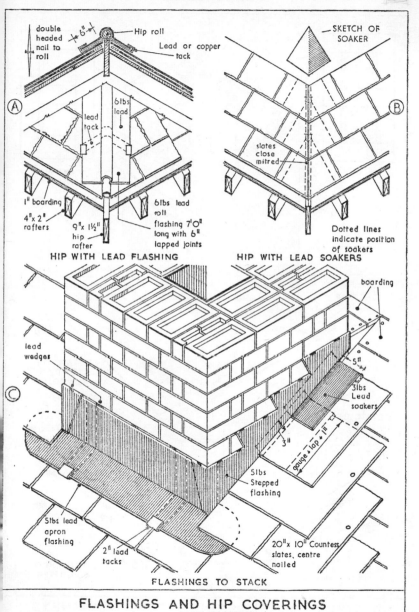

A — HIP WITH LEAD FLASHING

double headed nail to roll — 6" — Hip roll
Lead or copper tack
6lbs lead
lead tack
1" boarding
4" x 2" rafters
9" x 1½" hip rafter
6lbs lead roll
flashing 7'0" long with 6" lapped joints

B — HIP WITH LEAD SOAKERS

SKETCH OF SOAKER
slates close mitred
Dotted lines indicate position of soakers

C — FLASHINGS TO STACK

boarding
lead wedges
5"
3lbs Lead soakers
gauge + lap 1"
3"
5lbs Stepped flashing
5lbs lead apron flashing
2" lead tacks
20" x 10" Countess slates, centre nailed

FLASHINGS AND HIP COVERINGS

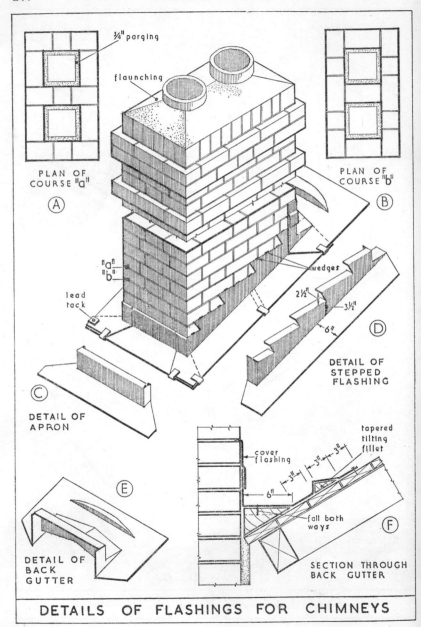

¾" parging

flaunching

PLAN OF COURSE "a"

(A)

PLAN OF COURSE "b"

(B)

"a"
"b"

lead tack

wedges

2½"

3½"

6"

(D)

DETAIL OF STEPPED FLASHING

(C)

DETAIL OF APRON

(E)

DETAIL OF BACK GUTTER

cover flashing

tapered tilting fillet

3" 3"

6"

fall both ways

(F)

SECTION THROUGH BACK GUTTER

DETAILS OF FLASHINGS FOR CHIMNEYS

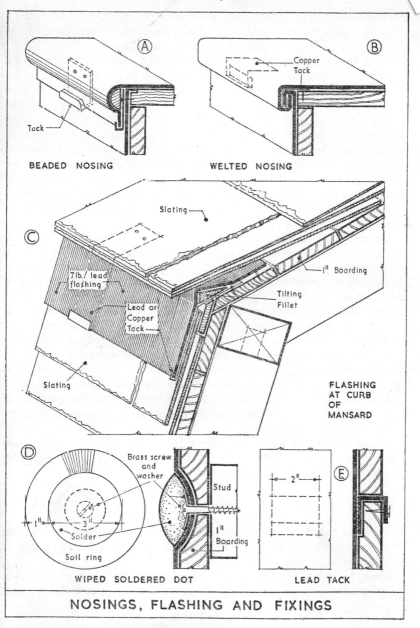

A   BEADED NOSING

Tack

B   WELTED NOSING

Copper Tack

C   FLASHING AT CURB OF MANSARD

Slating

7 lb./ lead flashing

Lead or Copper Tack

Slating

1" Boarding

Tilting Fillet

D   WIPED SOLDERED DOT

Brass screw and washer

Stud

1" Boarding

Solder

1"

3"

Soil ring

E   LEAD TACK

2"

NOSINGS, FLASHING AND FIXINGS

centre outwards. The gutter usually has a cover flashing, F. P. 244 C, D and E show the apron, stepped flashing and gutter piece before being fixed. At E, a straight fillet is more often used than a tapering fillet.

Secret Gutters. When flashings are fixed beneath instead of lying on the slates, secret gutters are constructed, as shown on p. 241 B, D and E.

These secret gutters derive their name from their being hidden from view by the slates. In some situations the slates are carried over the secret gutter so as nearly to touch the wall. This protects the lead from the sun, but the arrangement is bad in any position where leaves of trees or any rubbish might drift into and choke the gutter. To obviate this, the gutter is constructed as shown in D, where the tilting piece forms the depth of the trough, and the edge of the lead under the slates is bent to form a small hollow welt to guide away any water that might pass over the fillet; B shows the boarding cut short on the rafters to give depth to the gutter, and a hollow welt is turned on the edge of the lead for the purpose given above.

Soakers. The intersections of sloping roof surfaces with end gables or penetrating walls are sometimes made weathertight by pieces of lead termed soakers, fixed parallel to the walls, and resting on the slopes of roofs about 4 in. They are turned up against the walls from 2 to 3 in., and a cover stepped or raking flashing is fixed over the turned-up edges. The soakers should be the length of the slates minus the margin, and plus an inch for clipping over the heads of the slates. Page 243 C shows a soaker cut for Countess slates; and also an isometric detail of soakers, fixed with stepped cover flashings over them to prevent the water leaking between the soakers and the wall. Soakers are normally 4 in. wide and often half the width of the slate. This does not apply where a slate and a half slate is used. This is better than ordinary stepped flashings, as the wind cannot blow the rain between the roof and wall, and neither can the wind get under the edges as when ordinary stepped flashings are used.

In some cases each soaker turns up 6 in. against the wall and steps are cut and the edges tucked into a raglet, as in ordinary stepped flashing. This is a good plan, but takes a longer time to execute.

GUTTERS

Rain water that falls upon roofs naturally runs to the lowest part, and provision must be made to carry the water away. This is done by means of gutters fixed at the eaves or behind parapets.

These are the troughs or ducts provided at the lower edge of the slopes of all pitched or flat roofs, to convey the rain water to convenient points where it is discharged into rain-water pipes, through which it is directed into the drains. It is essential that the pipes and gutters should have an ample area to meet the needs in the case of sudden storms. The maximum distance between the pipes should be from 30 ft to 40 ft. The usual rule for the minimum area of the pipes is to allow 1 in. in area for every 75 to 100 ft super of roof drained, measured on plan.

The roofs may have either eaves or parapet gutters at the foot of the slope, the former may be of cast iron, asbestos, aluminium, etc.

Parapet Gutters. When the gutters are formed behind parapets as p. 248 A and B, at the bottom of pitched roofs, owing to the fall that must be given, the gutter becomes tapering in plan. The exact form of the gutter depends on the position of the down pipes, this again on the elevation and the position of drains. A and B show two plans for a tapering gutter, one with the down pipes at the end of the building and one in the centre; the principle is the same in both. The lengths of gutter are made as nearly as possible a multiple of 7 ft, with not more than two lengths if possible in any slope; if more than two lengths are employed the gutter becomes very wide at its highest end. The minimum size of the cesspool is 9″ × 9″ × 6″ deep. C shows the form of the cesspool before insertion, being 6 inches deep; the angles are soldered. D shows a section of the cesspool with the bottom dished for the down pipe. E shows a cesspool formed to run through the wall; the outer end is dressed over a cast-iron rainwater head into which it discharges. F shows the formation of a drip with detail of turn-up against wall, and the arrangement of the cover flashings, and G shows the view looking at the slope and illustrates the method of dressing over the tilting fillet and also the method of mitreing the tilting fillet to bring it lower down on the slope. H is a diagram showing the method of obtaining the width of the gutter at the various levels; to these widths must be added 6-in. turn-up against the wall and 9 in. up the slope.

Parapet parallel gutters usually occur with flat roofs. The gutter is made a minimum of 2 in. deep at its highest end; in other respects, with regard to fall and drip, it is similar to the tapering gutter. The turn-up and cover flashings against the wall is as shown on p. 248 F, and the turn-up which is fixed in a rebate on the roof side with the finish of the rolls is shown on p. 239 A, B, E and F.

Tapering Valley Gutters. A gutter constructed between the slopes of two adjacent roofs is called a valley gutter, and may be tapering when the common rafters of adjoining slopes rest on the same plate. Valley gutters are also available purpose-made in cast iron and asbestos.

Snow Boards. These should be provided in all gutters to preserve an

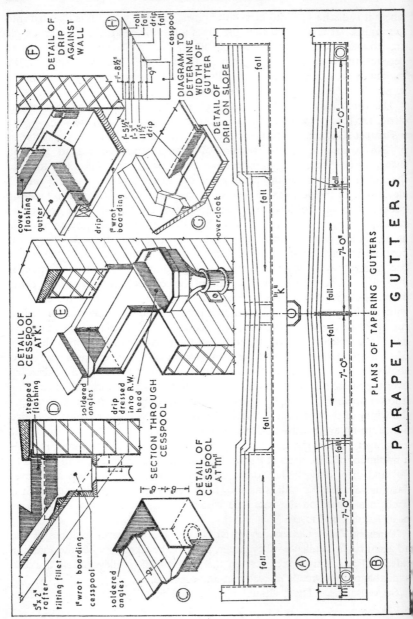

F — DETAIL OF DRIP AGAINST WALL

cover flashing
gutter
drip
1" wrot boarding

H

roll
fall
drip
fall
cesspool

1'-8½"
9"

DIAGRAM TO DETERMINE WIDTH OF GUTTER

1'-5½"
1'-3"
1'-1½"
drip

G — DETAIL OF DRIP ON SLOPE

overcloak

fall
fall

E — DETAIL OF CESSPOOL AT "K."

stepped flashing
soldered angles
drip dressed into R.W. head

D — SECTION THROUGH CESSPOOL

5" x 2" rafter
tilting fillet
1" wrot boarding
cesspool
soldered angles

C — DETAIL OF CESSPOOL AT "m"

9"
9"
9"

K

A

fall
fall
fall
fall

B

7'-0"
7'-0"
7'-0"
7'-0"
7'-0"
fall
fall

m

PLANS OF TAPERING GUTTERS

PARAPET GUTTERS

uninterrupted channel for draining away the water as the snow melts after a heavy snowstorm. The snow thaws on the underside first, through being in contact with the warm roof; and if the gutters and outlets be choked with frozen snow, that which is thawed will run through the joints in the roofing material. The gutters on the hospital at Basle in Switzerland are equipped with an electric heating element to melt the snow and keep the gutters permanently clear. The snow boards consist of a number of strips of wood 2″ × 1″, placed in the gutter with their length parallel to the current of the gutter and spaced ¾ in. apart; they are supported by and fixed to cross-pieces 4½″ × 2″. From the underside of these bearers a piece at least 2 in. wide is taken out from the centre, and extends to within 3 in. from each end to form an arch for the melted snow to flow through. These are also advantages on lead flats over which foot traffic passes.

Snow Guards. These consist of low iron railings fixed at the lower edges of all sloping roofs, for preventing large masses of snow slipping down the roof surface and falling over the eaves; they should be at least 1 ft high and the rails should be large enough to break the masses thoroughly. In severe climates on pitched roofs these should never be omitted; they are often dispensed with in the south of England and are necessary in the midlands and the north.

Burning In. Lead cover flashings for parapet gutters are sometimes secured to the stone blocking course by being turned into a groove or raglet, cut dovetail shape, on the top surface of the stone; molten lead is then poured into the groove, which thoroughly secures the flashing to the stonework. As the molten lead shrinks on cooling it is necessary to 'set it up', that is, to expand the surface with caulking tools or blunt chisels with a rounded end, to fill the groove, and thus ensure the lead being thoroughly secured.

Soldered Dots. Where large vertical surfaces have to be covered with lead, as on dormer cheeks, they are sometimes secured in the following manner: Round hollowings, 3 in. in diameter, are dished out of the boards, the lead is dressed into these hollowings and screwed to the boards and studs (the latter are best for screwing to if they come in the required positions). A tinned copper washer should be placed under the head of the screw to distribute the fixing over a greater surface of lead, so that when shrinkage or expansion takes place, the lead shall not be torn by the screw. The hollow is encompassed by a ring of soil (which is a composition of size, lamp black and chalk) to prevent the solder from adhering to the flush surface of the lead covering. The hollow is then filled up level with solder, and is then known as a soldered dot. Page 245 D shows the construction. Lead fixed in this manner is liable to crack near the soldered dots.

Secret Tacks. A better mode of fixing dormer cheeks is shown on p. 245 E, where a lead tack is soldered to the back side of the lead covering. The loose end of the tack is passed through a slot cut in the boarding, and secured by copper nails on the inside. The tack, or secret tack, as it is called, fixes the covering securely, is not so unsightly as is the former method, and allows more freedom for the lead cheek to expand.

Lead Dowel or Dot. Exposed parts of stone cornices, strings, etc., are covered with sheet lead, to prevent the absorption of the rain water that falls upon them. The lead is dressed down and over the cornice. It is fixed near the outer edge of the cornice by lead dowels placed at about 3 ft intervals. Circular holes exactly opposite each other are made in the lead and surface of the stone; the edges of the lead round the hole should be turned up slightly. An iron mould with a small hole through the top is held over the hole in the lead and stone, and molten lead poured in to fill up the holes prepared to receive it, and also the cup-shape hollow of the mould. This fixing is called a lead dowel or dot.

COPPER

Coverings. Copper sheet may be used for all roofing purposes as a covering. It has many advantages, the chief of which is the fact that it is practically everlasting. When exposed to the atmosphere a very thin protective coating is formed, which develops over the course of a number of years into the well-known and beautiful grey or grey-green patina. This patina, which consists largely of a basic sulphate of copper, is immune to further atmospheric attack and will permanently protect the underlying copper sheet even though the atmosphere may be polluted with corrosive matter, such as is to be found in many industrial areas.

Copper is tough, ductile and malleable. These properties enable the metal to withstand considerable physical damage and its freedom from creep is an attribute not possessed by the more plastic metals. There are no particular difficulties in the technique of working copper sheet or strip; but there are certain peculiarities of which it is advisable to be aware. Thus, copper can be hardened easily by hammering and working. For this reason copper used for roofing or flashing should be in dead soft temper, although, if during the working the copper becomes hard, it can be annealed by heating to a dull red and quenched in water or allowed to cool naturally in the air. In working copper, the various welts and folds should be achieved with a minimum of sharp blows as opposed to the succession of taps with which the plumber works lead sheet.

Copper roofing is light in weight. Taking comparative areas of roof, the weight of copper sheet covering compared to the weights of the following materials would be approximately as follows:

1/7th that of lead; 1/5th to 1/10th that of slates;
1/11th that of tiles; 1/3rd that of zinc.

The saving in weight may permit a reduction in the sizes of the constructional members of the roof.

The coefficient of linear expansion for copper is less than for other roofing materials and thus there will be less movement due to temperature changes. Also, it is shown that lead should not be used on inclinations above 10° because of its low tensile strength and poor degree of elasticity, unless special precautions are taken. Copper has good mechanical properties, a comparatively high tensile strength, and this, in addition to its light weight, enables it to expand and contract on a steep pitch without any tendency to ' creep ' or ' flow ' down the slope. In fact, sheet copper can be applied to a vertical surface without taking any special precautions other than those that would be used in normal roofing practice.

In the preservation of ancient buildings, copper or copper alloy rod has been used as reinforcement to concrete instead of steel; while for a roof covering it is favoured because it is found that insect pests, borers such as the death-watch beetle, do not thrive under copper.

Specification. Hot or cold rolled fully annealed sheet or strip copper in dead soft temper or half hard temper is used for external work and is supplied in the following gauges:

Roofwork, 22, 23 or 24 s.w.g. copper—ranging in thickness from 0·028 to 0·022 and weighing from 20·8 oz. per ft to 16·4 oz. per ft. Sheet— hot rolled. Strip—cold rolled—fully annealed.

Flashings, 24 to 26 s.w.g. copper—ranging from 0·022 in. to 0·018 in. thick and weighing 16·4 oz. per ft to 13·4 oz. per ft. Strip—cold rolled—annealed.

D.P.C.'s, 30 s.w.g. copper—0·01 in. to 4 in. thick, weighing 9·2 oz. per ft (cold rolled strip—annealed) laid with 3 in. minimum lap.

Fully annealed copper must be used for roofwork, but half-hard temper material is sometimes required for weatherings to window frames and cornices or coping edges.

Sheet sizes are usually 4′ × 2′ and 6′ × 3′. The definition of sheet is flat material of exact length over 38 s.w.g., but not over ⅜ in. thick and over 18 in. wide. Strip is material over 38 s.w.g. thick but not over ⅜ in. thick of any width and generally not cut to length. Usually supplied in coil but may be flat or folded.

Laying Sheet Copper. The preparation of the surface for sheet copper is exactly the same as for sheet lead (see p. 237). A layer of inodorous felt conforming to the following specification is first laid on the understructure with butt joints and secured with copper nails:

> B.S. 747 : 1952, Type 4A (ii) Brown, No. 1 Inodorous Flax Felt, 50 lb per roll.

This serves three purposes: it lessens any possibility of ' wearing ' the copper as it expands and contracts; it deadens the sound of wind and rain; and it acts as a measure of insulation. All sharp objects should first be brushed away from the understructure and nail heads punched well down into the boarding to prevent their coming into contact with the copper and setting up electrolytic action and consequent corrosion in the presence of moisture from condensation. All nails or screws should be either copper or copper alloy and, in the case of nails, there should be no shoulder under the flat head.

Laying Flats. There are two methods of laying copper in areas to cover a roof: (1) The Standing Seam; (2) The Batten Roll. The formation of joints with either of the types of roof just mentioned allow expansion and contraction to be taken up without risk of damage to the roof itself. Drips may be placed on roofs below 10° in pitch and spaced at 10 ft to 15 ft apart. Such drips should be not less than 2 in. deep.

Standing Seams. Page 253 D, E, F and G. The minimum pitch at which a standing seam roof may be laid is 10°. In general no area of any one individual piece of copper should be greater than 14 sq. ft. Thus, a piece 2 ft wide by 7 ft long should be a maximum. At the ends of the strip the pieces are joined together by double-lock cross-welts, p. 253. In forming the standing seam the edge of the overcloak is turned up $1\frac{1}{2}$ in. and the undercloak $1\frac{1}{4}$ in. Copper clips or cleats are fixed at 18 in. intervals to the prepared surface and turned up $1\frac{1}{2}$ in. against the overcloak. The illustration shows how this is done. The finished seam should stand approximately $\frac{7}{8}$ in. high. The double-lock cross-welts in the individual sheets are staggered in alternate bays to avoid too great a thickness of metal at the standing seams. The thickness of the double cross-welt does not exceed $\frac{1}{4}$ in.; therefore the water will not lie behind the welt if the fall is 1 in 60.

At the turn-up against the wall (see p. 254 A, B and C), the seam is flattened out and dressed tightly against the wall and a cover flashing fixed over the top. The edge of the cover flashing should have a bead worked on it to stiffen it.

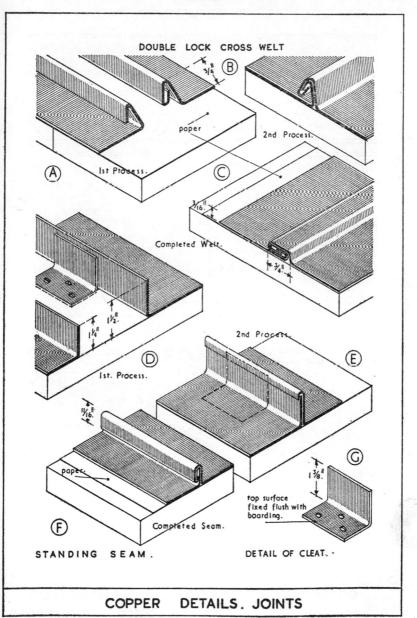

DOUBLE LOCK CROSS WELT

paper

2nd Process.

Ⓐ 1st Process. Ⓒ

Ⓑ

Completed Welt.

Ⓓ 1st. Process.

2nd Process. Ⓔ

paper

Ⓕ Completed Seam.

STANDING SEAM.

Ⓖ

top surface fixed flush with boarding.

DETAIL OF CLEAT.

COPPER DETAILS. JOINTS

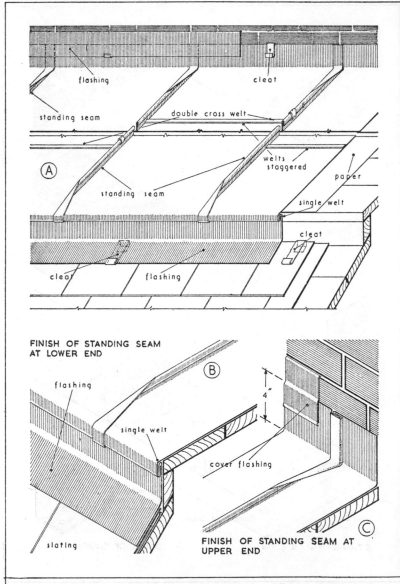

FINISH OF STANDING SEAM
AT LOWER END

FINISH OF STANDING SEAM AT
UPPER END

COPPER DETAILS: STANDING SEAM METHOD

The finish of the standing seam at the lower end, B, is flattened out and welted to the flashing below; A gives a general view of such a flat dressing against a brick wall at its upper end and its lower end with a flashing over a curb, with a slated roof. The standing seam can be used on all surfaces from the flat to the vertical.

Wood Roll Method. This method is preferable for flat roofs where there

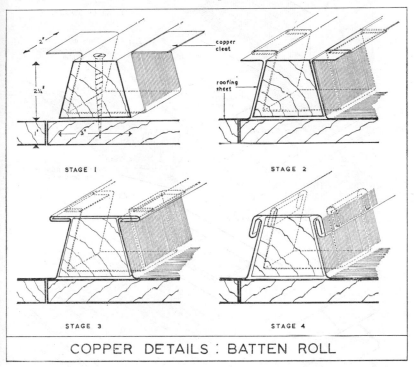

COPPER DETAILS : BATTEN ROLL

is likely to be any traffic, owing to the possibility of the standing seam being trodden flat. The latest form is the batten roll.

Batten Roll. The battens here are ex 2″ × 3″ and are slightly tapered (see p. 255); 2 in. wide cleats of copper and are fixed about 18 in. apart, the batten rolls themselves are fixed at about 2 to 6 in. centres with brass screws. The copper roofing sheet is turned up each side of the batten roll and flanged over at the top back parallel to the roofing sheet itself. A prepared capping strip is folded and slipped over these two flanges, the whole then being dressed down to the side of the roll. The sheets in the direction of the flow are

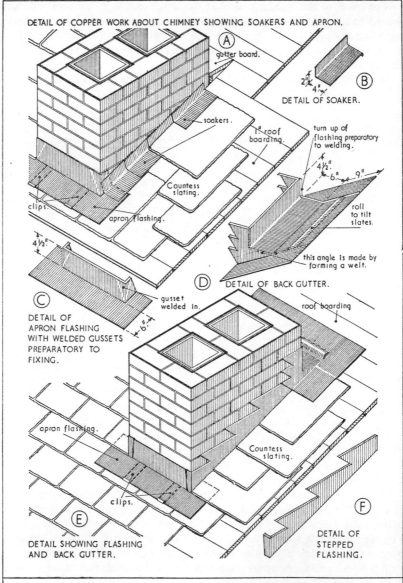

DETAIL OF COPPER WORK ABOUT CHIMNEY SHOWING SOAKERS AND APRON.

Ⓐ gutter board.

Ⓑ DETAIL OF SOAKER. 2" 4"

soakers.

1" roof boarding.

Countess slating.

turn up of flashing preparatory to welding.

clips.

apron flashing.

4½" 6" 9"

roll to tilt slates.

this angle is made by forming a welt.

Ⓓ DETAIL OF BACK GUTTER.

4½"

Ⓒ DETAIL OF APRON FLASHING WITH WELDED GUSSETS PREPARATORY TO FIXING.

gusset welded in.

6"

roof boarding

apron flashing.

Countess slating.

clips.

Ⓔ DETAIL SHOWING FLASHING AND BACK GUTTER.

Ⓕ DETAIL OF STEPPED FLASHING.

COPPER DETAILS: FLASHING TO CHIMNEY STACKS

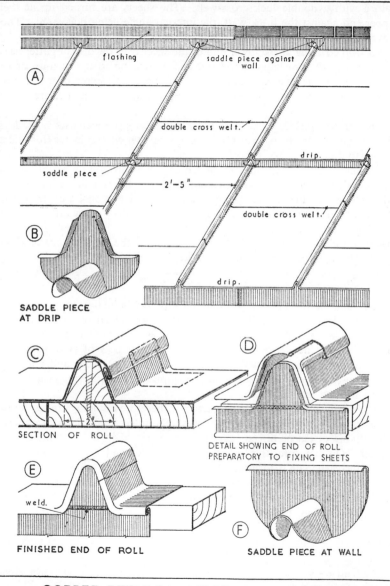

A — flashing — saddle piece against wall — double cross welt — saddle piece — 2'−5" — double cross welt — drip — drip

B — SADDLE PIECE AT DRIP

C — SECTION OF ROLL — 2'

D — DETAIL SHOWING END OF ROLL PREPARATORY TO FIXING SHEETS

E — weld — FINISHED END OF ROLL

F — SADDLE PIECE AT WALL

COPPER DETAILS: WOOD ROLL METHOD

joined with a double lock cross-welt. The sheets are turned up at their upper end against the brick wall, the internal angle being dog-eared. They have a saddle piece placed over the joint, as shown in B, p. 257.

The roll covering at the lower end of the sheet over the drip or gutter has a piece of copper the shape of the roll end welded on to the turn-up of the lower sheet or the flashing. The end of the sheets are welted over as shown in D and E. Specially stamped end pieces, as shown in B and F, are on the market.

Conical Roll (p. 257). This is an older method not so much used nowadays, the main difference being that no capping strip is used and it therefore takes longer to do.

Flashings for Chimney Stacks. When copper is dressed up about vertical surfaces there may be internal or external angles. Internal angles are formed with dog ears. For external angles on aprons a diagonal welt is formed between the front and side pieces as shown in the illustration on p. 256.

Where a number of aprons and back gutters have to be formed of the same size then welding is very often used. The sides of the stack are made waterproof with the slating by soakers and step flashings.

ZINC

Zinc is suitable for exterior work on all types of buildings and, if properly laid, provides one of the lightest and most economical of roof coverings. It will not last as long as lead or copper, but is cheaper than either of these materials. Its life depends mainly upon the thickness of zinc used; and forty years may be expected for 14 Z.G. (21 s.w.g.) sheet under average conditions,* although there are many examples of roofs having lasted much longer without maintenance.

Zinc is attacked by mineral acids, and will therefore last longer in residential areas, or along the coast, than in severely polluted industrial atmospheres, where a life of ten or fifteen years may be expected.† It is not affected by sea air. On exposure, the bright metal tarnishes and a protective skin of basic zinc carbonate is formed. This coating is strongly adherent, and since it does not flake or peel off, serves to protect the metal against further action.

Zinc should not be laid in contact with copper on account of the risk of electrolytic action, but contact with other metals used in building is not harmful. The sulphur acids present in industrial atmospheres are the chief agents causing atmospheric attack on zinc; soot in itself does not affect the

---

* *Post War Building Studies*, No. 13, Non-ferrous Metals.
† Cat's urine is very corrosive to zinc, so zinc-covered flat roofs should be inaccessible to cats.

metal. Cement and mortars (sand/cement, sand/lime/cement) made from clean materials do not effect zinc beyond causing superficial etching while setting is taking place. Materials such as breeze concrete or mortar made from ground ashes (black mortar) may contain appreciable amounts of soluble salt which may attack zinc. When the metal has to be laid in contact with these latter materials it should be coated with bitumen. Crude (i.e. unrefined) tar is likely to attack zinc, but such tar is probably never used in building work. Bituminous and asphaltic materials (coatings, paints, mastics) in use at the present time do not attack zinc. With the exception of Oak and Western Red Cedar, seasoned timbers do not affect zinc. Zinc gutters, soakers and aprons should not be used where they receive the drainage from Western Red Cedar shingles. Care must be taken where possible not to discharge water from iron or copper rainwater pipes on to zinc flat roofs.

The coefficient of expansion of zinc $(0.0000155—°F)$ is greater than that of copper, but slightly less than that of lead; provision for this is made in roofing. The metal has a relatively low melting-point (419° C.), but will not burn unless heated to much higher temperatures.

Zinc Sheet. The standard sizes of sheets specified in B.S. 849 are 3 ft wide and either 7 ft or 8 ft long; other sizes can be obtained to special order. The thickness of sheets is often designated by the special Zinc Gauge; and all British rolled sheets are stamped both with this and the nearest equivalent s.w.g. number. The gauges used in good building work are as follows:

Zinc Gauge No.	Nearest s.w.g. No.	Weight per square foot in oz.	No. of 8' × 3' sheets per 20 cwt	Approx. weight of zinc roll cap roofing per square in lb (100 feet super)	Remarks
12	23	15·0	100	118	Minimum thickness for zinc rainwater goods (B.S. 1431 : 1948). Temporary roofs.
14	21	18·6	80	144	Minimum thickness for zinc roll cap and standing seam roofs, flashings, soakers, weatherings, etc. (B.S. 849 : 1939).
16	19	24·6	61	192	Italianised and corrugated zinc roofs. Special work.

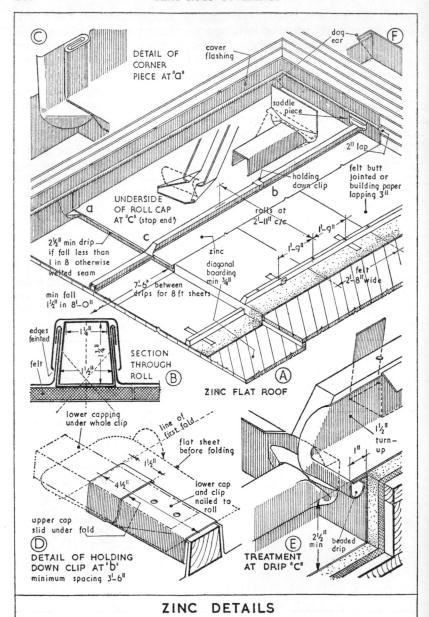

Ⓒ DETAIL OF CORNER PIECE AT "a"

cover flashing

dog ear

Ⓕ

saddle piece

holding down clip

2" lap

felt butt jointed or building paper lapping 3"

UNDERSIDE OF ROLL CAP AT "C" (stop end)

rolls at 2'-11" c/c

1'-9"

1'-9"

2½" min drip if fall less than 1 in 8 otherwise welted seam

zinc

diagonal boarding min ¾"

felt

2'-8" wide

min fall 1½" in 8'-0"

7'-6" between drips for 8 ft sheets

edges feinted

1¼"

1¾"

1½"

SECTION THROUGH ROLL Ⓑ

felt

lower capping under whole clip

ⒶZINC FLAT ROOF

line of first fold

1½"

flat sheet before folding

lower cap and clip nailed to roll

1½" turn-up

4½"

upper cap slid under fold

1"

Ⓓ DETAIL OF HOLDING DOWN CLIP AT "b"
minimum spacing 3'-6"

2½" min

beaded drip

Ⓔ TREATMENT AT DRIP "C"

ZINC DETAILS

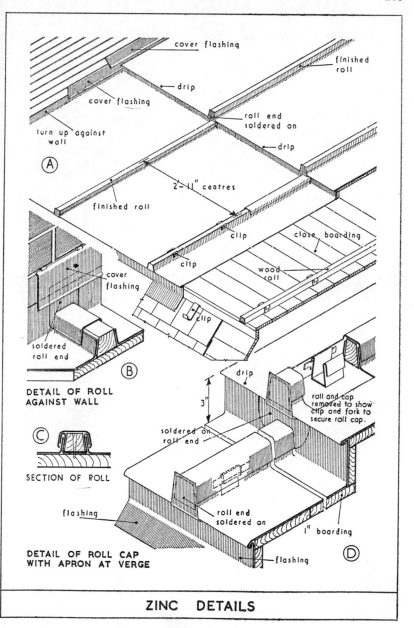

- cover flashing
- cover flashing
- drip
- turn up against wall
- finished roll
- roll end soldered on
- drip
- (A)
- 2'-11" centres
- finished roll
- clip
- close boarding
- clip
- wood roll
- cover flashing
- clip
- soldered roll end
- (B)

DETAIL OF ROLL AGAINST WALL

- (C)

SECTION OF ROLL

- drip
- roll and cap removed to show clip and fork to secure roll cap.
- 3"
- soldered on roll end
- flashing
- roll end soldered on
- 1" boarding
- (D)
- flashing

DETAIL OF ROLL CAP WITH APRON AT VERGE

ZINC DETAILS

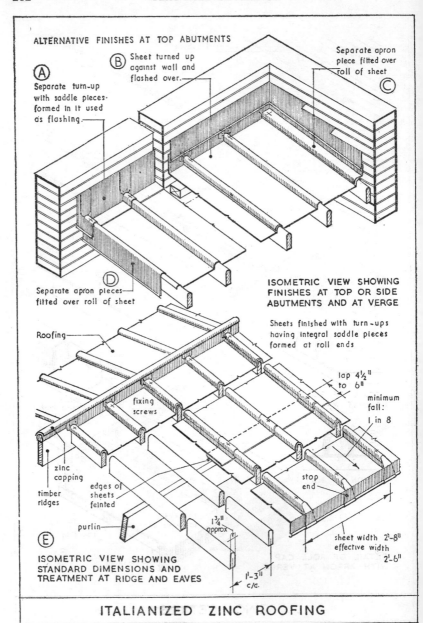

ALTERNATIVE FINISHES AT TOP ABUTMENTS

Ⓐ Separate turn-up with saddle pieces formed in it used as flashing.

Ⓑ Sheet turned up against wall and flashed over.

Ⓒ Separate apron piece fitted over roll of sheet

Ⓓ Separate apron pieces fitted over roll of sheet

ISOMETRIC VIEW SHOWING FINISHES AT TOP OR SIDE ABUTMENTS AND AT VERGE

Sheets finished with turn-ups having integral saddle pieces formed at roll ends

Roofing

lap 4½" to 6"

minimum fall: 1 in 8

fixing screws

zinc capping

timber ridges

edges of sheets feinted

stop end

purlin

1¾" approx

sheet width 2'-8" effective width 2'-6"

1'-3" c/c.

Ⓔ ISOMETRIC VIEW SHOWING STANDARD DIMENSIONS AND TREATMENT AT RIDGE AND EAVES

ITALIANIZED ZINC ROOFING

Zinc Roofing Systems. Several methods are in use; and the oldest, the roll cap system, which has undergone minor improvements during the last 100 years, is still the most useful method of laying zinc roofs today in this country.

The Italianised roofing system, which does not require a continuous decking under the sheets, comes next in importance and is widely used for buildings such as warehouses and railway stations. In this system the sheets are provided with three machine-made lengthwise corrugations, and are supported on round-topped rafters.

On the Continent, standing seam zinc roofs are common, and there are several examples in this country. Either zinc sheet or strip may be used, and the method of laying is the same as that used for standing seam copper roofs.

Roll Cap Roofing. Felt or paper is laid over the roof boarding under the rolls (felt is butt jointed) prior to laying the sheets. This prevents condensation on the underside of the metal. The sheets are laid over boarding or other decking material, and are turned up against straight-sided wood rolls fixed in the direction of the fall. The wood rolls measure $1\frac{1}{2}$ in. across the base, tapering to $1\frac{1}{4}$ in. across the top and are at least $1\frac{5}{8}$ in. high (p. 260 B and see table). No soldering is required nor should it be used on straightforward work, and no nails or screws pass through the exposed surfaces.

The minimum fall for flat zinc roofs is $1\frac{1}{2}$ in. in 8 ft. Drips, which require to be built into the roof structure, must be at least 2 in. deep for a welted drip or $2\frac{1}{2}$ in. for a beaded drip (p. 260, detail E), and spaced not more than 7 ft 6 in. apart if standard sheets are to be used.

Dog ears are formed at the corners of sheets where the side turn-up meets the end turn-up, and so are required at corners between walls and under drips, p. 260 F.

The roof is covered from the bottom of the fall upwards, and operations commence with the spacing and fixing of the wood rolls. In standard practice the rolls are fixed with their bottom edges 2 ft $9\frac{1}{2}$ in. apart; that is at 2 ft 11 in. centres; this allows for a $1\frac{1}{2}$-in. turn-up along the long sides of the sheets, plus $\frac{1}{4}$-in. along each side for expansion. Sheets are held on to the roof decking by means of $1\frac{1}{2}$-in. wide zinc clips fixed under the rolls and bent over to grip the sheet turn-up. Clips are spaced not more than 3 ft 6 in. apart. When the sheets are in position, the wood rolls are covered with standard square capping. Stop ends are formed on the lower ends of capping, a forming block made of cast iron or hardwood being necessary for this operation. The tail of the stop end is either beaded or welted to hook on to the ends of the sheets already in position. Cappings are fixed in lengths of not more than 6 ft, by means of holding-down clips (p. 260, detail D). These are bent up to the same shape as the capping and are 4½ in. long with a 1½-in. turn-back across the lower end. Clips are fixed over the top end of the lower length of capping by galvanised screws or nails, and the next length of capping fixed into the fold of the clip.

Saddle pieces are formed on the ends of cappings at walls and drips, and are worked up from the capping by simple folding (p. 260, detail A). Where the roof sheets abut a wall at a drip, a corner piece is welted into the upper sheet (p. 260, detail C).

Standing Seam Roofing. This method of roofing, which is more popular abroad than in Great Britain, provides an excellent watertight roof, and is particularly suitable for slopes of very considerable pitch. For flat or nearly flat surfaces it does not compete with the roll cap roof, nor is it suitable where considerable traffic is expected, since the standing seams, if trodden down flat, would lose their value as expansion joints.

The details of the system are already described in the section dealing with copper roofing, and when zinc is used only minor modifications are needed. Either sheet zinc or strip zinc can be used, although generally speaking the zinc should be softer than that used for the roll cap system. When sheets are used, the ends are joined by single welts. As in the roll cap roofing system drips are needed where the fall is less than 1 in 8. The minimum fall should not be less than 1½ in. in 8 ft. By the use of strip zinc, which can be supplied in long lengths, the need for welted joints or drips is completely eliminated.

In fixing a standing seam roof, zinc clips, 1½ in. high, are first nailed to the boarding at about 12-in. centres. The side of the first sheet is turned up 1¼ in. and fixed by bending over the clips. The side of the second (adjacent) sheet is turned up 1½ in. and secured to the first sheet by a single and then a double welt, the finished seam being about ⅞ in. high. Care must be taken to leave ¼ in. free space between lower edges of turn-ups to allow for expansion.

Box Gutters. Box gutters are constructed with falls and drips as for flat roofs. The depth at the highest point should be at least 2 in. and their width at least 9 in. Sides of box gutters against walls are turned up at least 4 in.

Flashings. Flashings are made in 7 ft or 8 ft lengths from the same gauge metal as the roof. They should be turned into the wall at least ¾ in. and secured with zinc, lead or hardwood wedges spaced not more than 2 ft apart, and then pointed up in the usual manner. The free edge of flashings should lap over the turned-up roof or gutter sheets at least 2 in., and have their bottom edges stiffened by means of a half round bead, or alternatively a welt.

Flashings for Chimney Stacks. These are formed in a manner similar to that described and shown in the section on Copper, with the exception that the gussets in the aprons are soldered on, not welded; and in the back gutter the side pieces and gutter bottom are also soldered.

ASPHALT

Materials. *Trinidad Lake Asphalt.* This is quarried in the Island of Trinidad and consists of a mixture of bitumen, colloidal clay and fine silica.

Natural Rock Asphalt. This is mined in Switzerland, France and Sicily. It occurs in a calcareous rock naturally impregnated with bitumen. Both the bitumen and the limestone vary in quality and in the degree of impregnation. The imported material has at least 6% bitumen content, it is crushed and ground in this country for the manufacture of Mastic Asphalt.

Application

Preparation and Laying. The asphalt is brought to the site in blocks weighing about half a hundredweight each. They are melted in a boiler, care being taken to see that the temperature does not rise over 400° F. The molten material is kept continually stirred by means of rods, and is then carried by pails to the spreaders who apply the material to the surface by means of floats and small trowels.

When properly applied, the material is jointless and can be applied to both horizontal and vertical surfaces.

Roofing. On a concrete surface it is usual to ensure that there is a minimum fall of $1\frac{1}{2}$ in. in 10 ft, although in some circumstances the roof can be perfectly flat, e.g. permanently flooded roofs. The asphalt is applied direct in two thicknesses of $\frac{3}{8}$ in. each to a total of $\frac{3}{4}$ in. The drawing on p. 266 indicates treatment at internal and external angles, eaves, rainwater outlets, standards, vent pipes, etc.

At all internal angles fillets are built up in three coats to guard against splitting at this point.

Vertical surfaces should be roughened in the case of concrete, or courses raked out in the case of brickwork, to provide a key. The asphalt may be taken horizontally through a wall to form a damp-proof course. If the wall above is likely to be heavy the asphalt may squeeze out in hot weather, so that in this particular instance a metal or bituminous felt D.P.C. may be preferable.

Where it is necessary to avoid exposing the asphalt vertically on a concrete fascia (note the key shown on the detail) then a lead or aluminium

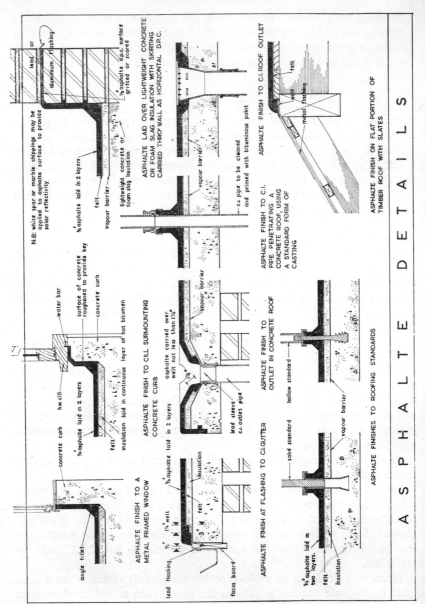

N.B. white spar or marble chippings may be applied to asphalte surface to provide solar reflectivity

lead or aluminium flashing

¾" asphalte d.p.c. surface gritted or scored

¾" asphalte laid in 2 layers

felt

vapour barrier

lightweight concrete or foam slag insulation

ASPHALTE LAID OVER LIGHTWEIGHT CONCRETE OR FOAM SLAG INSULATION WITH SKIRTING CARRIED THRO' WALL AS HORIZONTAL D.P.C.

vapour barrier

c.i. pipe to be cleaned and primed with bituminous point

ASPHALTE FINISH TO C.I. PIPE PENETRATING A CONCRETE ROOF, USING A STANDARD FORM OF CASTING

ASPHALTE FINISH TO C.I. ROOF OUTLET

felt

metal flashing

ASPHALTE FINISH ON FLAT PORTION OF TIMBER ROOF WITH SLATES

water bar

surface of concrete roughened to provide key

concrete curb

concrete curb

hw. cill

¾" asphalte laid in 2 layers

felt

insulation laid in continuous layer of hot bitumen

layer of hot bitumen

ASPHALTE FINISH TO CILL SURMOUNTING CONCRETE CURB

asphalte carried over welt not less than 1½"

vapour barrier

lead sleeve

c.i. outlet pipe

ASPHALTE FINISH TO OUTLET IN CONCRETE ROOF

hollow standard

solid standard

vapour barrier

ASPHALTE FINISHES TO ROOFING STANDARDS

concrete curb

¾" asphalte laid in 2 layers

felt

insulation

angle fillet

ASPHALTE FINISH TO A METAL FRAMED WINDOW

lead flashing

½" 1¼" welt

"3" welt

insulation

felt

¾" asphalte laid in two layers

facia board

ASPHALTE FINISH AT FLASHING TO C.I. GUTTER

ASPHALTE   DETAILS

flashing may be used. This may be turned down into a rainwater gutter, or if an upstand is formed, the metal flashing can be turned neatly over the top edge of the fascia board.

Special cast-iron fittings are available for forming and making good the asphalt finish where pipes pass through a roof. Similarly solid or hollow standards are provided with rimmed flanges to receive the top edge of the asphalt upstand.

Special cast-iron outlets, slightly funnel-shaped, are available with flanges to receive the asphalt. Sumps should never be used with this type of rain-water outlet; they collect leaves and rubbish and are so easily broken when too vigorously rodded. Outlets may alternatively be formed with the aid of lead sleeves formed like flat funnels, and providing a spigot for the socket of the rainwater pipe. The outside edges of funnel are turned over to provide an additional key for the asphalt.

It is important to provide a layer of insulation under which it is essential to provide a continuous vapour barrier. Insulation may consist of insula-tion board, cork slabs, or a substantial lightweight screed. Vapour permea-ting the concrete or other structure will not then condense out on the cold underside of the asphalt.

Finished asphalt roofs are not intended to take traffic; ideally they should be surfaced with a macadam or other suitable wearing layer for this purpose; otherwise it is valuable to reduce solar heat absorption by covering the surface with white spar, marble chips, limestone chips, asbestos cement roof tiles, or light concrete tiles. As asphalt over a long period of time is broken down by the ultra-violet light content in the sun's rays, such surfacing greatly increases the life of the roof.

Asphalt becomes more brittle in cold weather and is therefore more liable to damage by structural movement in the winter than at other times. Struc-tural, thermal, and moisture movements in different degrees for each different building material are all liable to occur, e.g. there is liable to be movement between the edge of a large concrete roof and adjacent brick wall (or parapet). In this case, the asphalt is turned up 6 in. to form a skirting and a metal flashing is taken through the brickwork a course or so above, and dressed down over the asphalt skirting. This allows relative movement to occur with less danger of cracking.

BITUMINOUS FELTS

Material. There are four main types of roofing felts.*

    Class 1. Bitumen felt (fibre felt); the base consists of close textured

                     * See British Standard 747: 1952.

absorbent sheet made from a mixture of animal and vegetable fibres saturated with bitumen. It is coated with oxidised bitumen which softens at temperatures over 80° C. It is surfaced with finely divided talc, natural sand, mineral granules or other approved material. Depending upon the finish, it can be used as either the top or cap layer or the under layers in built-up roofing.

Class 2. Bitumen felts (asbestos base); the base consists of an absorbent sheet of asbestos fibre containing not less than 80% asbestos. It is saturated with bitumen and has a coating of oxidised bitumen as before. One variety is obtainable which is not coated and is therefore not suitable for the top layer of built-up roofing. This class of felts is useful where fire resistance is required (see later reference to By-laws).

Class 3. Fluxed pitch felts; the base consists of a close-textured absorbent sheet made from a mixture of animal and vegetable fibres. It is saturated and coated with a fluxed coal tar pitch of a certain standard. The uncoated variety is used for lower layers of multiple layer roofing. The coated variety for use for this and for the cap layer. It is used in single layers for unimportant structures.

Class 4. Impregnated flax felts and hair felts; the flax felt consists of a loosely felted mixture of flax, jute or vegetable fibres. The black felt is a similar loosely felted mixture of animal hair, the brown felt has 50% cow hair or other animal hair, the balance being jute or other vegetable fibres. The seare impregnated, in the case of black felt with fluxed coal tar pitch and in the case of brown felt with brown wood tars, wood pitches or similar roofing materials. These felts are used mainly for heat insulation and sound absorption treatments or for isolating underlays.

Weights. Roofing felts are specified by weight, i.e. the weight of one roll, 1 yd wide by 12 yds long, and may vary from 15 lb to 80 lb. Although some felts are supplied in 24-yd rolls the weight is still specified per 12 square yards.

Fire Resistance. For normal domestic buildings,* adequate fire resistance is provided by asbestos-based roofing felt (to British Standard 474), or organic-based roofing felts on a $\frac{1}{2}$-in. screed or other non-combustible material, or if it is covered with $\frac{1}{2}$ in. of non-combustible material, e.g. asbestos roofing tiles or light concrete slabs, or if it is covered with bituminous macadam (not more than 7% bituminous material) and fine gravel or stone chippings.

In the case of public buildings, warehouses, large houses, terraces, the covering must be able to withstand the spread of fire and is decided by the local authority to suit each particular case.

* Other than houses of more than 36,000 cu. ft capacity, or houses forming blocks of more than two houses.

Where the roof covering does not comply with the foregoing the building must be twice its height from the boundary.

Life. As with asphalt, ultra-violet light in the sun's rays breaks down the bitumen in the course of time, so that a surface finish of preferably a white material such as spar limestone chippings, marble chippings, asbestos tiles or light concrete tiles will increase the life of the roof considerably, as well as assisting in the insulation value of the roof.

Vapour Barrier. Once again it is necessary to stress the importance of providing a continuous vapour barrier below the insulating layer under the felt so that moisture laden air from within the building cannot condense out on the cold underside of the felt.

Application. The drawing on p. 270 shows how the three layers are applied each sealed in a continuous layer of hot bitumen. A two-layer felt is sometimes specified but a three-layer specification is more satisfactory. It is usual to make the top layer the heaviest, e.g. first layer 55 lb, second layer 55 lb, top sheet or layer 80 lb.* Alternatively all the layers could be 60-lb sheets, there are many varieties possible. The side joints overlap 2 in. and the end joints overlap 6 in. No joints in succeeding layers should coincide (they should all break bond).

The layers are sealed together with oxidised bitumen applied at the rate of 3 lb per square yard.

On a timber roof a first layer of 60-lb felt is stud-nailed with large galvanised clout nails to the timber. Where the roof is laid on a lightweight concrete screed a 50-lb layer is laid loose over the concrete and sealed only at the outside edges of the roof with oxidised bitumen applied at the usual rate. The laps in this case are 3 in. and are sealed in turn with oxidised bitumen. The roof is then continued as before, e.g. second layer 60 lb and a third layer of 80 lb (plus protective tiles, etc.).

The general principles of application are similar to those of asphalt, roofs may be laid flat or they may be laid to a minimum fall of 1 in 80.†

Rainwater outlets may be provided in a similar way to asphalt technique, i.e. with cast-iron funnels, the first two layers being taken beneath the flange, the top layer being dressed into the outlet.‡ 'Fulbore' outlets are a recent

---

* The 80 lb sheet may be a two-ply sheet, which is bonded together at the factory.

† There are two schools of thought; the absolutely flat-ists say that to keep bitumen or asphalt moist prolongs its life; the 1 in 80 fallers say that puddles on a roof look bad and that puddles drying out in hot sun subject the water-proofing to great local differences in temperature. On account of the bumps over seams a roof has to be very much steeper than 1 in 80 to be clear always of puddles!

‡ Another method of forming outlets in flat roofs is to form a lead or Nuralite flanged sleeve as in section BB p. 146, this goes between the second and third layers, the third or cap layer being dressed down into the outlet. The sleeve enters the top-most socket of the R.W.P.

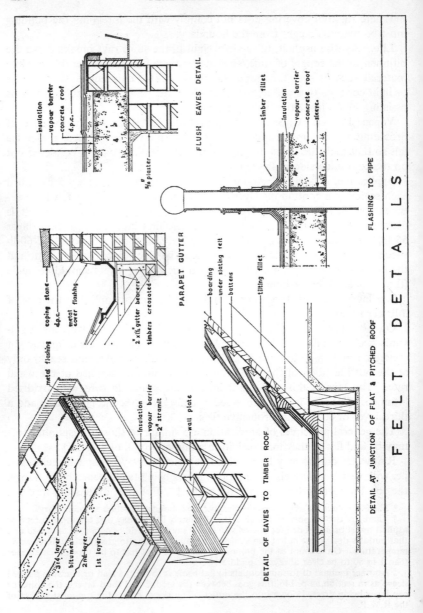

FLUSH EAVES DETAIL

FLASHING TO PIPE

PARAPET GUTTER

DETAIL OF EAVES TO TIMBER ROOF

DETAIL AT JUNCTION OF FLAT & PITCHED ROOF

FELT DETAILS

development in which the flanged grating can be screwed down, pressing the felt to the funnel all round. This is a great improvement. The outlets from the funnel may be vertical, at 45°, or practically horizontal.

At the eaves the felt may be formed to a drip over a gutter attached to a fascia as in the alternative detail section CC on p. 146. Where gutters are not provided and rainwater outlets are used, then it is necessary to form an upstand round the roof as in sections AA and BB, etc., p. 146. This upstand prevents gusts of wind blowing water from puddles over the edge of the eaves. They are formed by means of 3″ × 3″ wood triangular fillets up which the felt is dressed. The fillet and the top edge of the fascia is then flashed with a metal or Nuralite cover flashing fixed by means of dots or tacks.

At the junction between the tiled or slated pitch roof and the flat roof (see p. 270) the felt is again taken up a triangular fillet and a flashing of heavy felt or, preferably, metal, is taken down under the bottom course of the tiles and dressed over the turned-up felt. Pipes passing through flat roofs are treated as shown in the detail on p. 270. Parapet and valley gutters are easier to form as the material is a continuous one, so that drips and cesspools are avoided. ' Fulbore ' parapet R.W. outlets are the most effective way of coping with rainwater disposal from parapet gutters. The rectangular grating in this case can be clamped against the flanged outlet gripping the felt all round.

NURALITE

This material is coming into use as a substitute for roofing metals because of its cheapness. It is supplied in sheet form 8 ft by 3 ft. It is black in colour and is composed of asbestos and certain bitumens.

It can be used for flat roofing with the roll cap method, but because of its lightness extending to brittleness, it must be fixed frequently to prevent damage by high winds.

It is useful for forming most types of flashings. Those with long exposed edges can be finished off neatly with a small corrugation or bead, which provides greater rigidity.

The material is formed by softening with a blow lamp or with special irons. It is easy to cut and can be welded with the aid of ' welding plastic '. Nuralite ' dots ' can be formed, for fixing away from edges, with the aid of a circular cupped iron.*

---

* See Nuralite Technical Handbook, The Nuralite Co. Ltd., Whitehall Place, Gravesend, Kent.

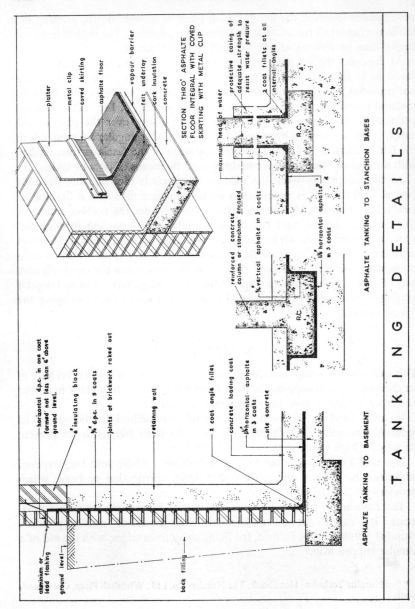

plaster

metal clip

coved skirting

asphalte floor

vapour barrier

felt underlay

cork insulation

concrete

SECTION THRO' ASPHALTE FLOOR INTEGRAL WITH COVED SKIRTING WITH METAL CLIP

maximum head of water

protective casing of adequate strength to resist water pressure

2 coat fillets at all internal angles

R.C.

reinforced concrete column or stanchion encased

½"vertical asphalte in 3 coats

R.C.

1½" horizontal asphalte in 3 coats

ASPHALTE TANKING TO STANCHION BASES

horizontal d.p.c. in one coat formed not less than 6" above ground level.

6" insulating block

¾" d.p.c. in 3 coats

joints of brickwork raked out

retaining wall

2 coat angle fillet

concrete loading coat

1½"horizontal asphalte in 3 coats

site concrete

aluminium or lead flashing

ground level

back filling

ASPHALTE TANKING TO BASEMENT

TANKING DETAILS

TANKING

This subject is dealt with more fully in *Advanced Building Construction*, but the drawings on p. 272 indicate the principles.

It is not always possible to excavate a trench clear of the outside walls of the basement, but, where it is, then it is much better to apply the asphalt or felt (either may be used) direct to the outside surface of the main retaining wall. Otherwise a semi-structural wall has to be built and tanked on the inside, the retaining wall proper being cast up against it in lifts as the waterproofing is applied. Subsequent water pressure may then press the waterproofing off the outside wall and on to the retaining wall proper in spite of careful consolidation of the retaining wall; this transfer may cause cracking of the waterproofing.

The procedure is to cast the site concrete and base to the retaining wall, and on this to lay the $1\frac{1}{8}$ in. horizontal asphalt or two layer felt tanking. A strengthening triangular fillet is formed at the corners and the waterproofing taken without a break up the vertical surfaces. The concrete loading coat has to be sufficiently reinforced to resist the upwards water pressure which may develop.*

Where concrete or steel column bases have to be accommodated it is better to take the tanking underneath them as shown in the first detail. Alternatively the reinforced concrete casing may be taken round the asphalt, dressed up the column, as shown in the second detail (p. 272). This may be more economical where the basement is a shallow one.

* During the construction of basements a sump is dug in one corner which is kept dry by pumping, when the concrete loading coat and the structural retaining wall are strong enough, the sump is filled in and asphalt or felt carefully sealed before the water has time to rise.

14

Water Supply—Cold and Hot

COLD WATER SUPPLY

FOR town supply the water is drawn off from rivers or wells, fed to closed or open reservoirs, sterilised and pumped either to high storage tanks with a gravity feed to the mains or pumped direct into the mains. In the country away from mains, supply may be by well when a pump may be fitted to the well for direct supply or the pump may deliver the water to storage tanks whence it may be drawn off as required. The Water Company's main is usually situated in the road. When a new supply for a building is required the main is tapped and a pipe taken to a stop tap and guard pit either in the pavement or just outside the boundary of the site. This stop tap enables the Water Company to isolate the supply to the building in case of leakage or failure. This 'communication pipe' (i.e. the pipe from the main to the building) is taken to the internal stop tap which is usually located just above the site concrete at the foot of the rising main (supply pipe). This stop tap should have a draining outlet incorporated in it so that the rising main can be drained off.

The rising main is turned into the storage cistern through a ball valve which stops the supply when the cistern is full (see drawing on p. 277).

The communication pipe should enter the building through a sleeve of drain pipe to eliminate fracture due to movement by the building settling. The point of entry should be away from external walls so as to avoid frost.

Storage System. For cold water service only, the minimum is usually 50 gallons (actual capacity), if the storage system supplies the hot water service as well, minimum size should be at least 80 gallons. A feed system for a hot water supply system only must be a minimum of 30 gallons.*

For other types of buildings the Code of Practice lays down a recommendation for each fitting, i.e. shower 100 to 200 gallons, w.c. 40 gallons, lavatory basin 20 gallons, sink 20 gallons, urinal 40 gallons, plus each person served 30 gallons (dwellings and boarding schools 30 gallons, etc.).

One of the objects of the storage cistern is to prevent the possible sucking

---

* 80 gallons—3′ × 2′ 6″ × 2′2″
 50 gallons—2′ 6″ × 2′ × 2′
 30 gallons—2′ 3″ × 1′ 8″ × 1′ 8″

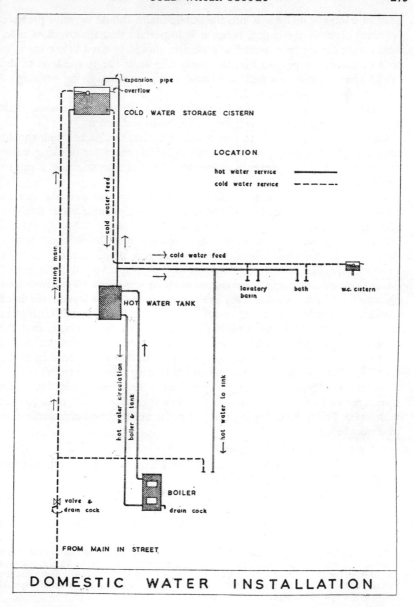

DOMESTIC WATER INSTALLATION

back of contaminated water into the public mains should negative pressure (suction) occur in the mains, hence it is important that the overflow pipe, which must always be provided to a cistern, should be fixed below the inlet level of the supply pipe so that the water can never rise to the level of the inlet. The overflow pipe must discharge into a position giving warning of overflow (see drawing on p. 277).

From the storage cistern are taken the cold feeds to the hot water tank and the cold feeds to w.c., lavatory basins, baths and sinks.

One important exception to this principle is that the kitchen sink should have a cold water supply straight from the rising main for drinking water (drinking water from the cistern where the water has been standing, is not so beneficial to health).

The expansion pipe from the hot water tank may turn over the storage cistern so long as its end is well above the highest possible water line (see drawing on p. 275).

Materials—Cisterns. The most usual, because it is the cheapest, is galvanised steel. Asbestos-cement cisterns are a very practical proposition as they do not suffer from rust. Alternatively, copper is very durable but of limited strength, making the maximum possible size about 60 gallons; lead cisterns built in a softwood case are too expensive nowadays (avoid hard woods). In the best practice, ' safes ' are provided underneath cisterns in the form of trays with outlet pipes running to roofs or gutters, in case the cistern springs a leak. In larger buildings the cisterns are often put on the roof so that the floor of the tankroom is part of the water proofing of the roof. In all cases cisterns should be lagged to keep them free from frost.

Materials—Pipes. Lead or compo (lead alloy) communication pipes should not be laid in earth containing a lot of vegetable matter, or in contact with lime. From the Company's stop tap the underground communication pipe may be in:

(a) Compo or lead (see above).

(b) Copper to B.S.S. 1386/1947 which may, if long distances are involved, be laid by mole plough.*

(c) Iron and Steel.

(d) Plastic.

(a) *Lead* has the advantage that it is very easy to cut, and form, although it

---

* A mole plough is winched along by tractor and will cut a 2½ in. diameter mole drain at an operational depth adjustable between 12 in. and 21 in. in any soil which is reasonably free of large boulders or tree roots. An entry trench is dug to the required depth and the ' knife ' of the plough cuts a slit and the tip of the knife is attached by means of a special fitting to the end of the pipe.

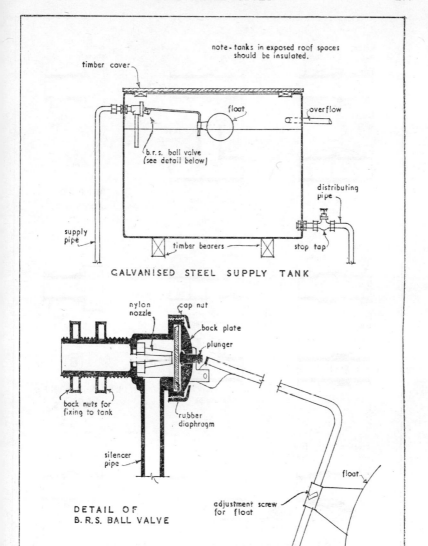

note - tanks in exposed roof spaces should be insulated.

timber cover

float

overflow

b.r.s. ball valve (see detail below)

distributing pipe

supply pipe

timber bearers

stop tap

GALVANISED STEEL SUPPLY TANK

nylon nozzle

cap nut

back plate

plunger

back nuts for fixing to tank

rubber diaphragm

silencer pipe

DETAIL OF B.R.S. BALL VALVE

adjustment screw for float

float

SUPPLY TANK & BALL VALVE

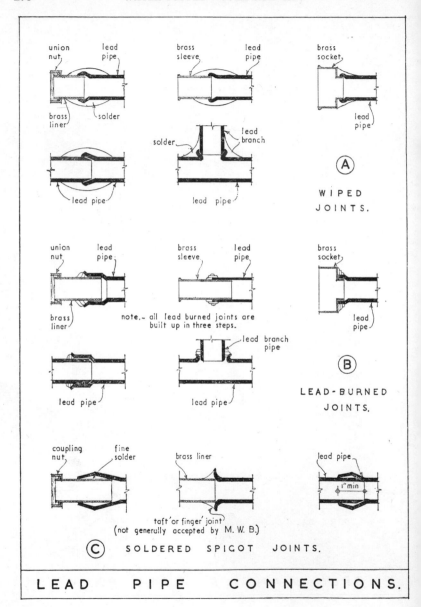

union nut   lead pipe

brass liner   solder

lead pipe

brass sleeve   lead pipe

solder   lead branch

lead pipe

brass socket

lead pipe

(A)

WIPED JOINTS.

union nut   lead pipe

brass liner

note.~ all lead burned joints are built up in three steps.

lead pipe

brass sleeve   lead pipe

lead branch pipe

lead pipe

brass socket

lead pipe

(B)

LEAD-BURNED JOINTS.

coupling nut   fine solder

brass liner

taft 'or finger' joint
(not generally accepted by M. W. B.)

lead pipe

1"min

(C)   SOLDERED SPIGOT JOINTS.

LEAD PIPE CONNECTIONS.

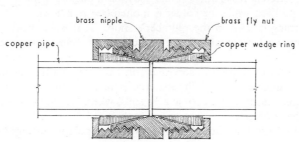

brass nipple — brass fly nut
copper pipe — copper wedge ring

① non-manipulative fitting

nuts are tightened to compress
copper wedge ring

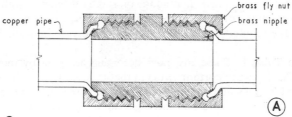

brass fly nut
copper pipe — brass nipple

② manipulative fitting

pipe ends opened out & fitted to
rounded ends of nipple-fly nuts are tightened
forming metal to metal joint.

Ⓐ

COMPRESSION
FITTINGS

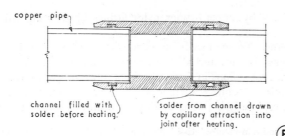

copper pipe

channel filled with
solder before heating.

solder from channel drawn
by capillary attraction into
joint after heating.

Ⓑ

CAPILLARY   FITTINGS

COPPER   PIPE   CONNECTIONS

is inclined to be expensive. It has to be supported frequently because it is not particularly stretch resistant. Joints may be made by wiping; solder is wiped into position while the solder is molten (see p. 278 A).

Lead burning is used in the plumber's shop. It is a form of ' welding ', the lead forming the actual joint being built up in three steps or layers (see p. 278 B).

(b) *Copper* for underground service is soft temper and a thicker gauge than that used for internai work. The material is very durable except where free sulphates are present, and in some acid soils, where it is advisable to lay the pipes in a bed of sand.

Jointing underground should be done with manipulative fittings (where the pipe ends must be shaped for gripping) or with capillary fittings (see drawings on p. 279).*

(c) *Iron and Steel* Tubes. These are usually galvanised and should not be formed, but are supplied in random or standard lengths with screwed ends. There are numerous galvanised fittings available to suit a great variety of layouts. The screwed joints are made tight with yarn and jointing compounds.

(d) *Plastic* Tubes.† These are now becoming accepted by most Water Authorities, having an important virtue in that they are frost resistant. They are unaffected by soils and waters which may be corrosive to metals. They become plastic when warmed and therefore can be formed easily. They are, however, not suitable for use in hot water service as they become too soft in the presence of boiling water, but they are satisfactory as waste pipes. Plastic can be had ' natural ', i.e. transparent, but where exposure to light is possible the tubes are supplied blackened, so that green organic growths cannot form in the water.

Jointing is effected by copper fittings, nylon fittings, or by fusing with heat— welding.

Flushing Cisterns. These must be supplied with overflow pipes in a similar manner to storage cisterns, and should deliver 2 gallons in 5 seconds for a high-level cistern or 2 gallons in 6 seconds for a low level cistern (p. 281).

It is inadvisable to connect them (Croydon or Portsmouth valves) to mains pressure, especially if this is 60 lb per sq. in. or over, as the washers

---

* Manipulative and non-manipulative joints are tightened up with a spanner, whereas capillary fittings incorporate an internal solder sleeve. When the sleeve is heated up with a blow lamp the solder melts, and by capillary attraction 'flows' to all parts of the joint. If this is correctly done with plenty of heat a very satisfactory joint is produced. Instead of an incorporated solder sleeve, solder may be fed into the joint either through a special hole or at the edge of the socket.

† British Standard 1972 : 1953 covers polythene tube.

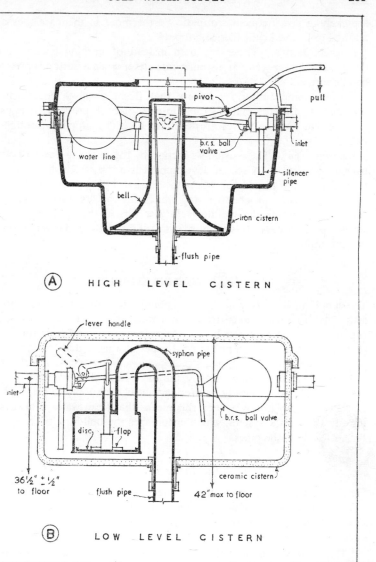

are likely to give frequent trouble. Furthermore in this case they are not allowed to be fixed with silencing tubes.*

Flushing Valves. These are used instead of flushing cisterns and are designed to deliver water at a similar rate either when a button is pressed or a handle turned.

Because some authorities believe that flushing valves could cause the contamination of the mains supply in case of back pressure, it is usual to arrange that flushing valves are fed from a cistern supplied through a ball valve.

Draw-off Taps. These usually function by the screwing down of a washer over a flow orifice. A recent development is a tap which does not need to have the supply turned off when the washer is being replaced. Another development is a ' progressive ' tap which, for the first turn or so, supplies cold water, and as the handle is further turned the cold water becomes warmer progressively. It is supplied with a spray outlet and is very economical in consumption.

HOT WATER SUPPLY

The supply of hot water to draw-off points—taps in baths, lavatory basins, sinks, etc., is usually taken from a hot water storage tank. This in turn is supplied from the hot water boiler. As water is drawn off from the hot water storage tank, the feed from the cold water storage cistern replaces the displaced water.

There are two systems, namely the *direct* and the *indirect*. The direct system should not generally be used, as hot water supply to draw-off points is heated directly in the boiler; this means that fresh water is always being introduced into the system, which encourages the build-up, over a period of time, of scale in the pipes.

The Indirect System

Here the hot water storage is in an indirect cylinder, or calorifier (see p. 283).†

The stored hot water occupies the bulk of the cylinder and is heated indirectly through the coil or annular heater connected to the boiler or primary circuit.

* The Building Research Station has just developed a new type of ball valve with a washer less liable to be damaged by ' cavitation ' and so this advice may need to be revised (see drawing on p. 271).

† There are two types of calorifier, one heated by a coil of pipe supplied from the primary circuit, or an annular heater—an enclosed hollow sleeve similarly connected.

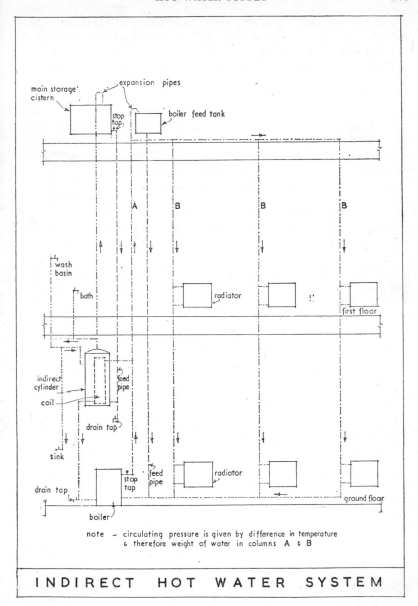

main storage cistern

expansion pipes

stop tap

boiler feed tank

A

B

B

B

wash basin

bath

radiator

radiator

radiator

first floor

indirect cylinder

coil

feed pipe

drain tap

sink

drain tap

stop tap

feed pipe

radiator

radiator

radiator

ground floor

boiler

note — circulating pressure is given by difference in temperature
& therefore weight of water in columns A & B

INDIRECT   HOT   WATER   SYSTEM

The primary circuit may also serve radiators. The temperature in the secondary system, the water of which is always being replaced, is lower than that in the primary system and is therefore less likely to suffer from scaling.

Where several hot water supply points are widely spaced as in schools or in blocks of flats, a calorifier plus ' break pressure ' tank can be fitted as a unit served by a primary circuit.

Electric Storage Water Heaters. *Non-Pressure Type.* These are mostly of small capacity for implementing hot water service during summer months, e.g. at kitchen sinks.

Pressure Type. These are usually of, say, 20 gallons capacity and incorporate a ' pressure break ' tank with its own ball valve.

Multi-point Gas Heater. Here the gas turns on automatically by means of a thermostat as soon as hot water is drawn off, and is a useful device for summer use when the boiler fire is out.

A similar device can be arranged with an electric immersion heater, except that this immersion heater is usually placed in the hot water cylinder.*

---

* The operating temperature of the thermostat on the immersion heater should not be more than 140° F. otherwise scaling may occur. It is vital that all the hot water service and especially the hot water cylinder is very efficiently lagged, otherwise the system will be most uneconomic.

15

Drainage

RAW sewage will decompose readily by the action of myriads of bacteria. This causes the production of unpleasant gases and the bacteria can be dangerous to health. The main object of a drainage system is to conduct the sewage away by means of pipes which are water tight and gas tight.

The sewage may be treated in the local authority's sewage works or it may be treated in a septic tank and filter bed. In either of these cases the principles of reduction of sewage to a relatively safe product is the same (p. 299).*

Principles of Drainage. The following principles must be adhered to in order to produce a satisfactory system.

1. *Falls.* If sewage moves too slowly because the fall is too shallow, the drains will block. If the drains are laid too steeply the solids will be left behind. If the drains are very steeply inclined the rush of sewage may damage the drain unless it is adequately constructed.

2. *Depth.* The drain must be laid deep enough in the ground to be free from damage by vehicles or by the movement of the ground due to ' Seasonal Movement ' (p. 21).

3. *Ventilation.* All parts of the system must be properly ventilated to prevent the build-up of noxious gases.

4. *Seals.* Terminations of soil drains must be fitted with seals— U shaped bends in the pipe to retain a water seal—to prevent gases escaping into the building.

5. *Access.* Manholes, rodding eyes, etc., must be provided so that all parts of the drain can be rodded in case of blockage. These access positions enable the drains to be tested.

6. *Materials.* These must be non-corrosive and able to withstand any stress which is likely to occur.

7. *Joints.* These must be made so that they will not leak during the life of the drain, nor become loose, nor obstruct the bore of the pipe.

8. *Support.* In every part, the drain pipes must be adequately supported. Where they pass under the foundations of the buildings these must be arched or bridged so that no load comes on to the drain.

* This is dealt with more fully in *Advanced Building Construction.*

9. *Interaction.* Pipes must be arranged so that the effect of the discharge of one fitting does not break the seal of another, or cause flooding through blockage.

By-laws. Every local authority is empowered to ensure that the construction of drains is in accordance with their By-laws. Building inspectors visit work in course of construction to see that the By-laws are carried out.

MATERIALS

Salt Glazed Ware. This is the most common material used in the manufacture of drain pipes and is suitable for most applications. Pipes and other fittings are made from clay, and are fired and glazed. They are made usually in 2 ft lengths, each pipe having a socket which is larger to allow the next pipe to be jointed into it. They are brittle and inclined to fracture under impact or excessive weight (see p. 287).*

Pipe Laying. Trenches should not be left open longer than is necessary. The weather tends to loosen the soil and excessive settlement is likely to occur. Flooding and accidents are other hazards caused by unnecessarily opened trenches. Each pipe should be examined before laying to see that it is free from cracks.

Start laying pipes at the lower end of the trench. Each pipe has to be checked for line and level by means of boning rods (see p. 19). A hand hole should be left under each joint so that the jointing can be completed properly. Trenches that are too deep should be filled to the proper level with a 1 : 12 weak concrete. Alternatively the pipes may be laid on small concrete blocks; this is a good method when the pipes have to be laid on a concrete bed as the blocks can then be the same thickness as the bed.

Pipe Jointing. Tarred Hemp Gasket is wrapped round the spigot (straight end) of each pipe. This has two functions, first it prevents mortar used for jointing being forced into the bore of the pipe, and secondly it centres the spigot in the socket, so that the bore of the drain pipes when joined are properly in alignment. The end is caulked tightly home so that it does not fill more than a quarter of the depth of the socket. A 1 : 1 cement/sand mix is used, never neat cement. This is pressed by hand into the joint all round, and struck off with a small trowel to form a neat fillet. Only fresh water

---

* B.S. 65 concerns materials, dimensions and performance of British Standard pipes and British Standard tested pipes. B.S. 540 concerns Enamelled Fire Clay pipes and fittings. B.S. 784, 1953 concerns methods of test for chemical stone ware and B.S. 1143 of 1955 concerns salt-glazed ware pipes with chemical-resistant properties.

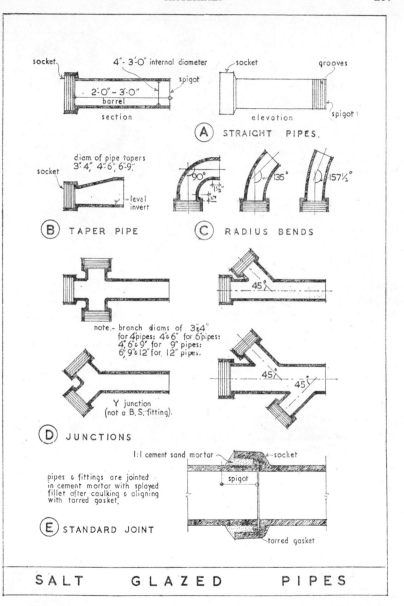

A STRAIGHT PIPES.

B TAPER PIPE

C RADIUS BENDS

D JUNCTIONS

E STANDARD JOINT

SALT GLAZED PIPES

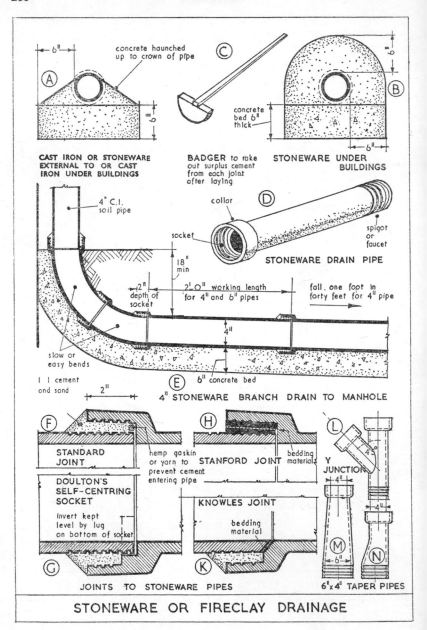

STONEWARE OR FIRECLAY DRAINAGE

should be used and the joints should be allowed to cure slowly by placing wet sacks over them (except in frosty weather).

Manholes (Inspection Chambers) (see p. 291). These can be made of brickwork, concrete or pre-cast concrete sections, and must be big enough to enable rodding operations to be carried out. If they are shallow they can be small, i.e. 1′ 6″ × 1′ 6″. If they are deep then they must be big enough for a man to descend them.

Another factor influencing the size of manholes is the number of branches the manhole is to accommodate. With a 4-in. drain allow 12 in. per branch. For a 6-in. drain allow 15 in. per branch. For the width allow 12 in. for each side with branches, plus 6 in. for the diameter of the main drain—whichever is greater.

The concrete base should be at least 6 in thick, this base carries the walls of the manhole and the half-round channel bends or alternatively junctions (see drawing and notes on p. 291). Branch pipes should discharge into the main run as nearly as possible in the direction of flow in the main channel.

' Concrete benching ' should rise vertically at each side of the channels at least to the height of the top of the outlet pipe; it then slopes more gently to the manhole walls to provide room to stand. This benching guides the sewage in the right direction and is formed at a minimum slope of 1 : 6 so that no sewage can be trapped on it. Concrete should be finished in a 1 : 1 rendering, trowelled with a steel trowel to produce a smooth impervious surface.

Brickwork should be at least 9 in. thick, preferably vitrified bricks and laid in English bond, the mortar should be 1 : 3 and the joints, especially the perpends, must be completely full of mortar. If there is danger of external ground water pressure then it is advisable to render the outside of the manhole; internal rendering is not recommended.

A cast-iron frame is then set on the top of the manhole level with the ground and the lid fitted on to it. The frame must be properly bedded and fixed.

For larger manholes pre-cast concrete sections with preformed bases and channels are often more economical to use.

Connections to Public Sewer. This is usually done under the supervision of the Sanitary Inspector. A small hole is made which is carefully enlarged, bit by bit, until a saddle piece can be fitted in. When this has been jointed the whole connection is cased in 6 in. of concrete.

Inlets to Drains. Any sanitary fitting must first discharge through a trap containing a water seal. This prevents the gases in the drain pipe, either from the sewer or from deposits on the side of the pipe, escaping into the room. Soil fittings are always connected directly to the drains or soil stacks. Waste

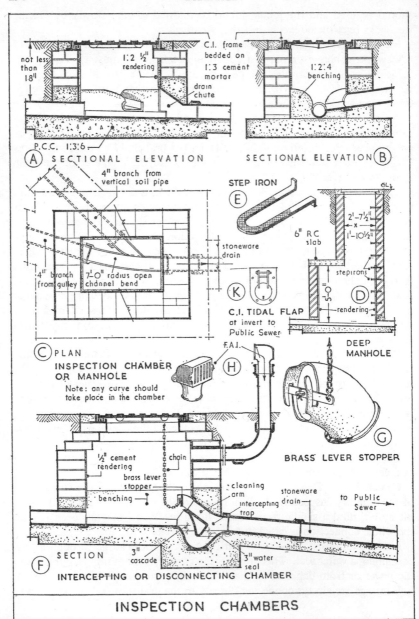

not less than 18"

1:2½" rendering

C.I. frame bedded on 1:3 cement mortar

drain chute

1:2:4 benching

P.C.C. 1:3:6

(A) SECTIONAL ELEVATION

SECTIONAL ELEVATION (B)

STEP IRON
(E)

4" branch from vertical soil pipe

stoneware drain

4" branch from gulley

7'-0" radius open channel bend

(K)

C.I. TIDAL FLAP at invert to Public Sewer

6" RC slab

2'-7½" x 1'-10½"

stepirons

5'-0"

rendering

(D) DEEP MANHOLE

(C) PLAN

INSPECTION CHAMBER OR MANHOLE

Note: any curve should take place in the chamber

F.A.I.
(H)

BRASS LEVER STOPPER
(G)

½" cement rendering

chain

brass lever stopper

benching

cleaning arm

intercepting trap

stoneware drain

to Public Sewer

(F) SECTION

3" cascade

3" water seal

INTERCEPTING OR DISCONNECTING CHAMBER

INSPECTION CHAMBERS

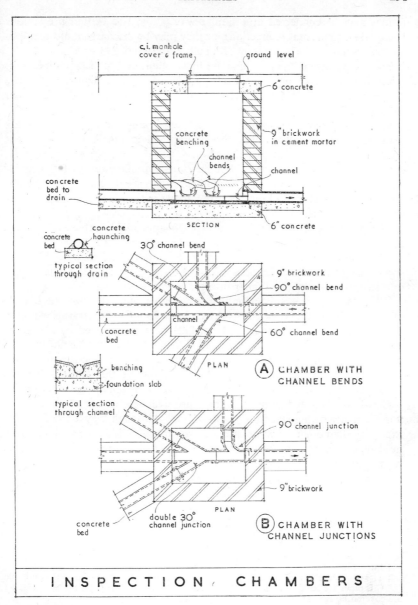

c.i. manhole cover & frame   ground level

6" concrete

concrete benching

channel bends

9" brickwork in cement mortar

channel

concrete bed to drain

SECTION

6" concrete

concrete bed

concrete haunching

typical section through drain

30° channel bend

9" brickwork

90° channel bend

channel

60° channel bend

concrete bed

benching

foundation slab

typical section through channel

PLAN

Ⓐ CHAMBER WITH CHANNEL BENDS

90° channel junction

9" brickwork

PLAN

Ⓑ CHAMBER WITH CHANNEL JUNCTIONS

concrete bed

double 30° channel junction

INSPECTION CHAMBERS

fittings may be connected in a similar way (subject to certain precautions being taken to prevent interaction), or they may be discharged into the open air over or above the water level of a gully trap (see p. 293 A).*

Pre-cast Concrete Pipes. These are most often used for sewer pipes over 6 in. diameter. They are available from 6 in. to 48 in. in diameter. 6 ft is a common standard length. Jointing technique is similar to that used for stoneware.

Pitch Fibre Pipes. These pipes, which are coming into general use, are made of blended wood-cellulose fibre and refined coal-tar in the proportions 25% fibre and 75% pitch by weight.†

One important advantage is that they are manufactured in 8-ft lengths, thus reducing the number of joints required in any particular run and thereby the chance of leakage. Jointing is not made with mortar, but by tapping the pipes into tapered sleeves (see p. 293 C).

The pipes are flexible and can accept an appreciable degree of bowing, and are not inclined to rupture under uneven ground settlement. Pipes are available in diameters of 2 in., 3 in., 4 in., 5 in. and 6 in.; they can be cut to special lengths and can be fitted using the normal 1 : 1 mortar technique into stoneware gulleys and other fittings.

When laying, pipes should receive continuous support along the bottom of the trench to true grade. Pegs driven in at about 15-ft intervals will keep the pipe-line in true alignment. Even falls may be achieved by laying the pipes on a thin layer of sand or fine ashes. When back filling use fine material tapped along both sides of the pipe to ensure that it is continuously supported, sharp stones and rocks must be excluded. Continue this selected back fill for 3 in. or 4 in. above the pipe and then back fill the remainder of the spoil.‡

Cast-iron Pipes and Fittings. These are available in sizes from 2 in. to 9 in. diameter with a standard length of 9 ft. Although they are much more expensive than other forms mentioned they are suitable for conditions which need great strength and resistance to leakage.§ Cast-iron pipes are coated with a protective coating of tar-based composition, even so, special precautions should be taken in acid soils containing sulphates, or when acid effluents are to be carried (in such cases, bitumen impregnated wrappings or vitreous enamelled pipes are used).

Joints are made either by pouring molten lead into the joint and then

* Soil fitting, e.g. w.c., urinal, slop sink.
   Waste fitting, e.g. lavatory basin, bath, kitchen sink, bidet, shower.
† Pitch Fibre Pipes are covered by B.S.S. 2760, 1956.
‡ The procedure in B.S. Code of Practice 301, Building Drainage Class 308 is suitable.
§ C.I. pipes are covered by B.S. 437, 1211, and 78. Fittings, gulleys, traps, bends, etc. are covered by B.S. 1130.

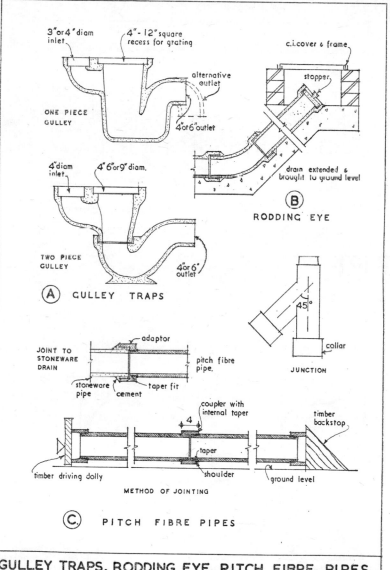

3" or 4" diam inlet

4" – 12" square recess for grating

alternative outlet

ONE PIECE GULLEY

4" or 6" outlet

c.i. cover & frame

stopper

RODDING EYE Ⓑ

drain extended & brought to ground level

4" diam inlet

4" 6" or 9" diam.

TWO PIECE GULLEY

4" or 6" outlet

Ⓐ GULLEY TRAPS

JUNCTION

45°

collar

adaptor

JOINT TO STONEWARE DRAIN

pitch fibre pipe.

stoneware pipe

cement

taper fit

coupler with internal taper

timber backstop

timber driving dolly

taper

shoulder

ground level

METHOD OF JOINTING

Ⓒ PITCH FIBRE PIPES

GULLEY TRAPS, RODDING EYE, PITCH FIBRE PIPES.

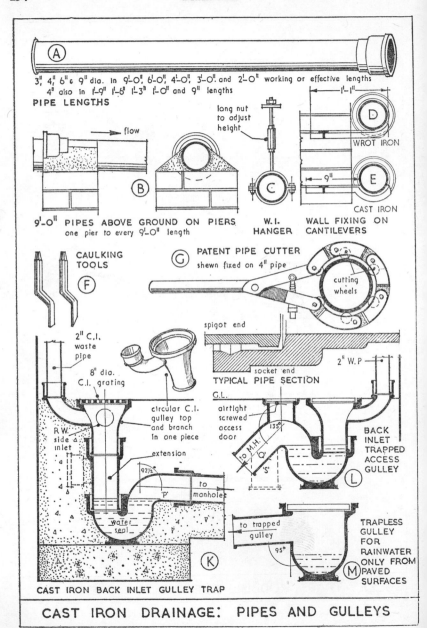

PIPE LENGTHS

3", 4", 6" & 9" dia. in 9'-0", 6'-0", 4'-0", 3'-0" and 2'-0" working or effective lengths
4" also in 1'-9" 1'-6" 1'-3" 1'-0" and 9" lengths

flow

9'-0" PIPES ABOVE GROUND ON PIERS
one pier to every 9'-0" length

long nut to adjust height

W.I. HANGER

WROT IRON

CAST IRON

WALL FIXING ON CANTILEVERS

CAULKING TOOLS

PATENT PIPE CUTTER
shewn fixed on 4" pipe

cutting wheels

spigot end

socket end

TYPICAL PIPE SECTION

2" C.I. waste pipe

8" dia. C.I. grating

circular C.I. gulley top and branch in one piece

R.W. side inlet

extension

92½°

'P'

to manhole

water seal

CAST IRON BACK INLET GULLEY TRAP

G.L.

airtight screwed access door

135°

to M.H.

'Q'

'S'

2" W.P

BACK INLET TRAPPED ACCESS GULLEY

to trapped gulley

95°

TRAPLESS GULLEY FOR RAINWATER ONLY FROM PAVED SURFACES

CAST IRON DRAINAGE: PIPES AND GULLEYS

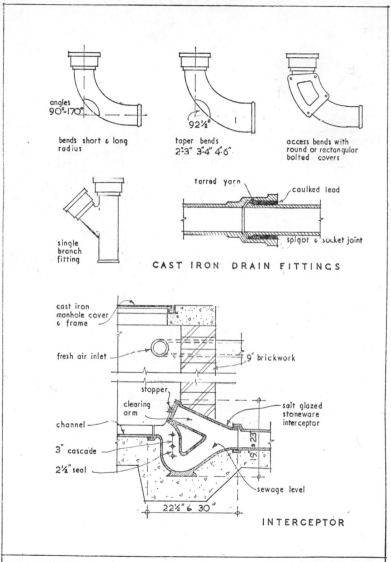

angles
90°-170°

bends short & long
radius

92½°

taper bends
2'3" 3'4" 4'6"

access bends with
round or rectangular
bolted covers

single
branch
fitting

tarred yarn

caulked lead

spigot & socket joint

CAST IRON DRAIN FITTINGS

cast iron
manhole cover
& frame

fresh air inlet

9" brickwork

stopper

clearing
arm

salt glazed
stoneware
interceptor

channel

3" cascade

2½" seal

19" 23"

sewage level

22½" & 30"

INTERCEPTOR

C. I. DRAIN FITTINGS & INTERCEPTOR

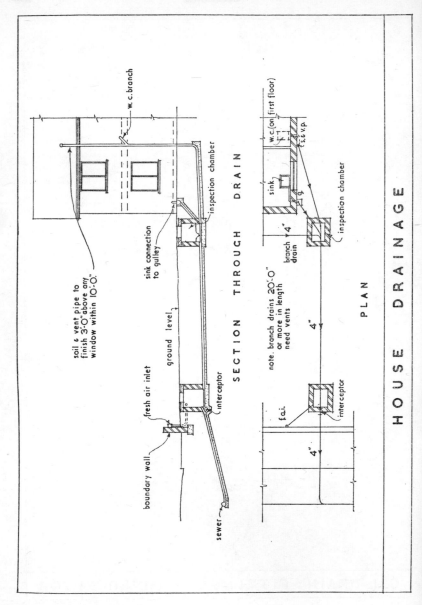

soil & vent pipe to
finish 3'-0"above any
window within 10'-0".

w. c. branch

inspection chamber

sink connection
to gulley

ground level

fresh air inlet

interceptor

boundary wall

sewer

SECTION THROUGH DRAIN

w.c.(on first floor)

s.& v.p.

sink

inspection chamber

branch
drain

4"

note. branch drains 20'-0"
or more in length
need vents

4"

f.a.i.

interceptor

4"

PLAN

HOUSE DRAINAGE

caulking to expand the lead to counteract the shrinkage, or alternatively caulking lead wool into a solid mass. Tarred gasket is used as for stoneware pipes in order to align the pipes and prevent the lead ' escaping ' into the bore (see p. 295).

Large variety of bends and junctions are available with or without bolted covers. These access junctions are used in manholes instead of half-round channels, they are gas- and water-tight having a gasket of rubber or fibre.

Many forms of gulleys are available (see *Advanced Building Construction*).

LAYOUT OF EXTERNAL DRAINS

Every part of the drainage system must fall towards the sewer. At the highest end (usually the farthest from the sewer) the drain is turned up to form a vent pipe (see p. 296).

Vent Pipe. This terminates at least 3 ft above any window within 10 ft of it, and has a galvanised balloon grating fixed in the end to dissuade birds building their nests in it, or to prevent the formation of other obstructions. It must be made of durable material such as cast iron or asbestos cement and the minimum permitted diameter is 3 in. Vent pipes may be placed on outside walls. It is often necessary to place them internally in the building, in which case most local authorities require them to be made of cast iron.*

Any part of a drain longer than 20 ft must be provided with a vent pipe.

Soil Pipe. The vent pipe usually collects w.c. branches and other connections; and then becomes a soil pipe. This will be discussed in greater detail later on.

Sewer Ventilation. To prevent the build-up of gases in the public sewer some local authorities require through ventilation from sewer to each vent pipe.†

Other local authorities require that close to the boundary wall or fence a disconnecting chamber and trap is constructed (see p. 296). This is a special sort of trap with a rodding arm closed by a removable stopper, so that the length of drain between the sewer and the disconnecting chamber can be effectively rodded, in case of obstruction. The trap prevents the sewer gas from escaping into drainage system of the building concerned. But to complete the through ventilation of the drain a fresh air inlet must be provided to the disconnecting chamber.

If no disconnecting chambers and traps are required then no fresh air

---

* Some local authorities object to the use of asbestos cem nt internally.
† If there is a great length of sewer between each vent pipet en these vents might have to pass an abnormal amount of gas, which may be dangerous to householders.

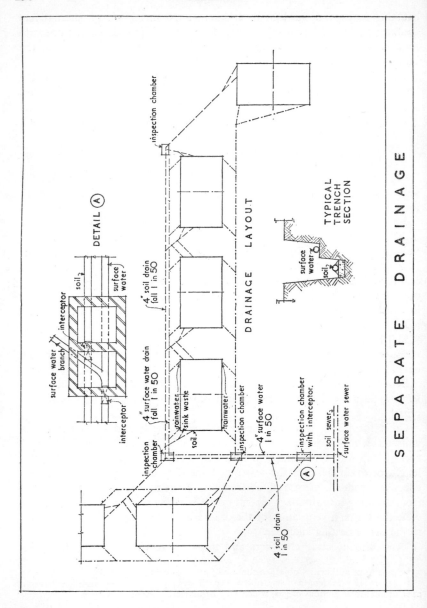

DETAIL Ⓐ

soil₂

surface water

interceptor

surface water branch

interceptor

inspection chamber

4" soil drain fall 1 in 50

4" surface water drain fall 1 in 50

inspection chamber

rainwater

sink waste

rainwater

soil₁

inspection chamber

4" surface water 1 in 50

inspection chamber with interceptor.

Ⓐ

soil sewer₂

surface water sewer

4" soil drain 1 in 50

DRAINAGE LAYOUT

surface water₁

soil₂

TYPICAL TRENCH SECTION

SEPARATE DRAINAGE

inlets are required and would in fact be dangerous (the mica flaps do not always work effectively).

Junctions and Bends. At all important junctions of drains an inspection chamber is constructed (i.e. where more than one branch joins the main drain run). Although some local authorities still insist upon it, it is usually unnecessary to build inspection chambers over single junctions.*

The maximum distance between manholes is 250 ft and the runs between manholes should be straight, as should the runs between stacks and their junctions to private sewers.

Avoid turning a drain (in a manhole) through more than a right angle wherever possible and reduce the number of manholes to an absolute minimum.

Separate or Dual System of Collection. More recently constructed public sewage schemes provide both main foul-water sewers and main surface-water sewers. All soil and waste fittings are connected to the foul-water sewer and all rainwater pipes and other surface drainage are connected to the surface-water sewer. If the local authority permits, it is advisable to connect one rainwater pipe to the head of the foul-water drain in each installation to assist in flushing the drain of solid matter.

Combined System of Collection. In older systems both surface and foul water are carried by the same sewer. The local authority may provide weirs within its system to carry off excess storm water, this is obviously not a very satisfactory method.†

Some local authorities in country districts where the subsoil is permeable, i.e. not in clay, encourage the surface water to be taken to soakaways. Soakaways are usually pits 4 ft or more square, dug down into the permeable strata. In this case only foul water is taken into the main sewer. This is an economical method of disposal which cannot be employed in built-up areas where there may be danger of flooding basements, etc., by raising the local water table.

SEPTIC TANK

If no public sewer is available, a septic tank and filter bed, i.e. a sewage treatment plant, may be constructed (see p. 300). A ' crust ' forms on the surface of the liquid in the septic tank sealing off the surface and enabling

---

* Post-war Building Study No. 26. H.M.S.O. stresses the importance of cutting out unnecessary manholes and gulleys as these cause most of the blockages that occur.

† The L.C.C. require drains connected directly to sewers (without disconnecting traps) to have bolted cast-iron covers at all points of access. Many local authorities with combined systems require separate drainage systems to be installed up to the last manhole so that a separate system can be installed later.

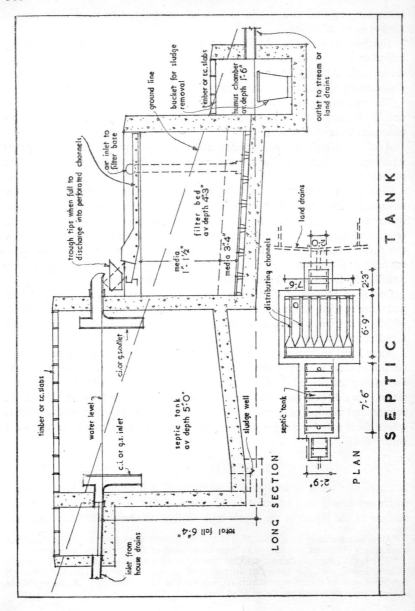

SEPTIC TANK

LONG SECTION

inlet from house drains

Total fall 6'4"

c.i. or g.s. inlet

water level

timber or t.c. slabs

septic tank
av depth 5'0"

sludge well

c.i. or g.s.outlet

trough tips when full to
discharge into perforated channels

air inlet to
filter base

ground line

bucket for sludge
removal

timber or t.c. slabs

media 1"-1½"

media 3'-4"

filter bed
av depth 4'3"

humus chamber
av depth 1'-6"

outlet to stream or
land drains

PLAN

septic tank

distributing channels

land drains

2'-9"

7'-6"

6'-9"

2'-3"

7'-6"

anaerobic bacteria to reduce the solids mainly to liquid (over a period sludge collects in the bottom of the septic tank and is pumped out at intervals).

This sludge when dry makes excellent manure. The liquid in the septic tank discharges through a junction outlet to tipper troughs which dose it over a filter bed. The filter bed consists of graded clinker or other aggregate fairly large at the bottom, getting smaller towards the top, and around which air can circulate from air inlet pipes. A 'gel' forms round each particle of aggregate, which is composed of aerobic bacteria which purifies the septic tank effluent and makes it relatively safe. The effluent from the filter bed will smell slightly if allowed to puddle, and is conducted via a humus chamber to land drains; these should be spigot and socket pipes laid reversed (to discourage tree roots growing into the joints and up the pipes). The humus chamber collects humus matter which precipitates out of the effluent in the spring and would otherwise block the land drains (humus is excellent for the garden).

Rainwater Shoes and Gulleys. If the rainwater is conducted to sewers, then it is advisable to insert back inlet gulleys with a sealed access plate to prevent any noxious gases which may be in the sewer coming up the rainwater pipe and escaping to the air at eaves level, which is too low for safety.

If the rainwater is taken to soakaways then it is advisable to use rainwater shoes with or without gratings.

Depth. Drains should be protected by 1 ft of earth, but otherwise should be kept as close to the surface as possible. Excavation is expensive. If possible drains should run with the contours. It may sometimes be cheaper to run a drain beneath the building instead of round it, but this is not always desirable in case of fracture of the drain beneath the building.*

Gradients must be properly maintained throughout all drain runs. Gradient must be sufficient to clear the drains of solids.

Satisfactory minimum gradients are:

1 in 40 for 4 in. pipes
1 in 60 for 6 in. pipes
1 in 90 for 9 in. pipes.

Experience also seems to justify using minimum gradients of:

1 in 50 for 4 in. pipes
1 in 75 for 6 in. pipes

---

* Drains beneath buildings should be of cast iron, or clay ware surrounded by 6 in. of concrete. Pitch fibre being flexible may come into common use for this purpose.

where falls are restricted and where the drains are well designed and well laid.

Where there is insufficient fall available never use a 6 in. pipe where a 4 in. pipe will do, in order that the drains can be laid at 1 in 60 (or 1 in 75). The increase in the size of the pipe does not increase the flow, in fact it reduces it, because the depth of the sewage is reduced.*

Private Sewers (Common Drains). Where a group of buildings are in common ownership the sharing of private sewers shows great economy in layout. Where there is no common ownership then easements have to be granted and agreements have to be reached regarding maintenance, between the individual owners. Local authorities usually discourage an unnecessary number of sewer connections.

Junctions of individual drains or private sewers to the main sewer is usually done without an inspection chamber. The exact position of the junction being recorded on the local authority's plans.

The surface- and foul-water drains may be run in the same trench (see p. 298). Economies can be achieved by this double manhole arrangement. Alternatively both drains can be made accessible from the same chamber by putting the foul drain through a cast-iron pipe at that point with a sealing cover.

DRAINAGE ABOVE GROUND TO BUILDINGS

Materials

Soil Stacks. These must be strong enough to support themselves adequately between fixings, every 6 ft or so vertically. Cast iron is the commonest material used. It is painted with bituminous paint when concealed, or with a good paint system when exposed. Joints are made in the usual way (see p. 297).†

Galvanised steel pipes are sometimes used. They are more rigid and lighter. They lend themselves to standardised branch assembly, but they

---

* British Standard Code of Practice 301, Building Drainage, recommends that the site of drains and their gradients be related to the volume of flow. Allow two thirds of a cubic foot per minute per 100 persons (assuming 30 gallons of water per head); maximum flow would be twice this amount. Surface water flow at the rate of $1\frac{1}{2}$ in. of rainfall per hour over the horizontal area of the surface drained.

Minimum self cleansing velocity in a pipe is 2·5 ft per second $\frac{1}{4}$-depth. The Code gives volumes of flow and gradient which will give this in pipes of different diameters.

Maximum desirable speed to flow is 10 ft per second, i.e. 6 in. drain at 1 in 9. For steeper falls, drop manholes or open channel ramps have to be provided. See *Plumbing in Building* by Sydney Webster (Batsford).

† British Standard 416 specifies requisite wall thickness for different diameters of pipe, the nature of the coating, freedom from defects, etc.

pose the problem of galvanic corrosion where branches of dissimilar metals are introduced.* Insulating washers are used to separate the metals.

Asbestos cement pipes are accepted by some authorities and are satisfactory so long as they are protected from possible impact. They are covered by B.S. 582 and show economy over cast iron. They are painted with a bituminous solution.

Branches. These invariably are bent in many directions to reach the outlet traps of the sanitary fittings. This applies especially to waste pipes from lavatory basins, baths, and sinks (usually $1\frac{1}{4}$ in. or $1\frac{1}{2}$ in. diameter pipe) but occasionally the much larger $3\frac{1}{2}$ in. diameter waste from a w.c. to the soil stack needs to be manipulated round obstructions in lead or copper pipe.

Jointing between pipes of dissimilar metal may involve the use of a ' thimble ' of stronger metal to reinforce the weaker pipe.

Various joints are shown on p. 305.

(a) Cast iron to cast iron described on p. 297.

(b) Lead to cast iron. First, a brass sleeve is fitted over the end of the pipe (this sleeve is the strengthening thimble); the end of the lead pipe is turned into a rim to retain the jointing material. The joint is caulked with tarred hemp (gasket) and lead caulked in as before. A wiped joint is then made in the brass sleeve and the lead pipe.

(c) Copper to cast iron. This is made similarly to (b), but instead of a wiped joint the brass sleeve is welded to the copper pipe. The brass sleeve strengthens the end of the copper pipe as before.

(d) Cast iron to stoneware. The same technique as for jointing stoneware pipes.

(e) Lead to stoneware. This is the same as (b) except that Portland cement and sand (1 : 1) jointing is used.

(f) Copper to stoneware. As for (c) but with a cement and sand jointing.

(g) Stoneware to stoneware. See p. 286.

(h) This shows a special type of joint which can be made a tighter fit making the gasket unnecessary. The taper aligns the pipe automatically.

(k) Cast-iron R.W.P. joint. Traditional material used in the joint is red lead putty, but several proprietary mastics are also available.

Copper to copper joints may be capillary solder, manipulative or non-manipulative (tightened with a spanner) described on p. 280.

* Electrolytic action is set up between the two dissimilar metals in a similar way to the action which goes on in a (car) battery. Moisture has to be present for this action to occur.

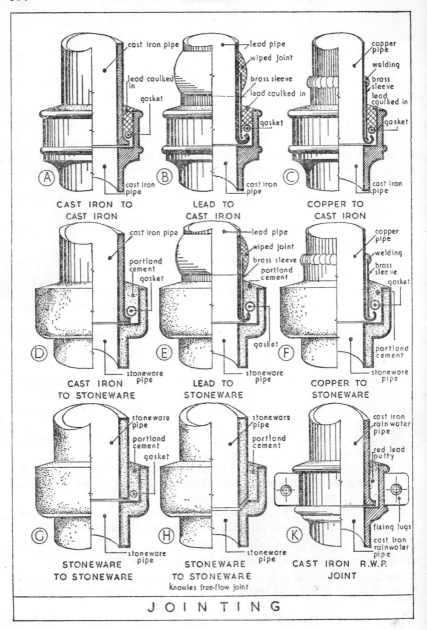

CAST IRON TO CAST IRON

LEAD TO CAST IRON

COPPER TO CAST IRON

CAST IRON TO STONEWARE

LEAD TO STONEWARE

COPPER TO STONEWARE

STONEWARE TO STONEWARE

STONEWARE TO STONEWARE
knowles free-flow joint

CAST IRON R.W.P. JOINT

JOINTING

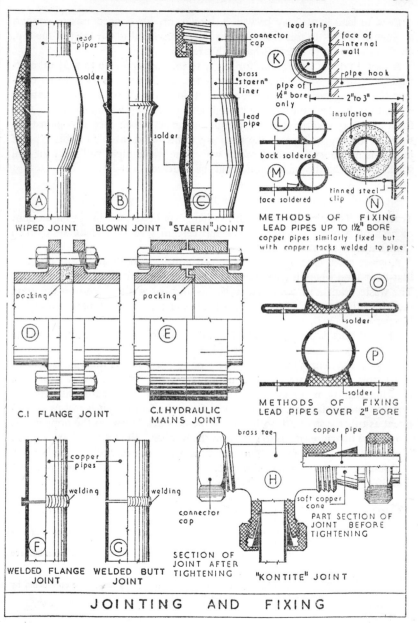

WIPED JOINT   BLOWN JOINT   "STAERN" JOINT

lead pipes

solder

solder

connector cap

brass "staern" liner

lead pipe

lead strip

face of internal wall

pipe hook

2" to 3"

pipe of ½" bore only

insulation

back soldered

face soldered

tinned steel clip

METHODS   OF   FIXING
LEAD PIPES UP TO 1½" BORE
copper pipes similarly fixed but
with copper tacks welded to pipe

solder

solder

METHODS   OF   FIXING
LEAD PIPES OVER 2" BORE

packing

packing

C.I. FLANGE JOINT   C.I. HYDRAULIC
MAINS JOINT

copper pipes

welding

welding

WELDED FLANGE   WELDED BUTT
JOINT   JOINT

brass tee

copper pipe

connector cap

soft copper cone

SECTION OF
JOINT AFTER
TIGHTENING

PART SECTION OF
JOINT   BEFORE
TIGHTENING

"KONTITE" JOINT

JOINTING   AND   FIXING

Lead to lead joints may be wiped, blown, or, for connections to copper, a ' staern ' joint. In this case a tail or liner is coupled to the inlet of the tap, etc., as shown on p. 305 (left-hand illustration).

A useful type of connection for say a $1\frac{1}{2}$ in. copper waste to a $3\frac{1}{2}$ in. cast-iron stack which is now becoming more frequently used, is for a $1\frac{1}{2}$ in. cast-iron boss compression fitting to be welded on to the stack (a shop operation) so that on site the joint is made by tightening up a nut with a spanner. One form of this type of joint uses a Neoprene gasket which expands against the sides of the copper pipe as the nuts are tightened down. For this type of joint it is necessary to know exactly where the waste pipes will meet the soil stack so that the shop-made joints can be ordered.

Layout

Traditional Two-pipe System. This system has been used in a vast amount of housing between the wars, but it has certain severe disadvantages which render it now obsolescent.

A waste stack is taken from a trapped gulley at the head of the drain to first-floor level where it terminates in a hopper (similar to a rainwater head). The waste branches from lavatory basins and baths discharge into the open mouth of the hopper. Frequently a rainwater pipe also discharges into this hopper (see p. 307).

The soil stack is a separate pipe from the manhole and continues above the branch to the highest w.c. as a vent pipe.*

Whatever system is used, the waste pipe to every fitting must have its own trap; this prevents smells from deposits on the sides of waste branches, entering bathrooms or kitchens. For this reason this traditional two-pipe system is unsatisfactory, because apart from the fact that it is not as economical as other systems, deposits on the waste stack (between the hopper and the gulley) do cause smells to rise from the hopper. Furthermore as so much pipe work is exposed, freezing up is not uncommon, especially at the hopper.

Two-pipe System (without hoppers). This is illustrated on pp. 307 and 309. It is a system frequently used for buildings of several stories.

---

* Definitions—*Waste* is the water from lavatory basins, baths, sinks and bidets.
  Soil is the effluent from w.c's and urinals.
  Foul water is the term used for either waste or soil or both, usually in a drain sewer.
  Storm water is the term used for rain water from roofs or from surface drains.
  Surface water—as for storm water.
  Stack—a vertical pipe of say $3\frac{1}{2}$ in. diameter to which are connected by means of branches sanitary fittings.

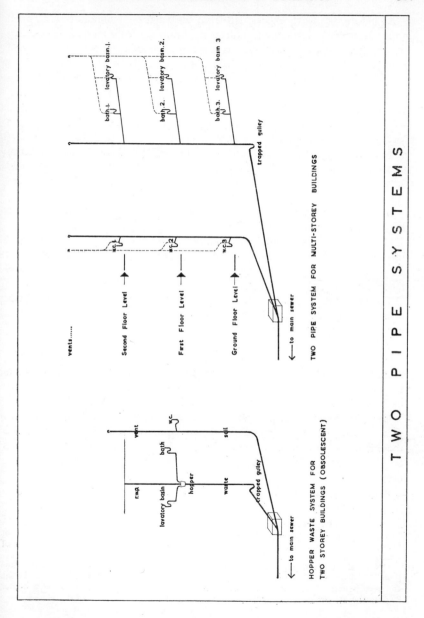

TWO PIPE SYSTEMS

TWO PIPE SYSTEM FOR MULTI-STOREY BUILDINGS

HOPPER WASTE SYSTEM FOR TWO STOREY BUILDINGS (OBSOLESCENT)

As before, the waste pipe is led from the adjacent manhole to a trapped gulley and thence vertically to collect the branches from baths and lavatory basins, etc. This trapped gulley is a second line of defence to the trapped gulleys on the sanitary fittings (whose seals need only be $1\frac{1}{2}$ in. deep).

The soil stack (without a gulley at its foot) follows a similar route collecting on its way the branches from w.c.'s. Above the highest w.c. it becomes a vent pipe.

This system poses the problem of *syphonage*. If w.c. No. 1 containing a lot of paper is flushed, a ' plug ' travels down the soil stack; as this ' plug ' passes w.c. No. 2 the zone of rarefaction immediately behind this plug tends to suck out the water seal in the trap of w.c. No. 2. The same thing would happen to w.c. No. 3. If any other branches to fittings are connected to this stack their traps may suffer in the same way.

In order to overcome this, smaller diameter vent pipes are connected to the branch close to the trap.*

Usually one vertical vent pipe is employed, connected by branches to the traps of each fitting. The vent pipe is then returned and connected to the main vent pipe above the topmost fitting or terminated above roof level independently.

The vent pipe works by counteracting the sucking effect in the soil stack caused by the discharge of fittings above by allowing free air to come in, this leaves the water seal in the traps undisturbed.

Self syphonage may occur in waste branches that are too long and too steep. A ' plug ' of water travelling down the pipe from the farthest fitting tends to draw its own seal, this is liable to occur in lavatory basins and sinks but not with baths, as there is always a final trickle of water from the empty bath which reseals the trap. Venting to each trap overcomes this (see p. 309).

One-pipe System (see p. 309). In this case only one stack and one vent pipe is used, showing greater economy over previous systems described. As there is no trapped gulley at the bottom of the stack (because the soil also is emptied into the stack) the seals to the sanitary fittings must be at least 2 in. deep.†

Although great economy is achieved in this system the pipework at inter-

---

* The Code of Practice requires this distance to be between 3 in. and 18 in. (The L.C.C. 3 in. to 12 in.) The diameter of the vent pipe for soil fittings is $1\frac{1}{4}$ in. minimum (Code of Practice) and 2 in. minimum for the L.C.C. For waste traps it is 1 in. minimum (Code of Practice) and $1\frac{1}{4}$ in. minimum for the L.C.C.

† Normally the vent pipe starts by venting the lowest fittings, but if the drain is less than 10 ft from the lowest floor then the bottom of the vent pipe should be joined to the soil pipe between 9 in. and 14 in. below the floor, or it should be returned at a higher level to the nearest manhole (soil).

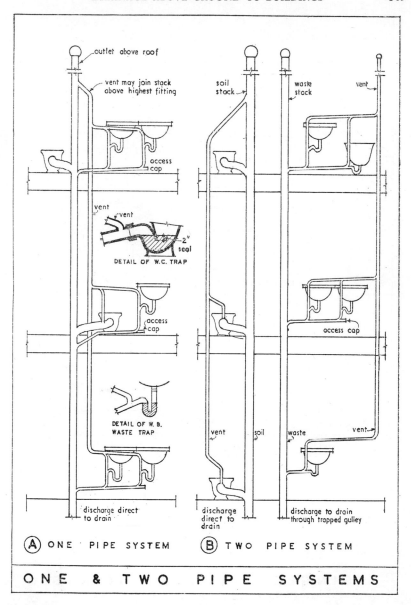

ONE & TWO PIPE SYSTEMS

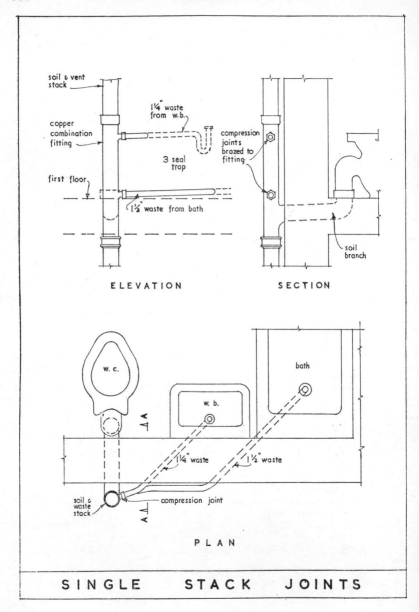

soil & vent stack

copper combination fitting

1¼" waste from w.b.

3 seal trap

compression joints brazed to fitting

first floor

1½" waste from bath

soil branch

ELEVATION   SECTION

w. c.

w. b.

bath

A

1¼" waste

1½" waste

soil & waste stack

compression joint

A

PLAN

SINGLE   STACK   JOINTS

mediate floor levels is inclined to be complicated, and there are several proprietary prefabricated plumbing units available on the market to simplify this.

Single-Stack System. If certain straightforward rules are followed it is possible to connect soil and wastes to the same stack without venting the traps. Recent research has made this method reliable. It is, for multi-story buildings, the most economical system of all.*

W.C. branch entries to the stack are made below the branch entries to waste fittings (lavatory basins, sinks, baths, etc.), by this means the only problem to resolve is that of self-syphonage.

The usual stack size is $3\frac{1}{2}$ in. in diameter, but this is increased to 4 in. at the large radius bend at the foot. This large radius reduces a pressure build-up at the bottom of the stack, should many fittings be discharged together. This condition increases the possibility of flooding fittings whose branches enter the stack at ground floor level (near the bend) (see *Advanced Building Construction*). Where branches join the stack the T must be ' swept ', that is, the underside of the junction must be radiused.

Waste branches must not enter the stack opposite a w.c. branch, as there is then risk that the w.c. discharge would enter the waste branch. In this case the connection should be made at right angles.

Risk of self-syphonage is eliminated if (*a*) the water seal in traps to sanitary fittings is 3 in. and (*b*) if both the slope and the length of branches (distance between trap and stack) is limited.

The minimum desirable slope of a branch is 1 in 48 for a maximum length of 5 ft 6 in. (1 in 24 for 3 ft, and 1 in 12 for 1 ft branches).

Basin and bath wastes can be combined if they are remote from the stack. It is important to use an easy bend on the combined $1\frac{1}{2}$ in. diameter waste pipe. This pipe is turned back into the stack as a vent above the basin branch. The combined waste should not be longer than 1 ft. 6 in. from the stack to the easy bend.

Standard fittings are available accurately made to suit these rather precise requirements.†

The system described is suitable for buildings up to five storeys high. Plumbing for taller buildings than this is described in *Advanced Building Construction*.

---

* See *Drain Pipework in Dwellings—Hydraulic Design and Performance*, published by H.M.S.O.
† See *Plumbing in Building*, by Sydney Webster, (Batsford).

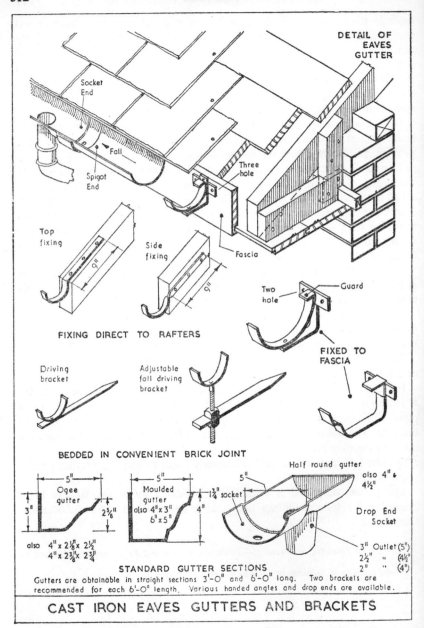

DETAIL OF
EAVES
GUTTER

Socket
End

Fall

Spigot
End

Three
hole

Top
fixing

Side
fixing

Fascia

FIXING DIRECT TO RAFTERS

Two
hole

Guard

FIXED TO
FASCIA

Driving
bracket

Adjustable
fall driving
bracket

BEDDED IN CONVENIENT BRICK JOINT

Half round gutter

also 4" &
4½"

Ogee
gutter

Moulded
gutter
also 4" x 3"
6" x 5"

1¾" socket

Drop End
Socket

also 4" x 2⅛" x 2½"
4" x 2⅜" x 2¾"

3" Outlet (5")
2½" " (4½")
2" " (4")

STANDARD GUTTER SECTIONS

Gutters are obtainable in straight sections 3'-0" and 6'-0" long. Two brackets are recommended for each 6'-0" length. Various handed angles and drop ends are available.

CAST IRON EAVES GUTTERS AND BRACKETS

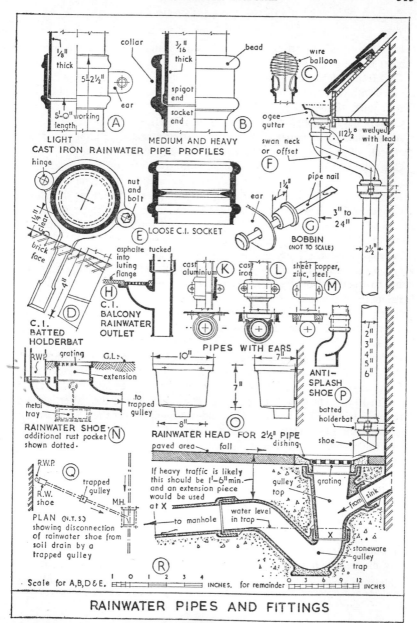

RAINWATER PIPES AND FITTINGS

RAINWATER DISPOSAL
Materials

Rainwater pipes and fittings are permitted by standards to be lighter and thinner than for soil systems.

Cast Iron. Here the light grade is permissible. Joints may be left dry or caulked with yarn and red lead putty (this is essential if the R.W.P. is internal). Gutter joints (in red lead) are bolted (p. 312).

Gutters should be laid to a fall of a ½ in. in 10 ft.

Aluminium. This material is effective, strong and light though not the cheapest. Pipe jointing is by the use of a bituminous compound.

Galvanised Mild Steel. This material is inexpensive but must be carefully maintained and painted to resist corrosion permanently. It should not be used for draining roofs of other metal, i.e. copper, zinc, or cedar shingles.

Copper, Zinc. These materials need more staying than those previously described. Gutters can be soldered together to form links of a maximum of 50 ft. This limit is set because of thermal expansion.

Asbestos-cement. These goods are very commonly used, they are rigid, very inexpensive and are free from corrosion troubles, though they are liable to fracture from impact. For this reason it is advisable to have the first length of the rainwater pipe from the ground in ' soil quality ' weight. Jointing may be made with yarn caulking and sand and cement. Alternatively a bitumen compound can be used.

Lead Valley and Parapet Gutters (see p. 248). Lead has been traditionally used for valley and parapet gutters. The valleys are formed on boarding, and follow normal plumbing practice (see p. 246). Drips are provided every 7 ft in long gutters to accommodate joints. The gutter falls at the rate of 1½ in. in 10 ft. The drips require 2 in. The upper end of the gutter is therefore much wider. The lower end should not be narrower than 8 in. between the slates (or tiles), to provide foot room. ' Cesspools ' are provided at R.W. outlets—these are the wells formed by drips from two converging gutters. Parapet gutters have falls and drips in the same way. A chute is formed in lead, through the parapet wall to a R.W. head. Alternatively the R.W.P. can descend direct from the cesspool.

SANITARY FITTINGS AND CONNECTIONS
Materials *

The finish of sanitary fittings must be non-porous, smooth, durable and easily cleaned. Of the ceramic materials available, earthenware, vitreous

* Materials are dealt with more fully in *Advanced Building Construction* and *Plumbing in Building* and *Plumbing Materials and Techniques*, by Sydney Webster, (Batsford).

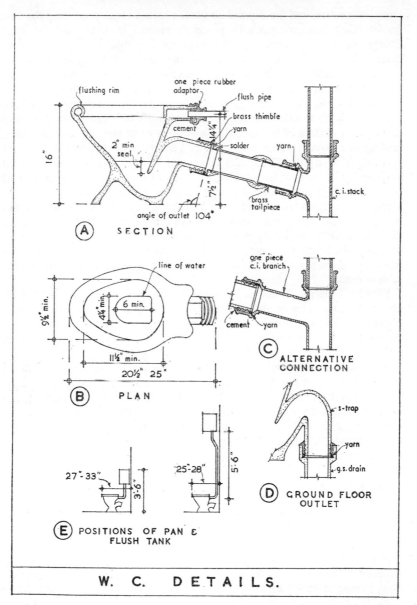

flushing rim
one piece rubber adaptor
flush pipe
brass thimble
cement
yarn
solder
yarn
4¼"
2" min seal
7½"
brass tailpiece
c.i. stack
16"
angle of outlet 104°

(A) SECTION

line of water
9½" min.
4¼" min.
6 min.
11½" min.
20½" 25"

(B) PLAN

one piece c.i. branch
cement yarn

(C) ALTERNATIVE CONNECTION

s-trap
yarn
g.s. drain

(D) GROUND FLOOR OUTLET

27°-33"
3'-6"
25"-28"
5'-6"

(E) POSITIONS OF PAN & FLUSH TANK

W. C. DETAILS.

x 2

china, stoneware, and fireclay are all used, vitreous china producing the best finish. Cast iron covered with porcelain enamel is often used for large fittings, e.g. baths. Pressed metal fittings are very light and are inclined to drum unless sound-deadened on the reverse side. They may be enamelled or may be made of stainless steel or monel metal, which are corrosion-resisting and can be polished or provided with a 'machined' finish.

Water Closets. These fittings have an inlet for the attachment of a flush pipe which leads to a flushing rim which distributes the flushing water around the exposed surface of the pan. A water seal of at least 2 in. is provided, leading to an outlet which may be turned nearly horizontally ('P' trap) or vertically ('S' trap). This outlet is serrated to form a spigot for a cement and sand joint (with yarn caulking) into a cast-iron branch (see p. 315 c) or it may be jointed with a brass thimble to a lead branch to the stack. Here another brass tail is used to make the joint into the cast-iron junction (see p. 315 A). The brass thimble and tail prevent the soft lead pipe being distorted during the jointing process. Alternatively the 'S' trap of the w.c. can be jointed into a stoneware outlet, i.e. the socket of a stoneware drain just clear of the surface of the floor (see p. 315 D), here a yarn and cement joint is made.

Flushing Cisterns. These may be fixed either at a high level, i.e. at 5 ft 6 in. above the flush entry or at low level ('low-level suite'). By-laws require a high-level cistern to deliver two gallons in five seconds, and a low-level cistern to deliver two gallons in six seconds. The cisterns should refill in two minutes (see p. 281).

Siting of W.C. Compartments. They should be entered through a ventilated lobby, except from the open air or from a bedroom or dressing room only. They should have permanent ventilation of 20 sq. in. either from an external wall or through the roof (a single w.c. compartment should have a permanent ventilation area of 2 sq. ft). A lantern light ventilating a cloakroom containing several w.c's. should, in plan, be at least 1/5th of the floor area of the cloakroom and half of the lantern must provide permanent ventilation.

Baths. These are provided with holes formed for taps, overflow and waste. Traps and overflows are usually made of copper or copper alloy (although the illustration shows lead). It is possible to purchase the overflow and waste as the unit, saving awkward plumbing work. Baths have adjustable feet like large bolts which raise or lower the bath when turned. This enables the 'fall' of the bottom of the bath to be correctly adjusted. The mouths of the taps must be well above the level of the overflow, in case of back-pressure in the mains. The edge of the bath is finished

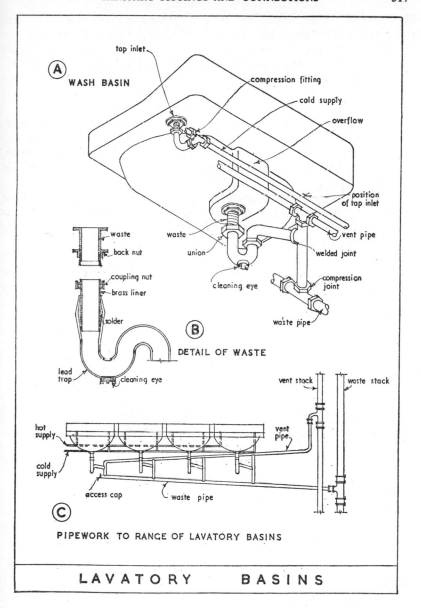

(A) WASH BASIN

tap inlet

compression fitting

cold supply

overflow

position of tap inlet

waste

back nut

waste

union

vent pipe

welded joint

coupling nut

brass liner

solder

cleaning eye

compression joint

waste pipe

(B) DETAIL OF WASTE

lead trap

cleaning eye

vent stack

waste stack

hot supply

cold supply

vent pipe

access cap

waste pipe

(C) PIPEWORK TO RANGE OF LAVATORY BASINS

LAVATORY   BASINS

so that bath panels can be fitted, e.g. glass, asbestos-cement, tiles, etc. These panels should be removable so that plumbing can be got at if necessary.

Lavatory Basins. These incorporate their own overflow, many sorts of trap are available. When using a single stack system the trap should be 3 in. deep and preferably of a re-sealing variety. The basin may be supported on brackets, or legs, or on a pedestal. Once again the mouths of the taps should not project below the level of the overflow (see p. 317).

Sinks. There is a very wide range of patterns available. Some incorporating drainers, some double, of cast iron, pressed metal, ceramics, etc. Sink units should be provided with an overflow. In the case of double sinks, so long as the division is lower than the edges, only one sink need have an overflow. Trapped wastes should be accessible in case of obstruction.

Wastes are bedded white lead to the fitting outlet, and a nut is screwed down to draw a flange tightly against it. The ' tail ' of the waste fitting is then attached to the waste pipe by either a non-manipulative fitting (to copper) or by wiping a soldered joint to a lead pipe.

16
Electricity*

THE PUBLIC SUPPLY

ELECTRICITY is produced in the power station by alternators driven by steam turbines or other form of power, the alternator consists of three coils inside which is rotated an electro-magnet, the movement of which induces electricity in the coils. Every time a pole of the electro-magnet passes a coil, electrical

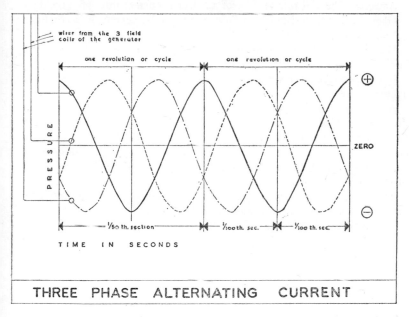

THREE PHASE ALTERNATING CURRENT

pressure rises and falls away within the coil, alternating in direction. The speed of the alternator is adjusted so that each peak in the pressure occurs in each coil every 1/50th of a second. The above diagram illustrates this.

The main distribution system consists of four wires, three of which are

* It is only appropriate here to give the broad outline of the way electricity is used in building. This subject is dealt with more fully in *Advanced Building Construction*.

' the phases ' which are connected at the generating station to each coil of the alternator. The fourth wire is the ' neutral ' and is solidly earthed at each sub-station.*

The pressure or voltage between any pair of phase wires is 415 volts (the line voltage) and between a phase wire and a neutral 240 volts (the phase voltage).

DEFINITIONS

Conductor. E.g. copper or aluminium wire—a substance through which electricity flows easily. Sometimes it is uninsulated, as with high-tension transmission lines, or busbars in factory trunking, or insulated as with domestic or other wiring.

Ampere. The unit rate of flow of an electric current through a conductor.

Ohm. The unit resistance to flow of an electric current in a conductor.

Volt. The unit pressure.†

Watt. The unit of measurement of the rate of the use of electrical energy in equipment.

In all these definitions a circuit is implied, i.e. current *flowing* in a conductor.

A useful analogy in the understanding of volts and amps is that of water flowing in a pipe. If a certain quantity of water is passed through a very large pipe, a large quantity of water (amps) can flow slowly at low-pressure (volts). But if a small pipe is used in order to pass a similar quantity of water very much higher pressure (volts) will have to be used to get the same quantity of water (amps) through the pipe.

This helps to show why relatively small wires can be used to carry a large amount of electricity if the voltage is high.

Relationships. Ohm's Law states that

$$\text{Ohms} = \frac{\text{Volts}}{\text{Amps}}$$

$$\text{Hence, Volts} = \text{Amps} \times \text{Ohms}$$

This is useful when considering resistance in circuits and helps to explain why the voltage decreases or ' drops ' when conductors are too long. Nevertheless the electricity supply authority are by statute required to provide electricity over specified minimum voltages.

---

* It is more economical to distribute electricity in high or medium voltage, it is stepped down by means of transformers at substations to low voltage, 415–240 volts.

† Volt = Electro Motive Force—E.M.F.—or Difference of Potential of electricity supplied to a conductor.

Watts are the product of volts and amps, i.e. Watts = Amps × Volts.

Distribution. Without going into detail, the National Grid links and distributes the supply from power stations throughout the country at very high voltage (132,000 volts and over). This high voltage is broken down regionally by means of transformers in sub-stations to local high voltage distribution (11,000 volts). Local sub-stations break this down to 415–240 volts. Schools, factories and public buildings are usually supplied with the four-wire distribution, i.e. 3-phase and neutral, whereas private houses are supplied with 1-phase (single-phase) and neutral. Large buildings may be supplied direct by the high-voltage distribution (11,000 volts) through a private sub-station.

SERVICE ENTRY AND DISTRIBUTION BOARD

Supplies to smaller buildings (say 240 volts) may come from overhead or underground cables. (The latter will probably become more common.) The incoming cables are lead to the ' Distribution Board '. This is usually a wooden board to which are fixed (in the order in which the current passes through them):

- (*a*) Sealing Chamber (underground supply) where the end of the cable is sealed from moisture.
- (*b*) The Electricity Company's fuse on the live (phase) wire.
- (*c*) The Meter.
- (*d*) Consumers' Service Unit. This contains the main switch from which are led busbars (copper-bar conductors) to the fuseways supplying the various final circuits. The fuseway is a gap in each of these circuits which is bridged by a clipped-in fuse cartridge.

It is important that the fuse to each final circuit is weaker than the wiring in the circuit it protects.

A typical schedule of fuseways would be as follows:

Cooker	30 amp
Ring main No. 1	30 amp
Ring main No. 2	30 amp
Immersion heater	10 amp
Lighting No. 1	5 amp
Lighting No. 2	5 amp
Spare way No. 1	— amp
Spare way No. 2	— amp

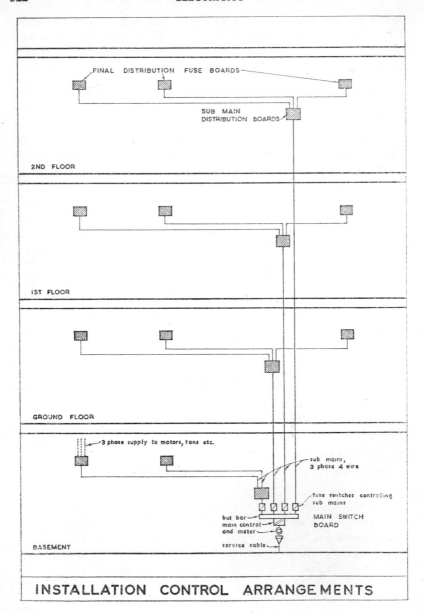

FINAL DISTRIBUTION FUSE BOARDS

SUB MAIN
DISTRIBUTION BOARDS

2ND FLOOR

1ST FLOOR

GROUND FLOOR

3 phase supply to motors, fans etc.

sub mains,
3 phase 4 wire

fuse switches controlling
sub mains

bus bar
main control
and meter

MAIN SWITCH
BOARD

service cable

BASEMENT

INSTALLATION CONTROL ARRANGEMENTS

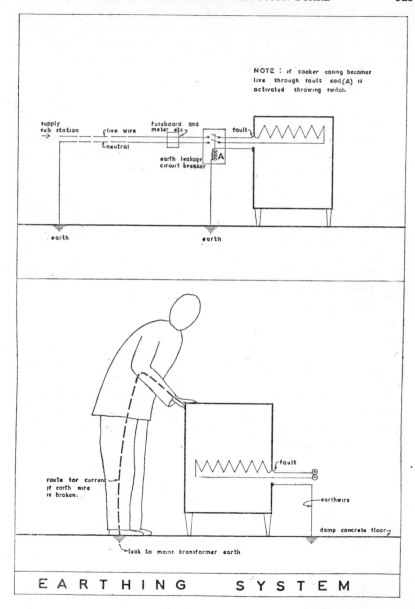

EARTHING SYSTEM

Earth. If a fault should develop in any appliance, e.g. the live (phase or 'line') comes in direct contact with the casing or structure, there must be a ready and ample path for the current to return to earth—rather than through the body of anyone who may happen to touch the casing of the appliance.

This is provided by connecting an earth wire to the structure of all metal appliances. It is taken back to the distribution board where it may be connected (via a collecting busbar) to:

(*a*) A rising metal water main, though not all water companies will approve this, especially if there are sulphates present in the ground, or there are local earthing peculiarities, or

(*b*) the supply company's earthed cable sheath, and/or

(*c*) an earth leakage circuit-breaker ('trip switch') which will immediately open a switch in the circuit if there is any lack of balance in the circuit, i.e. if current starts to flow in the earth wire. These give added protection to normal circuits in certain areas (e.g. infants' schools and houses). They are mostly used where earth conditions are poor, when they must be provided with an earth (e.g. copper rods or buried plates) and they must be tested regularly—a jammed trip switch could be dangerous.

Ring Main. This is now the recognised method of supplying socket outlets (for radio, fires, floor lamps, cleaners, etc.). The outlets have a maximum rating of 13 amps. The plugs which fit them each contain a 13-, 7- or 3-amp fuse selected to protect the appliance the plug serves, e.g. 3 amp—light, 7 amp—toaster, 13 amp—large electric fire.

The ring main consists of a pair of conductors (and earth wire) which start at a 30-amp fuseway in the consumer unit, travels round several rooms, being connected to several socket outlets on the way; they then return to the same fuseway. Current can therefore reach each outlet from two directions, which very much reduces the chance of over-loading in any part of the circuit. The drawing on p. 325 indicates a typical arrangement. (Only a few fuseways are indicated for the sake of clarity.)

There are certain rules to be observed when installing a Ring Main:

(1) Maximum number of 13-amp socket outlets is 10, except in houses and flats where there may be an unlimited number of socket outlets if the area is less than 1,000 sq. ft.

(2) Spurs may be taken from socket outlets on the ring main—maximum 2 per spur (see drawing, p. 325).

(3) The ring main wiring should not be cut when making connections to

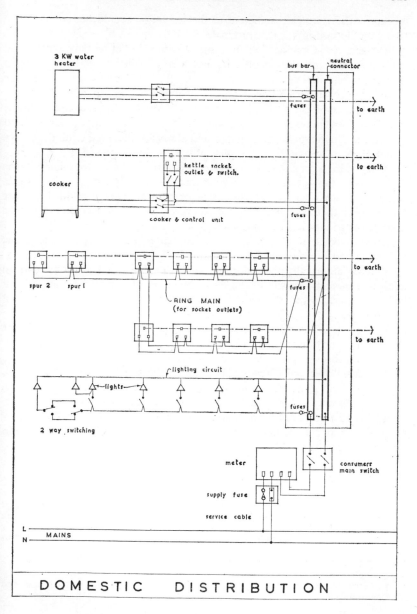

3 KW water heater

bus bar

neutral connector

fuses

to earth

cooker

kettle socket outlet & switch.

cooker & control unit

fuses

to earth

spur 2   spur 1

RING MAIN
(for socket outlets)

fuses

to earth

to earth

lighting circuit

lights

fuses

2 way switching

meter

consumers main switch

supply fuse

service cable

L
N   MAINS

DOMESTIC   DISTRIBUTION

socket outlets; instead, sufficient of the insulation should be removed, and the wire ' looped-in ' to the terminal.

Ordinary Sub-Circuits. When using 13-amp socket outlets with fused plugs, on ordinary sub-circuits, i.e. not a ring mains, regulations permit a maximum of 6 outlets on one sub-circuit. If only 2 outlets are required, the fuse in the consumer unit must be 20 amps; if over, then 30 amps.

Distribution of Socket Outlets. Generally, far too few socket outlets are provided, which results in the dangerous practice of using adaptors to provide additional outlets. A list should always be prepared of all the equipment likely to be used so that sufficient outlets can be provided.*

Socket outlets must not be provided in bathrooms or in other damp-prone locations. Many deaths have been caused, for instance, by people in baths touching faulty electric heaters—when the bath plumbing provided a better route to earth than the heater's earth wire. Socket outlets should not be sited close to taps in kitchens, garages, etc.

Damp concrete solid ground floors are dangerous, as they provide a fine, tempting earth through people touching faulty equipment.†

Cookers are usually permanently wired through a switched cooker control unit to a 30-amp fuseway in the distribution board. Immersion heaters are often similarly wired through a switch to, say, a 15-amp fuseway for a 3 kW heater.‡

Refrigerators and washing machines are often served through a spur box with a fuse cartridge from a ring main. This is a more satisfactory arrangement than through plugs and socket outlets.§

Lighting Points and Circuits. Because of the small load usually carried, lighting circuits most often consist of a pair of conductors (twin cable) from a 5-amp fuseway in the consumer unit. (The maximum load normally permitted is 15 amps, i.e. 15-amp fuse and cable.)

With a 5-amp fuse, assuming 100-watt lamps (240 volts), the maximum number of points would be:

$$\frac{5 \times 240}{100} = 12 \text{ points.}$$

* See p. 28 *Electricity in Building* by A. L. Osborne, (Batsford).

† *Post War Building Study*, No. 11. ' Electrical Installations ' recommends, that socket outlets should be located 9 in. above floor (minimum 5 in.), except in kitchens where they should be 4 ft 6 in.

‡ 1 kW = 1,000 watts. With a voltage of 240, the fuse necessary is calculated as follows:— $\frac{3{,}000 \text{ watts}}{240 \text{ volts}} = 12 \cdot 5 \text{ amps.}$

therefore a 15 amp. fuse and wiring is adequate.

§ *Electric Wiring* (*Domestic*) by E. Molloy, (Newnes), illustrates many fittings and wiring techniques.

Thus a small house with, say, 18 points would have 2 lighting circuits each using a 5-amp fuse in a fuseway in the consumer's service unit distribution board.

There are several methods of wiring lighting points:

(a) Looping-in, using 2-plate roses.

(b) Looping-in, using 3-plate roses (probably the best).

(c) Looping-in, using 3-terminal switches.

(d) Joint box method.

These methods are described in detail elsewhere, but whichever is selected it must satisfy the following:

(a) The switch must be on the live (phase) wire so that the lamp-holder is dead when the switch is off. (The Supply Authority may refuse to connect an installation where the lampholders are directly connected to the phase wire.)

(b) There must be not less than one final sub-circuit per 1,000 sq. ft.

(c) Ceiling pull switches only are used in bathrooms and similar earth-dangerous locations.

Wiring Systems. (a) *Steel Conduit.* In this system, steel tubes or conduits are fixed wherever wiring is neeeded, the wires being drawn through. As the conduit is itself the earth continuity conductor, and is earthed at one end, so much depends on the method of jointing. The best work is done in heavy solid drawn conduit with screwed joints. There are lighter grades of conduit —with welded, brazed or merely close-jointed seams. Joints can be made by means of grip screws in sleeves.

Vulcanised India Rubber (V.I.R.) insulated cables or P.V.C. insulated cables are drawn through the conduit. Many steel fittings are available for forming junction ceiling outlets, socket outlets, switch points, etc.

Conduit is traditionally regarded as a high quality job, and has the advantage that it can be laid in floor screeds and it protects wiring from nail damage in walls. It is, however, susceptible to corrosion from external dampness and condensation with consequent loss of earth continuity. But it does permit rewiring to be carried out, thus providing a flexible installation.

(b) *P.V.C. Conduit.* This has many of the virtues of the last method. Earthing is provided by an earth wire. There is no risk of corrosion, though it may soften in high temperatures. It is not so resistant to nail damage.

(c) *M.I.C.S.* (*Mineral Insulated Copper Sheathed*). An extremely reliable system with an indefinite life, in which the single-strand conductors, surrounded by highly compressed insulating mineral, are carried in a relatively small bore copper tube. Connections to junctions, etc., involve rather an elaborate technique using a compressed plastic waterproof compound

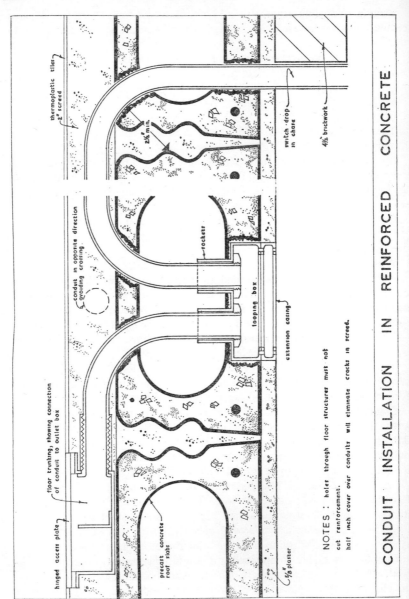

thermoplastic tiles
2" screed

switch drop
in chase

4½ brickwork

conduit in opposite direction
avoiding crossing

sockets

looping box

extension casing

floor trunking, showing connection
of conduit to outlet box

hinged access plate

precast concrete
roof slabs

⅝" plaster

2½" min.

NOTES : holes through floor structures must not
cut reinforcement.
half inch cover over conduits will eliminate cracks in screed.

CONDUIT INSTALLATION IN REINFORCED CONCRETE

which prevents water getting at the mineral insulator. The cable can be used in the most difficult conditions—water, corrosive atmosphere, heat, inflammable vapours (e.g. garages).

If it is cast into screeds, it does not provide the same degree of flexibility as good conduit.

(d) *P.V.C.* (*Polyvynyl-Chloride*) sheathed and insulated cable is satisfactory where the wiring can run freely in ceiling spaces and in studding. Where it has to run in chases down walls, it should be protected against nail damage with metal channelling or conduit. Structural movements, e.g. loose floor boards, have been known to damage this type of loose wiring. Renewing or altering wiring involves taking up floors, and opening up the structure.

(e) *Polythene.* This provides serviceable sheathing and insulation as for (d), but becomes softer at lower temperatures—which may be caused by overloading, or externally. Cheaper than P.V.C.

(f) *T.R.S.* (*Tough Rubber Sheathing*). Similar to (d) and (e) and is used a great deal for agricultural work. It should be kept away from ultra-violet light (sun) as this causes deterioration.

(g) *Lead Sheath.* V.I.R. insulated cables may be covered with a lead-alloy sheath. These metal sheaths must be bonded together throughout the installation by means of bonding clamps on each junction, etc. Kinks in the cables may damage the lead and break the continuity. Wet plaster and alkaline atmospheres are deleterious.

17

Plastering

FOR internal use there are five main types of calcium sulphate (gypsum) plaster. These may be mixed with sand or gauged with cement or lime. Plaster may also be made with lime (calcium hydroxide) on its own, which is the traditional form of plaster.

Both gypsum plaster and lime plaster should not be used externally as they are slightly soluble in water; instead, cement and sand is used.

In addition to plastering walls and ceilings the plasterer screeds concrete floors to provide a smooth surface for floor finishes.

INTERNAL PLASTERING

Gypsum. Deposits are found between certain sandstones and marls in Staffordshire, Derbyshire, Nottinghamshire, Sussex and North Lancashire. The gypsum is factory-processed and bagged for sale.*

Trace impurities make the plaster pink or grey, but the colouring does not affect the properties of the plaster. When sulphate plasters set they expand slightly. (On the other hand, lime plasters contract slightly on setting.) This slight expansion has the virtue that it reduces cracking during drying out. The strength of a 1 : 1 plaster/sand mix is about the same strength as a 1 : 3 Portland cement/sand mortar.†

Generally, anhydrous plasters give harder finishes than the hemihydrate groups.

In most cases hemihydrate plasters adhere better to smooth backings, e.g. plaster-board and smooth concrete.

Partial wetting of a plaster is dangerous, as the setting of some of the plaster may be delayed, which may cause disruption. As calcium sulphate is soluble, damp conditions will cause eventual deterioration.

---

* Naturally occurring calcium sulphate ($CaSO_4 2H_2O$) is heated at the factory to drive off some of the water to form calcium sulphate hemihydrate ($CaSO_4 \frac{1}{2}H_2O$). This hemihydrate will set in the presence of water to become $CaSO_4 2H_2O$—the original calcium sulphate. This setting process is used by the plasterer.

† Anhydrous calcium sulphate ($CaSO_4$) is taken a stage further in manufacture, all the water being driven off. Thus:—

' Hemihydrate '—with ' half ' a molecule of water.
' Anhydrous '—no molecules of water.

Some calcium sulphate plasters will corrode metal lathing because of the presence of soluble salts or acids, e.g. accelerated anhydrous plasters. Lime helps to inhibit corrosion. It is usual either to render metal lathing first with cement and sand (allowing this to set for at least twenty-four hours), or to paint the lathing thoroughly with a bituminous paint before applying the plaster.

Cement. Cement can be used for internal renderings. It is most useful in damp situations, as it is insoluble, and where strength is important. It is heavy to apply and difficult to trowel unless a small amount of plasticiser is added to the mix. The plasticiser acts as a 'wetting agent', and makes the mix more 'buttery' and easier to apply. A satisfactory mix is 1 : 6, cement/sand with plasticiser, without which a 1: 4 mix would be more usual. The alternative is to gauge the mix with lime, i.e. 1 : 1 : 6 or 1 : 2 : 9, cement/lime/sand.

Sand. Sand must be clean and well graded. It must be free from iron, coal-dust, mica, shale, flaky material, salts, vegetable or animal impurities and clay. Rough tests can be made with a magnifying glass, by rubbing the sand between the fingers to see if it balls too easily, and by shaking samples with water in a glass jar. In this case, sand will settle quickly and a layer of silt will appear on the top surface of the sand—this occurs in about fifteen minutes. After an hour the clay will have slowly settled out and the water will still look dirty.*

Water. Water should be drinkable, i.e. free from salts and other impurities.

Classes of Gypsum Plasters

There are five main classes of gypsum plaster, the last (Class ' E ') being the naturally occurring 'anhydrite'. It is important to know the difference between the classes, and it is dangerous to mix them.

Class 'A'—Plaster of Paris. This plaster must be used in small batches because it sets quickly. It is useful for stopping and repair work, used either neat or with the addition of lime (gauging). It is used in the proportions ¼–1 : 1 plaster/lime, with or without sand. It should be trowelled as little as possible.†

---

* British Standard 1198–1199 and 1200 of 1944, incorporated in British Standard 882.
  National Building Studies Bulletin, No. 7, ' Sands for Plaster, Mortars and External Renderings ' (H.M.S.O.).
  ' Sands for Plasters, Mortars and Renderings,' *Ministry of Works Advisory Leaflet*, No. 15.
  Builders Materials, by B. H. Knight (Edward Arnold).
  † *Makes:* Plaster of Paris; Gauging Plaster; C.B. Plaster.

Class ' B '—Retarded Hemihydrate Gypsum Plasters. These plasters must be allowed to dry out quickly. They must not be knocked up or retempered after they have started to stiffen. Class ' B ' plasters usually contain a retarder which slows the setting down to give sufficient time for mixing and application. Addition of lime will accelerate the set. Too much water with the finishing coat will spoil the work. For undercoats use a 1 : 1½–3 plaster/sand mix. The amount of sand varies according to the background; for instance, absorbent brickwork will require more sand in the mix than for plaster-board or concrete. Class ' B ' plasters can be used in some cases for metal lathing as an undercoat to a gauged lime finishing coat. The mix used for the undercoat is ¼–1 : 1 plaster (unhaired)/lime, with sand if appropriate.

Alternatively, Class ' B ' is used as a finishing coat only in two- or three-coat work. Then it is used neat or with the addition of lime up to 1/3rd part of the plaster. It can be used for single-coat work on concrete, gypsum plaster board or insulating fibre board, when no lime is added. Plasters used for work on plaster-board or insulating board single-coat work, have low expansion characteristics on setting, and are used neat with no additional lime.

Other varieties are dual-purpose, i.e. they can be used for both undercoats and finishing (these should not be used mistakenly for single-coat work) and are used in the same way as the undercoat and finishing coat types.

Yet other varieties of this class are manufactured specially for application to smooth concrete surfaces either as preparatory work or as a finishing coat, and in this case they are used neat.

Acoustic plasters (of this class) are used with an aggregate as a finishing coat to give additional sound absorption, and are also used neat.*

Class ' C '—Anhydrous Gypsum Plasters. These plasters set slowly and should not be allowed to dry too quickly. Some harden sometime after the initial set. These plasters can in fact be retempered within an hour of mixing. They have rather poor bond to plaster board or fibre board backgrounds and should not really be used for this type of work. Their usefulness lies in the fact that the surface can be worked over after the initial set has taken place.

The undercoat type is used with sand with or without lime in the proportions 1 : 1–2 plaster/sand (the sand proportion varies with the

---

* *Makes:* Adamant; Adamantine; Aegrit; Battle-axe; Belpite; Carlisle Hardwall; Faspite; Gothite; Granite; Gypstone; Keenapco; Murite; Napco; Paristone; Pytho; Seigniorite; Silver Seal; Sirapite Board Plaster; Sirapite Browning; Sirfix; Thistle.

background). Alternatively it can be used in the proportions 2 : 1 : 5–6 plaster/lime/sand.

For finishing coats in two- or three-coat work it is used neat or with the addition of lime up to 1/3rd part of the plaster. It can be used with lime in the proportions ¼–1 : 1 plaster/lime with sand if appropriate. There is also a dual-purpose type made, the proportions being the same as for undercoat and finishing-coat types.*

Class ' D '—Keene's or Parian. These are like the Class ' C ' plasters and, in the same way, they should not be used directly on building boards, a difference being that for finishing-coat work they are invariably used neat.†

Class ' E '—Anhydrite Plaster. This is made as a dual-purpose plaster. Sanded undercoats are mixed in the proportions 1 : 1½ plaster/sand. It is used neat for finishing coats either in two or three applications, and for single-coat work on concrete or boards. No lime should be added to the mix, and once again the mix should not be retempered after one hour from mixing.

Background. This affects the choice of plaster. Porous bricks or blocks provide a reasonable surface for plaster so long as it is not too strong, i.e. a 1 : 3 cement/sand mix.

Dense concrete is difficult to plaster if the surface has been ' polished ' with a trowel. In such cases, a splattered coat of cement and sand on the concrete first will help adhesion.

Rich mixes should not be used on metal lathing as they distort it. A common mix is cement/lime/sand 1 : 2 : 8.

Plaster boards and fibre building boards have special plasters made for use with them. Lime should be excluded from the mix as it has a bad effect on adhesion. Two-coat work with sanded gypsum plaster for an undercoat is satisfactory, or a single coat of neat gypsum plaster, e.g. ' no-setting-expansion quality ' Class ' B ,' or alternatively, dual-purpose Class ' E.'

Lime Plasters. Lime for plaster is produced by ' burning ' chalk, calcium carbonate, in a lime kiln.

$$CaCO_3 \quad = \quad CaO \quad + \quad CO_2$$

Calcium carbonate = calcium oxide (lime) + carbon dioxide.

The lime (quicklime) reacts with water very readily producing heat and carbon dioxide gas. This forms calcium hydroxide, and is what happens when the builder slakes quicklime on the site to form the putty for plastering.

* *Makes:* Sirapite; Glastone; Statite; Victorite; Xelite.
† *Makes:* Keene's; Parian; Astroplax; Pixie Keene's; Superite.

This used to be seen frequently not so long ago, but is now hardly ever seen owing to the increasing popularity of gypsum plaster.

The calcium hydroxide is plastered on to the walls, dries out, and over the course of time carbonates slowly back into calcium carbonate—the original compound. This carbonation only occurs on the surface exposed to the air.

$$Ca(OH)_2 \ + \ CO_2 \ = \ CaCO_3 \ + H_2O$$

Calcium hydroxide + carbon dioxide = calcium carbonate + water

It will be seen from this that water is produced during carbonation which tends to harm decorations applied to lime plaster for a month or more after application.

Limes are classified according to their clay content. When they contain no clay at all they are known as 'fat' limes and these slake rapidly. On the other hand, limes containing clay up to 35% are known as 'hydraulic' limes and take a long time to slake. They set much more rapidly and are virtually hard at the end of one month, whereas a fat lime may take very much longer.

Hydrated lime is available in bags and is now commonly used in preference to slaking on the site. It is principally used for gauging mortar (i.e. mixing with mortar).

Plastering on Plaster Board and Insulating Fibre Building Board. The traditional base for plastering in the past has been timber laths, but these have been almost entirely superseded by plaster boards produced to receive skim coats of plaster, and insulating board which is a soft fibre board with insulating properties.

These sheet bases are most often used when a plaster finish is required to a timber framework, e.g. timber joist ceilings, stud partitions.

Plaster Board. This consists of a gypsum plaster core, either ⅜ in. or ½ in. thick, covered by a tough sheet of paper on each side.*

Fixing. Plaster board is fixed by means of galvanised or sherardised plaster-board nails 1¼ in. by 14 s.w.g.; they are spaced at 6 in. centres, and a space of ⅛ in. is usually recommended to be left at the joints to receive filler. The nails are driven slightly below the surface but without breaking

* There are several minor variations of plaster board, e.g.:
  Plaster Base Board, ⅜ in. thick and from 36 in. + 28 in. to 36 in. + 54 in.
  Plaster Lath, ⅜ in. thick and 16 in. wide, from 32 in. to 54 in. long.
  Plaster Wall Board, ¼ in., ⅜ in. and ½ in. thick, 2 ft, 3 ft and 4 ft in width, and in length varying from 6 ft to 12 ft. The board is supplied one side for plastering and the other side for decoration direct.
  Insulating Plaster Board has a sheet of bright aluminium foil added to one side to increase reflective insulation (to be effective this bright surface must always be fixed adjacent to an air space).

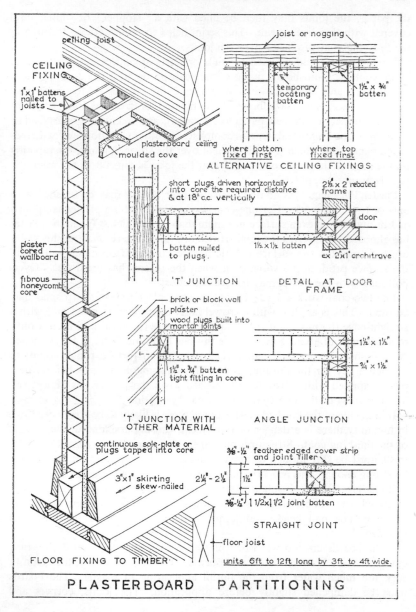

CEILING FIXING

ceiling joist

1"x1" battens nailed to joists

plasterboard ceiling
moulded cove

plaster cored wallboard

fibrous honeycomb core

joist or nogging

temporary locating batten

1½" x ¾" batten

where bottom fixed first

where top fixed first

ALTERNATIVE CEILING FIXINGS

short plugs driven horizontally into core the required distance & at 18" c.c. vertically

batten nailed to plugs.

'T' JUNCTION

2½" x 2" rebated frame

door

1½ x 1½" batten

ex 2"x1" architrave

DETAIL AT DOOR FRAME

brick or block wall
plaster
wood plugs built into mortar joints

1½" x ¾" batten tight fitting in core

'T' JUNCTION WITH OTHER MATERIAL

1½" x 1½"

¾" x 1½"

ANGLE JUNCTION

continuous sole-plate or plugs tapped into core

3"x1" skirting skew-nailed

2¼" - 2½"

1½"

⅜" - ½" feather edged cover strip and joint filler

⅜" - ½"   1 1/2"x1 1/2" joint batten

STRAIGHT JOINT

floor joist

FLOOR FIXING TO TIMBER

units 6ft to 12ft long by 3ft to 4ft wide.

PLASTERBOARD PARTITIONING

the paper, the joints may then be filled with a ' stopper ' or ' filler ' and covered with thin linen scrim. This scrim helps to reduce cracks forming in the finishing coat of plaster over the joints.

$\frac{3}{8}$-in. boards should be fixed to studs or joists at centres not greater than 16-in. centres; $\frac{1}{2}$-in. board fixing centres can go up to 2 ft. Jointing techniques vary and manufacturers' recommendations differ. Most manufacturers produce plaster wallboard with tapered or recessed long edges to receive stopper, reinforced paper (perforated), and a finishing slurry. The joint should be unnoticeable when complete. Another variation is a feathered-edged paper tape which is stuck straight over the stopped joints, the tapering on the edge of the paper being such that the joint is difficult to see when the tape is properly applied.

Plaster Finishing. As an alternative, plaster boards may be finished with one- or two-coat work. For one-coat work, neat finishing plaster is applied and brought to an even surface not more than $\frac{3}{16}$ in. thick. When the plaster has almost set it receives the final trowelling; the plasterer may use his water brush to moisten the surface a little if necessary, but too much will ' kill ' the surface producing a white dust when the plaster has dried out. Over-polishing with the trowel may have a bad effect.

For two-coat work a 1 : 1$\frac{1}{2}$ haired browing plaster/clean sharp sand may be used. This is applied with a trowel fairly quickly and ' ruled off ' with a straight-edge (by moving it from side to side over the surface to even it out), to a thickness of about $\frac{3}{8}$ in. Before this has had time to set, it is roughened (with a short batten with nails driven through to form a rough comb) to provide a key for the finishing coat. This finishing coat is, as before, neat plaster applied with a trowel and finished when the plaster has almost set. The thickness of the two coats should be about $\frac{1}{2}$ in.

If in the life of the finished plaster board there is likely to be large variations in humidity there is a danger of movement, causing cracking in the surface of the finishing coat. Structural movement can cause serious cracking. The joists must be stiff enough to prevent undue movement, and the studs must be strong enough and properly nogged to resist induced stresses.

Insulating Board. Insulating fibre boards are often fixed and left unplastered, but concealed fixing techniques are relatively expensive, and in order to hide nail heads and joints, a finishing of plaster is sometimes specified.

If the boards are too wet when plastered, their shrinkage on drying may crack the bond between board and plaster. If they are too dry, they tend to suck too much water from the initial application of plaster. The boards must be dampened slightly before application. The joints, corners and angles are then reinforced with galvanised wire mesh, 3 in. wide, embedded in the plaster and fastened, if necessary, with a few galvanised staples. For the large sheets (8′ × 4′, etc.) a $\frac{3}{16}$ in. finishing coat of neat plaster is satisfactory.*

Insulating board must either be plastered or must have the joints adequately ' expressed ', i.e. covered by a strip of aluminium, plastic or wood, or bevelled to form a V joint. The joints cannot otherwise be satisfactorily concealed.

Insulating board, once again, is sensitive to changes in humidity and it is important to fix the boards adequately.

Fixing. Battens, studs, joists or rafters should be spaced at 12-in. or 16-in. centres for 4 ft wide sheets, and 12-in. to 18-in. centres for 3 ft sheets ($\frac{1}{2}$-in. wall boards ; $\frac{1}{8}$ in. should be left all round. It is advisable to rest the sheet to be fixed on a piece of plank against the wall, then to nail along the top, then down the centre and finally down the sides and along the bottom. Nails round the edge should be at 3-in. centres and elsewhere at 6-in. centres.

PLASTERING TECHNIQUE

Rendering. The first coat applied to concrete, brick, or stone walls is termed ' rendering '. Its object is to fill in hollows in the surface ready to receive the floating coat. The rendering coat can be dispensed with if the brickwork is accurately laid, or the concrete is reasonably true and even.

To a lath surface this preparatory coat is termed the ' pricking-up coat '.

The surface to receive this preparatory coat must be rough and absorbent to help adhesion. Smooth surfaces should be hacked before the application of the plaster. Particularly difficult patches, i.e. large smooth stones, may be ' strapped,' i.e. 2″ × 1″ creosoted wood fillets or strips fixed to plugs in the wall; this aids the mechanical key of the plaster to the surface.

Before the rendering sets, it is scratched with a comb made of large nails or pointed laths.

Floating Coat. The object of this coat is to provide a true surface to receive the finish. For this purpose wood rules are fixed to all external angles and at up to 10 ft centres, being kept perfectly vertical and in the same plane one with another. The plaster is then trowelled on, and all superfluous material struck off with a long straight-edge known as a Derby float. This float is kept pressed against the rules and is moved from side to side upwards. The surface thus produced is scratched with a nail comb or bass broom to form a key for the setting coat.

---

* Plaster Base Boards (fibre) in similar small sizes as Plasterboard base (p. 334) need angles and corners reinforced with wire, but not the joints between the individual boards.

Setting Coat. The floating coat then receives a setting coat $\frac{3}{16}$ in. thick. Just before the plaster sets it is polished to an even surface with the trowel.

Grounds. It is usual to fix to the brick or blockwork, where the skirtings and architraves are to be fixed, rough grounds of timber which form in effect bottom rules for the floating process. The architraves and skirtings are then nailed to these grounds.

Two-coat Work. This is the most usual specification for even concrete and well-laid brick- and blockwork; the evenness of the background makes the rendering unnecessary. As in all plastering work, the background, i.e. bricks, blocks, etc., must be free from dirt, grease, dust and friable material. The courses of brickwork should be raked to provide additional key and if possible ' keyed ' bricks should be used. These bricks have grooves let into the stretcher faces which makes for much more reliable plastering. The floating and setting are carried out as described before.

One-coat Work. This is suitable for application to plaster boards, insulation boards and other exceptionally true surfaces. The $\frac{3}{16}$-in. setting coat is applied only, as before.

EXTERNAL CEMENT RENDERING

Functions. External cement renderings usually require the following characteristics: (*a*) attractive appearance and colour; (*b*) durability; (*c*) resistance to moisture penetration; (*d*) frost resistance; (*e*) uniform weathering.

Appearance depends upon choice of finishing technique, e.g. roughcast, pebble-dash, machine applied, scraped textures. Colour is supplied usually by employing coloured cements or by incorporating coloured aggregates in the mix of the finishing material.

Durability depends upon the degree of adhesion of the rendering to the background over the whole of the surface, and the detailing of sills and copings, the composition of the mix and the standard of the workmanship.

Water will penetrate a wall far more readily if it contains hair cracks (i.e. a strong rendering that has crazed) than it will through more absorbent and resilient rendering.

Frost resistance will depend upon whether or not the rendering will be saturated in any part during frost. This can be controlled by proper detailing at damp courses, sills and copings.

Uniform weathering depends upon texture of the finished surface, the amount of pollution in the atmosphere and the amount of overhang to sills, copings, etc.

Background. Dense, string, smooth surfaces, e.g. concrete. Key must be provided to these surfaces by means of a splatter-dash of 1 : 2 cement/sand mix, or by the application of proprietary bonding fluid, alternatively the surface may be hacked to provide a mechanical key. It is perhaps most satisfactory to arrange for a key to be cast into such surfaces to be rendered in the formwork, by, for example, the use of dovetail ribbed rubber formwork lining sheets.

Strong Porous Materials, e.g. clay, bricks and some concrete blocks. Here the joints should be raked out, to the depth of at least $\frac{1}{2}$ in. Care is required to make sure that no air pockets are left between the rendering and the background.

Weak Porous Materials, e.g. blocks or lightweight aggregate concrete. Here, weaker rendering mixes are necessary; if the rendering is too strong it is likely to fail on such surfaces.

Non-fines Concrete. This provides a first-rate key.

Weak Resilient Materials, e.g. wood-wool building slabs. So long as the area to be rendered is kept small and the edges are left unrestrained, rather strong rendering should be used which bonds very well with the slab and concentrates movement at the edges rather than at the centre of the panels. Bitumen-dipped galvanised wire further reduces likelihood of surface cracking.

Overhangs. It is usually recommended that sills, copings, eaves, etc., should overhang rendering for protection. If this is overdone in industrial areas, grime will accumulate under these overhangs to a line where the rain can reach the surface to wash it. But it is essential that the top edges of renderings should be adequately protected, and copings themselves should have throatings to throw the water clear from the upper edge of the rendering. There should always be a damp-proof course under copings to prevent the penetration of water into the brick or block background. This damp-proof course should project slightly over the edge of the rendering. Down-pipes and gutters should be arranged so that overflowing cannot discolour and damage the renderings.

Preparation. The surface must provide a good key for the first coat of the rendering and so it should be free from paint, oil, dust, dirt, soot, or friable material. Soft mortar in old brickwork should be raked out to $\frac{1}{2}$ in. Any material likely to disintegrate should be covered with stout bitumen-coated metal lathing securely fixed. Any timber to be covered by the rendering should be treated with a wood preservative.*

If the background is very porous and has a great deal of suction it should

---

* It need hardly be said that to render timber or disintegrating material is only a temporary measure, and cannot be regarded as good construction.

be damped sufficiently, but no free water should be left on the surface. If the weather is too dry it is inadvisable to work. Start on the shady side of the building first and work round towards the sun.

Application. Where exposure is severe, three-coat work may be necessary, but normally two coats are satisfactory.

The first coat, i.e. straightening coat, should not exceed $\frac{5}{8}$ in. or be less than $\frac{3}{8}$ in. A floating rule is worked over the surface which is then surface-combed.* If a machine is used for applying the finishing coat, then the combings should be omitted.

Coats should be left to dry out for as long as possible so that initial shrinkage can take place before subsequent coats are put on.

The final coat depends on the texture required, but should be not less than $\frac{3}{16}$ in. and not more than $\frac{5}{16}$ in. Protect renderings from frost, rain and drying winds.

Textures. *Smooth Finish.* Smooth rendering should never be left undecorated, but if finished with a wood float it can be decorated with two coats of external grade emulsion paint with excellent results.

Roughcast. The straightening coat may consist of 1 : 1 : 6 cement/lime/sand mix, or a 1 : 6 cement/sand with plasticiser. This is combed for key and left to dry out. A wet plastic mix is then made of $1\frac{1}{2}$ parts cement, $\frac{1}{2}$ part lime, 2 parts of shingle or crushed stone and 3 parts of sand. The stone may vary from $\frac{1}{4}$ in. to $\frac{1}{2}$ in. (depending on the texture required). This is made into a wet mix which is thrown on to the wall with a hand scoop or laying-on trowel. Coloured cements may be used. As with all textured finishes much depends on the skill of the operative.

Machine Applied Finishes. Special paddle-wheel machines are available which ' flick-on ' the mix when a handle is turned. This produces a Tyrolean type finish which is built up often in two or three applications. If too much is applied at once the texture is spoilt. Proprietary mixes may be used, in which case the manufacturer's directions should be followed.

Scraped Finish. Some hours after the application of the rendering the surface may be scraped with an old saw blade in order to remove the laitance and expose the larger pieces of aggregate. The final result depends upon the colour and texture of the aggregate.

* Indentations resulting from combing should be $\frac{3}{4}$ in. apart and not more than $\frac{1}{4}$ in. deep.

ALTERNATIVE MIXES FOR EXTERNAL RENDERING

Types of background	Examples	Severe exposure	Protected urban exposure
Strong and dense	Dense clay bricks or blocks, dense concrete blocks, and structural concrete	Spatter-dash, 1:3 followed by: Pebble-dash, 1:3 Roughcast, 1:3 or 1:1-1½:5-6 or Textured, 1:1-1½:5-6	Spatter-dash, 1:3 followed by: Roughcast, 1:3 or 1:1-1½:5-6 Textured, 1:1-1½:5-6 or 1:2:8-9 Smooth, 1:1-1½:5-6 or Pebble-dash, 1:3
Moderately strong, porous	Most bricks	As above, but spatter-dash treatment not so important in most cases	
Moderately weak, porous	Lightweight concretes, poured or cast *in situ*, or soft weak bricks	Roughcast, 1:1-1½:5-6 or Textured, 1:1-1½:5-6	Roughcast, 1:1-1½:5-6 or 1:2:8-9 or Textured, 1:1-1½:5-6 or Smooth, 1:1-1½:5-6
Open textured	No fines concrete	Roughcast, 1:3 or 1:1-1½:5-6 Pebble-dash, 1:3 or Textured, 1:1-1½:5-6	Roughcast, 1:3 or 1:1-1½:5-6 Textured, 1:1-1½:5-6 or 1:2:8-9 or Pebble-dash, 1:3
Weak, resilient	Wood wool building slabs	Textured, 1:3 Roughcast, 1:1-1½:5-6 or Pebble-dash, 1:3	Textured, 1:3 Roughcast, 1:1-1½:5-6 or Pebble-dash, 1:3

N.B.—Materials are implied thus: 1:3, cement:sand; or 1:1-1½:5-6, cement/lime/sand.

Notes:—1. Exposure: There are three factors taken into account in the compilation of the Table: (a) Severity of rainfall. (b) Likelihood of rapid alterations of rain and frost. (c) Greater importance of soot deposition in urban as against rural areas.
2. Spatter-dash is thrown on with no subsequent smoothing, and should be applied in just sufficient quantity to cover the surface and level up the suction of the background.
3. Textured finishes include machine-applied and scraped.
4. The final adjustment of the mix within the limits given in the above Table should be made having in mind the type of lime and sand available. With hydrated lime used unsoaked, the smaller volume of sand is desirable owing to the lower workability it gives to the resulting mix, and for the reason that the actual volume of lime is less than in a mix using lime putty.
5. Except where otherwise stated the mixes given above are normally used for both undercoats and finishing coats. A strong mix rich in cement should not be applied to a weaker undercoat.

Based on *Housing Manual* 1944: Appendix H (34), published by H.M.S.O., and *External Renderings*, by the Cement and Concrete Association.

SOME CHARACTERISTICS OF PLASTER MIXES

Mix	Shrinkage or expansion	Strength and hardness	Remarks
LIME AND CEMENT Lime/Sand	All shrink on drying. Too much clayey or fine material or sands of uniform particle size make for high shrinkage. Content of clayey or fine material should not exceed 5 per cent. Strong mixes tend to develop a few large cracks; weaker mixes, finer and distributed cracks.	Weak and soft	Takes a long time to harden. Each undercoat must be allowed to dry thoroughly before applying next coat.
Cement/sand		Strong and hard	Hardens fairly quickly. Undercoats as above. A workability aid helps application, i.e. plasticiser.
Cement/lime/sand. 1 : 1 : 6 1 : 2 : 9		Sufficiently strong and hard for most purposes	Hardens slowly. Undercoats as above. Addition of lime gives easier working. Lightweight aggregates may replace sand.
GYPSUM PLASTERS Neat gypsum plaster, Class B	All expand as they set and subsequent movements are small.	Hard	Sets quickly. Allow to dry as soon as possible.
Class C		Harder	Sets slowly and so allows ample time for finishing to smooth surface. Do not allow to dry too quickly.
Class D		Hardest	Ditto.
Gypsum plaster/ sand. Class B	The addition of sand reduces expansion and subsequent movement.		Lightweight aggregates such as expanded vermiculite or clay may replace sand.
Class C		Strength falls off increase in sand content	—
Gypsum plaster/ lime/sand. Class B	Lime reduces the expansion on setting.		Addition of lime gives easier working. Addition of lime accelerates set.
Class C			Normally used with lime for undercoats.

Note.—Class A gypsum plaster (plaster of Paris) is not included. It sets very quickly and is used in small batches for repair work. From *B.R.S. Digest*, 69, published by H.M.S.O.

18
Painting and Decorating

OBJECTS

THE principal objects of painting are for preservation, decoration and hygiene.

Preservation. Timber used externally in particular, is constantly adjusting itself to changes in the climate of humidity. It shrinks on drying and expands when its moisture content increases. This produces warping, twisting and cupping (see p. 137). It is therefore necessary to seal as far as possible the surface with a paint system to reduce the moisture movement. Paint will reduce chance of infection from fungus and reduce the incidence of attack from beetle.

Most metals deteriorate by corrosion unless protected by a suitable paint system. Other surfaces, such as plaster and fibre board, need the protection provided by a film of paint, against abrasive damage.

Decoration. Colour and light reflectivity are obvious aspects of painting and decorating.

Hygiene. Many painted surfaces must be able to withstand repeated washing. High-gloss paint is often best able to withstand this treatment, but modern eggshell and matt paints are reasonably good in this respect.

COMPOSITION

Paints usually contain the following: Pigments, Medium, Thinner and Drier.

Pigment. This colouring matter is provided in the form of a fine powder and gives the paint ' body '. It can be opaque or consist of transparent dyes used in conjunction with opaque pigments.

Pigments are provided mainly from metallic sources, e.g. lead (white), producing an elastic film which will expand and contract with the base as the temperature changes—a useful characteristic; zinc oxide produces a hard and inelastic film which may become brittle and crack and is more suitable for interior use. Both lead and zinc oxides discolour in industrial atmospheres, lead turning to the black sulphide, zinc turning to a sulphate which is soluble in water; titanium, a mixture of titanium oxide and barium sulphate has extraordinary spreading power, but is not altogether satisfactory used externally, unless mixed with other pigments.

Medium (Vehicle, Binder or Varnish). This is the binding material in the dry paint film and gives characteristics of penetration into the surface and adhesion thereto; it seals the surface of the background. It may consist of linseed oil, or natural or synthetic resins.

Thinners. This is an ingredient of the paint which evaporates during drying and makes paint suitably liquid in the tin for application. The amount in the paint has a bearing on the degree of gloss of the finished paint film. Turpentine and petroleum spirit are common thinners.

Driers. Paints usually dry by oxidisation and these help to speed up the natural oxidisation of the medium. If the paint contains too much driers, cracking and crazing may result.

PRIMERS

Wood. Primer should penetrate the wood and provide a good key for subsequent coats. It contains an excess of oil and a pigment which dries readily, e.g. red lead. It may also be made from white lead, linseed oil, turpentine or white spirit. White lead combines very well with linseed oil and is very suitable for wood priming. Aluminium primers are good for external work.

Ferrous Metals. It is thought that these metals corrode by electrolitic action in the presence of moisture. Current will flow over the surface of the metal in the moisture film and return within the body of the metal. Normal metal paint systems will stop the flow of current over the surface of the metal (by eliminating the moisture film). If the paint film is scratched corrosion usually spreads under the paint film as the ' circuit ' is not broken by the paint film. Some special pigments, e.g. calcium plumbate will break the circuit and prevent corrosion spreading under the film.

Primers for ferrous metals must adhere firmly to the surface, other examples are red lead, red oxide, zinc chromate and metallic aluminium. All mill scale, rust, dirt and grease must be completely removed from the surface of the metal before the application of the primer.

All primers will deteriorate if exposed for too long and should be under-coated as soon as possible.

Hardboard. Special primers are available which will not sink into the surface—which results in bad brush marks and laps. A primer which ' sinks ' too much will cause failure of gloss in the finishing coat.

Aluminium. Qualities of adhesion will be affected if the primer contains pigments which react with the metal, e.g. red and white lead. Zinc chromate is satisfactory.

P.V.A. Emulsions. These paints act as their own primers when suitably thinned and will adhere to surfaces which would otherwise be difficult to, paint, e.g. new plaster, cement rendering, asbestos cement, asbestolux hardboard, lining paper. P.V.A. emulsions are not satisfactory for metal surfaces unless primed specially.

UNDERCOATS

The principle object of the undercoat is to bring the surface close to the colour of the finishing coat. It also fills in small surface defects and must provide proper adhesion between the priming coat and the finishing coat. It provides an additional reserve against any danger of the sinking of the gloss finishing coat, and consequent loss of gloss.

Undercoats should dry out overnight ready for the finishing coats. An alkyd based paint—a modern type—is often applied coat on coat and does not dry out matt as do normal undercoats.

P.V.A. emulsions as mentioned before, are also applied coat on coat, the first coat being thinned either with a special thinner or with water to compensate for the suction of the background.

Size, which contracts vigorously on drying, should never be used under a flat oil paint. Size is also water soluble and so if water gets into the background, the paint film will flake off.

PAINT FINISHES

Gloss Finishes. Many are based on titanium oxide which has extremely good covering power, and may be carried in mediums such as varnish (natural gum or synthetic). Additional medium is provided which will produce the high gloss. The best high gloss finishes are able to withstand physical abrasion, weathering, resistance to moisture and have the virtue of elasticity for a long period.

Semi-gloss and Eggshell. The degree of gloss varies with the proportion of medium. These paints are not satisfactory for external use, but can give a reasonable degree of resistance to moisture penetration and can be used satisfactorily in bathrooms and kitchens.

Oil Gloss Paint. Here the medium is refined or boiled linseed oil (boiling gives a much higher gloss). Because white lead and linseed oil combine very well together, white lead is a very common pigment for an oil gloss paint, and is very suitable for painting timber in exposed positions.

These paints are difficult to apply because they do not level out or ' flow ' easily, the work has to be brushed lightly in different directions several times to reduce brush marks.

Matt Paints—Oil. These mostly produce a dead flat finish and are satisfactory for use on plaster but not on woodwork. The surface can be cleaned down, but owing to its texture it is liable to hold dirt.

Matt Paints—Emulsion. Many of these are now based on polyvinyl acetate (P.V.A.) and are extremely useful on many difficult surfaces such as new plaster, which takes other types of paint poorly. These emulsions are satisfactory for interior surfaces, but certain grades can be used externally on asbestos cement sheets, cement renderings, etc.

They should not be applied over other gloss paints as adhesion to this type of surface cannot be good. The usual specification is to thin the emulsion with a special thinner or water to counteract suction and to follow with a neat finishing coat.

Washable Distempers. These are otherwise called oil-bound water paints and consist of an emulsion and glue size.

The pigment is Lithopone usually, which is a mixture of zinc sulphide and barium sulphate. Another ingredient is whiting (the less of this the better the paint). Too many coats of these materials may flake because of the glue content, such surfaces should be sealed with a penetrating paint.

Distemper and Ceiling White. These are made from whiting (calcium carbonate) and glue size. They are cheap and satisfactory only for ceilings where there is no wear. The distemper must be removed completely if another paint system is to be applied. Distemper should not be applied over another paint film.

As a base for distemper, bare plaster is usually ' clearcolled ' soon after setting. This is size mainly, with a little colouring, which will provide a key for the distemper. Distemper is a satisfactory surface over lining paper.

Thixotropic Paints. This type of paint, pioneered in America, is coming on to the market in this country. In the tin the paint is in the form of a gel. The movement of the bristles of the brush breaks down the viscosity enabling the brush to pick up the paint. When the brush is applied to the surface the paint will spread out satisfactorily and will reassume its gelled or thixotropic structure after the mechanical disturbance of the brush has stopped.

This has the advantage that the paint cannot be spilled from the tin; it is especially useful when painting ceilings or soffits because drips do not run down the handle.

In this type of paint the proportion of pigment to vehicle has to be very carefully controlled so that the gel works properly. This means that thinners can only be added with extreme care. If the lid of the paint tin is not replaced properly the evaporated thinners are therefore difficult to replace. The paints have a tendency to ' skin ' in the tin rather more than normal paint. The chief advantage of this paint is that heavier coatings can be applied without the danger of curtaining or sagging because of their thixotropic nature, this means that fewer coats are necessary.

Epoxide Resin Paints. This is a remarkable paint, the finish of which is close to a fired vitreous enamelled surface, but without the firing. It dries to a very hard film with good gloss, adhesion and high mar resistance, and it has very good resistance to solvents and chemicals. It is suitable for use both externally and internally and can be applied satisfactorily on normally difficult surfaces such as cement, asbestos, rubber and concrete moulds. Imperfections in workmanship are more difficult to correct with this type of paint.

TECHNIQUE

Paint may be applied by brush, roller* or by spray, with the object of building up a film suitable for its purpose. The surface must first be prepared by cleaning, and may be scrubbed with abrasive to produce a flat surface. A priming paint is then applied to ' level out ' the suction of the surface which might otherwise effect the evenness of the finish. Note that the life of paint film depends on the adhesion and life of the primer. Hollows and small cracks are then filled with a suitable filler.†

Several undercoats are now applied, each being allowed to dry, and are rubbed down in turn with a fine abrasive, e.g. glasspaper, to reduce any slight lumps and ridges. The architect specifies the number of coats in accordance with the standard of finish and durability he requires. The finishing coat or coats are then applied.‡

Wood should be painted with the grain, the ripples produced by the brush are then inclined to lie in the ' valleys ' of the grain.

When a large surface has to be painted no edge of new paint must be allowed to dry so that ridges are formed. To keep the edge open (wet), sufficiently the paint must not dry too quickly. Very large areas, e.g. walls, can be effectively managed by two painters, the first starts in the right-hand

---

* Rollers may have a variety of coverings e.g. lambswool, synthetic sponge etc.

† E.g. Hemihydrate calcium sulphate plaster or a synthetic filler, for wood or plaster.

‡ Some finishing coats cannot be applied in more than one coat,—e.g. some lead-based high gloss paints. Many new paint formulations are on the market; many well-known paints now have ' synthetics ' added, so it is essential to follow the manufacturers' directions. (One manufacturer prints on the tins ' If all else fails,—read the directions!').

corner and works to the left doing the top half only. The second also starts on the right after the first has gone four feet or so, and does the bottom half.

The size (width) of the brush or roller should be smaller than the surface to be painted. Mouldings are painted with a small brush, or tool which is also used in conjunction with rollers to finish to a line or into an internal angle.

Some paints are thin and produce a curtaining effect unless brushed out well; others have more ' body ' and are not so troublesome, though they may not be so economical. Yet other paints need ' laying off '* to produce a ripple-free surface.

Brushes, rollers, spray-guns, and all other equipment must be cleaned carefully each time they are used, otherwise small lumps of old paint will spoil the work, and the equipment will deteriorate and become useless rapidly.

If a tin of paint is not used completely the first time, the remaining paint must be strained before use (through cloth, e.g. stocking material) to remove the dried paint skin.

* The brush is worked lightly across the wet paint at right angles to the direction in which it was put on.

SUMMARY OF PAINTING TECHNIQUES (GENERAL)

Equipment	Very high gloss, e.g. coachbuilding	Normal gloss, e.g. window frames	Semi-matt, e.g. walls	Matt, e.g. blackboards, special features
Brush	Prepare, prime, fill, followed by 2 or 3 undercoats, each one dried and rubbed down. Finishing coat or coats—very high gloss lacquer. (Labour costs make this method rare.)	Prepare, prime, fill, followed by 2 or 3 undercoats, each dried and rubbed down. Finishing coat—gloss paint.	Paint: as for normal gloss, but may not require so many undercoats, as irregularities are not so easy to see. Emulsion: 2 coats only, no rubbing down. The first coat may have to be diluted with water or special liquid if the background has too much suction.	Not suitable externally. Prepare, prime, fill, 1 or 2 undercoats, and matt finishing coat.
Roller	—	—	As above; roller produces a slightly stippled finish.	Satisfactory.
Spray	Many coats applied which may be rubbed down if the original surface was uneven. Last coats are not usually rubbed—the sprayed coats are thinner than brushed ones. Produces best obtainable finish.	Not used on site except where it is economical to make and use masks to protect other surfaces, i.e. in highly repetitive work. Excellent finish.	Satisfactory and economical for large amount of work. (The droplets of paint are said not to adhere quite so well as with brush application.) Excellent finish.	Satisfactory.

POROUS PAINTS FOR EARLY DECORATION ON NEW PLASTER AND CEMENT*

NAME	TYPE	GENERAL PROPERTIES	CONDITIONS OF USE
Distempers	Oil-bound washable	Can be used as a permanent decoration. Can be redecorated with distemper or oil paints. Will withstand occasional washing if allowed to harden for some time. Most of these distempers are liable to be attacked chemically.	Mainly for interior use, but some are made for exterior use. Should not be used where alternate wetting and drying, e.g. due to condensation, is likely. This might cause flaking, especially on highly trowelled surfaces.
	Oil-free washable (casein bound)	As oil-bound washable distempers, but resistant to chemical attack.	Less suitable for exterior use.
	Oil-free non-washable (size bound)	Not fast to dry rubbing. Can fairly readily be washed off, and should be removed before redecorating.	Used where rubbing is unlikely, e.g. on ceilings.
Flat oil paints	Porous, i.e. flat finish due to high pigment-filler content	Provide a serviceable permanent decoration, or a suitable base for redecoration. More permanent than distempers. Some forms resist chemical attack.	Can be used on all surfaces. Preferable to distempers where resistance to alternate wetting and drying or greater permanence is required.
Cement paints		Provide a hard durable matt surface. Resistant to chemical attack. Can be redecorated with cement paint, but are liable to cause chemical attack on oil paints applied over them, unless precautions are taken. (See Table.)	Mixing must be carried out strictly according to the manufacturers' directions. Especially suitable for use on exterior or interior surfaces of concrete, cement rendering or asbestos cement sheet. Should NOT be used on damp materials containing excess sulphates, e.g. gypsum and anhydrite plasters and some bricks.
Silicate paints		Resistant to alkali attack. Sometimes promote efflorescence.	Similar to cement paints, but less likely to be affected by excess sulphates.
Plastic paints		In spite of the thick coat usually applied, plastic paints are fairly porous, unless a glaze coat is applied.	Mixing and application must be carried out strictly in accordance with the manufacturers' instructions.

* From *Painting New Plaster and Cement*. M.o.W Advisory Leaflet, No. 1.

DEFECTS AND THEIR CAUSES IN PAINTING WOODWORK*

This table lists the main defects in paintwork and gives the possible causes of each. It shows that care is essential at every stage.

DEFECTS	POSSIBLE CAUSES			
	PREPARATION OF WOOD	PAINTING	PAINT	WEATHER OR EXPOSURE
Blistering.	Damp or unseasoned wood. Knots not properly treated.	Paint poorly applied.	Badly formulated paint.	Excessive heat.
Peeling. Poor adhesion. Flaking.	Damp or unseasoned wood. Surface not properly cleaned.	Paint poorly applied, particularly the priming coat. Insufficient drying between coats.	Unsuitable primer. Paint too brittle.	
Irregular cracks.	Damp or unseasoned wood. Paste or size left on wood.	Paint poorly applied. Insufficient drying between coats.	Bad combination of paints—undercoat too soft and finish too hard.	Excessive heat.
Delayed drying. Uneven drying.	Surface not properly cleaned. Residues of paint removers. Painting on creosote without sealing.	Finish applied before undercoat completely dry.	Poor quality undercoat and/or finish.	Damp, cold or frost.
Poor gloss. Dull patches on glossy finish. 'Sleepiness.'	Alkaline materials left on wood.	Paint poorly applied. Finish applied before undercoat completely dry.	Poor finishing paint—too much driers in it.	Damp, fog or frost.
Gloss on flat finish. 'Flashing,' 'Sheariness.'		Paint poorly applied. Finish applied before undercoat completely dry.	Poor quality paint.	
Discoloration.	Painting on creosote without sealing. Surface not properly cleaned. Knots not properly treated.		Bleeding of pigment from ' pink primers.'	Fog.
Resin coming through.	Knots not properly treated.			
Insufficiently opaque. Colour uneven.		Paint poorly applied. Undercoat too thin or uneven.	Poor quality undercoat or finish.	
Wood decaying or mouldy.	Damp or unseasoned wood. Entry of water through opening of joints or through end grain.			

* From *Painting Woodwork.* M.o.W. Leaflet, No. 25.

TYPICAL DEFECTS IN PAINTING

DEFECT	CAUSE
All defects	Moisture contributes to all failures.
Chemical attack or 'saponification' In mild cases, peeling and blistering. In severe cases, gives a soft sticky film, with watery blisters and yellow oily runs. In all cases, some pigments are bleached or discoloured.	Attack on oil paints and oil-bound distempers by lime, in the presence of certain salts and moisture. All Portland cement products, lime plasters and lime-gauged plasters may cause this attack.
Efflorescence A crystalline deposit, often white and fluffy, which may push off the decorations, or appear on top of them.	Salts from the structure are carried to the surface by water, and deposited there as drying occurs. This may happen with any material.
Loss of adhesion Peeling, blistering and flaking.	Water alone, or helped by chemical attack, efflorescence or friable plaster.
Coloured spots or patches Often grey, black, purple, red or pink.	Moulds, mildew or fungi encouraged by damp conditions, especially where paper, paste and size are present.
Dry out In mild cases, plaster does not attain full strength and hardness. In severe cases plaster is powdery and friable on the surface, or throughout, and paint applied on it may peel.	Too rapid removal of water from gypsum and anhydrite plasters.
Delayed expansion Slight rippling and softening, or wholesale rotting, expansion and blistering of the plaster.	If plaster suffering from dry out again becomes wet, delayed expansion occurs.

PLASTER AND CEMENT*

PREVENTION	CURE
Paint only when dry, or use porous temporary decorations until the wall has dried out.	Remedy the fault which has allowed entry of water, allow to dry, remove loosely adhering decorations, and redecorate.
Dry before painting. If decoration must be done before drying is complete, use porous alkali-resistant paints or distempers. If the decoration is non-porous, it should not be applied until the wall is dry. Alkali-resistant systems, or at least two coats of a primer of this type, give greater safety. Oil-bound distempers can be applied at an earlier stage than gloss paints.	Strip, allow to dry, and redecorate, as in preceding column.
Wipe away with a dry cloth or brush, and leave for a few days to see if further growth occurs. Do NOT decorate until growth ceases. Do NOT attempt to seal back. Do NOT introduce water into the wall. If distemper is to be applied, it may be necessary to prime the wall with a coat of sharp colour.	If efflorescence is pushing off the decorations, strip, allow to dry, brush down and redecorate. If efflorescence appears on top of the decorations, wipe off until no more comes.
Dry before painting.	Remedy cause of dampness, remove loose paint, dry and redecorate.
Remedy damp conditions. If damp conditions cannot be remedied, use special paints containing fungicidal ingredients. Some of these should not be used where they may contaminate foodstuffs. Hard-drying paints are less likely to be attacked.	Strip off old decorations. Treat the wall with a fungicidal wash (†). Dry. If the mildew continues to grow, give a second fungicidal wash. When dry, redecorate, using special paints containing fungicidal ingredients if attack was severe.
Avoid too rapid drying by restricting heat and ventilation in early stages after plastering. On Keene's and Parian, where chemical attack is not expected, prime following the trowel with a sharp primer (‡). This avoids other restrictions on drying, but no further coats may be applied until the plaster has dried.	In mild cases, if the plaster is allowed to dry and is kept dry, redecoration without replastering may be successful. In severe cases, hack off and replaster.

* From *Painting New Plaster and Cement*. M.o.W. Advisory Leaflet, No. 1.
† A suitable wash for destroying mould is Santobrite (1 lb in 10 gal of water) supplied by Monsanto Chemicals Ltd., or Shirlan NA (1 lb in 10 gal. of water) supplied by Imperial Chemical Industries Ltd., or zinc silicofluoride (6 oz. in one gallon of water). The manufacturers' directions should be closely followed in making up and using the proprietary materials.
‡ A sharp primer can be made by thinning white lead paste, and adding driers, and, if desired, a little red lead or a *little* gold-size.

19

Glazier

MATERIAL

Sheet Glass. This is usually produced by a vertical drawing from the molten glass. The two surfaces of the resulting sheet are never absolutely parallel, as a certain amount of distortion occurs.

Qualities:

  O.Q.—Ordinary Quality; for general glazing.
  S.Q.—Selected Quality; for better quality work.

Except for large sheets it takes an expert to differentiate between well selected S.Q. and Polished Plate.

It is specified by weight per sq. ft:

24 oz.	.	.	.	.	.	approximately $\frac{1}{10}$ in.
26 oz.	.	.	.	.	.	„ $\frac{1}{8}$ in.
32 oz.	.	.	.	.	.	„ $\frac{5}{32}$ in.

Usual maximum manufacturing size is 66″ × 44″. The safe glazing size depends on the degree of exposure.

Polished Plate. The two surfaces of the glass are ground and polished so that they are true and free from distortion. This increases the cost approximately five times, but produces the best results.

Qualities:

  G.G.—Glazing glass; for general work.
  S.G.—Selected quality; for the best glazing.
  S.Q.—Silvering quality; for mirrors.

It is specified by thickness, which ranges from $\frac{1}{8}$ in. to $1\frac{1}{2}$ in. The most common is $\frac{1}{4}$ in., for which the usual maximum manufacturing size is 175″ × 98″.

The surface(s) can be worked or obscured by acid etching or sand-blasting, in many ways.

Rolled and Cast Glass. Textured and translucent glass with many variations, the cost being generally comparable to sheet.

An average maximum manufacturing size would be 120″ × 48″.

Wired Glass—in which wire is embedded during manufacture. It is used mostly in roof glazing. In the event of breakage, splinters cannot fall to the floor below. It is also used in small panes in fire resistant doors and partitions, as it holds together better in high temperatures.

Square mesh is used for better-class work in polished plate or cast glass. Hexagonal mesh ' chicken wire ' is used for general glazing work in cast glass.

Toughened Glass. Various forms of toughened glass are available, but they are much more expensive than even plate glass. They are used for glazed doors and balustrades, etc.

Other Varieties, e.g. glass which absorbs to a large extent the heat of the sun, and is either a greenish tinge or is a sandwich of glass fibres; fly-killing glass, for food stores; diffusing glass (glass fibre sandwich) for borrowed lights and roof lights; opaque coloured glass for sill walls in curtain walling, etc.

GLAZING TECHNIQUE

The rebate in wood frames to take the glass should not be less than $\frac{3}{8}$ in. First, the rebate is ' back puttied ' with a layer of putty about $\frac{1}{4}$ in. thick. The glass is then ' offered ' into the opening and pressed in all round so that the back putty squeezes out to about an $\frac{1}{8}$ in., leaving no putty-less gaps. If the sheet of glass is a large one, it is usual to support its weight on two small chips of wood, each a quarter the width of the sheet in from each end. By adjusting the thickness of these chips, the sheet can be squared up in the opening. Sprigs are then lightly tapped in all round to retain the glass.

Smaller sheets may then be puttied in with a triangular fillet. Large sheets are finished with a puttied timber glazing bead which is pressed into place to leave about $\frac{1}{8}$ in. of putty between the bead and the glass. The beads are then pinned or screwed to the frames.

Wood frames should be primed before puttying. If varnish or a synthetic sealer is being used instead of a paint system, then the beads and frames must be varnished or sealed before glazing. It is customary that the carpenter cuts the beads ready for the glazier to fix.

Metal frames need a special putty which will harden on its own. (Linseed oil putty hardens through oxidation and because the wood absorbs some of the oil.) Metal beads replace wood beads for the larger sizes.

Appendix

Material	Thickness in inches	Weight lb per
Blocks, hollow . . .	2	9–12 sq. ft
Boards:		
Insulating . . .	$\frac{1}{2}$	0·75 sq. ft
Plaster-board . . .	$\frac{3}{8}$	2·00 sq. ft
Brickwork:		
Common . . .		125 cu. ft
Engineering . . .		150 cu. ft
Concrete:		
Reinforced . . .		150 cu. ft
Cork:		
Slabs	1	1·00 sq. ft
Compressed . . .	1	2·00 sq. ft
Flooring:		
Rubber	$\frac{1}{4}$	2·70 sq. ft
Hardwood . . .	$\frac{7}{8}$	3·3 sq. ft
Floors:		
Hollow	4	31·0 sq. ft
,, ...	5	40·0 sq. ft
,, ...	6	45·0 sq. ft
Glass	$\frac{1}{4}$	3·5 sq. ft
Glass silk quilted . .	1	3·5 sq. ft
Plaster:		
Acoustic . . .	$\frac{1}{2}$	2·0 sq. ft
Fibrous . . .	$\frac{5}{8}$	3·0 sq. ft
Cement . . .	$\frac{1}{4}$	6·0 sq. ft
Paving:		
Concrete . . .	2	25·0 sq. ft
York Stone . . .	2	25·0 sq. ft
Pavement lights . .	$2\frac{1}{4}$	25·0 sq. ft
Timber:		
Hardwood . . .		45·0 cu. ft
Pitch pine . . .		42·0 cu. ft
Softwood . . .		30·0 cu. ft
Weights of roof coverings:	each $\frac{3}{8}$ in. thickness	
Asphalt . . .		4–4$\frac{1}{4}$ sq. ft
1 in. boarding . .		2·5 sq. ft
Battens		2·0 sq. ft
Common rafters . .		3·0 sq. ft

Material	Weight
	lb per
Copper	1 sq. ft
Corrugated iron . .	2·3 sq. ft
	plus 20% for laps
Corrugated asbestos .	3·3 sq. ft
Plate glass . .	5·0 sq. ft
Felt	½ sq. ft
Glazing bars (metal) .	1½ sq. ft
	for 6 ft spans
Lead . . .	For 6 lb 8 ⎤ including
	7 lb 9 ⎬ rolls
	8 lb 11 ⎦ and laps
Pantiles . . .	12 sq. ft
Plain tiles . .	14·5 sq. ft
Purlins (wood) . .	2·0 sq. ft
(steel) . .	4·0 sq. ft
Shingles (Red Cedar) . .	1·5 sq. ft
Slates (ordinary) . .	Westmorland 9 to 15·5
Thatch . . .	8·5 sq. ft
Zinc	1 to 1¼ sq. ft

Some of these figures have been obtained from the *Building Technicians' Diary* published by the Association of Building Technicians; and Code of Practice No. 3 : 1952.

BY-LAW TIMBER SIZES

Limiting spans of joists, rafters and purlins of European redwood or whitewood, Eastern Canadian spruce, Douglas fir or Western Hemlock in dwellings of not more than two storeys designed for one occupation.

In the following tables:

Nominal size means the net sawn size in accordance with British Standard 1860. Douglas fir surfaced to give dimensions ¼ in. less than the nominal size may be used for the tabulated spans.

Floor Joists

Nominal size	Clear span			
	16 in. centres	18 in. centres	21 in. centres	24 in. centres
	ft in.	ft in.	ft in.	ft in.
$1\frac{1}{2}'' \times 3''$ . . .	2 8	2 4	2 0	1 9
$2'' \times 3''$ . . .	3 8	3 2	2 10	2 5
$1\frac{1}{2}'' \times 4''$ . . .	4 9	4 2	3 8	3 3
$2'' \times 4''$ . . .	6 4	5 9	5 0	4 4
$1\frac{1}{2}'' \times 5''$ . . .	7 4	6 7	5 9	5 1
$2'' \times 5''$ . . .	8 6	8 2	7 7	6 8
$1\frac{1}{2}'' \times 6''$ . . .	9 1	8 7	7 11	7 1
$2'' \times 6''$ . . .	10 3	9 10	9 3	8 8
$2\frac{1}{2}'' \times 6''$ . . .	11 0	10 7	10 0	9 7
$1\frac{1}{2}'' \times 7''$ . . .	10 8	10 1	9 4	8 8
$2'' \times 7''$ . . .	12 0	11 7	10 11	10 2
$2\frac{1}{2}'' \times 7''$ . . .	12 11	12 5	11 9	11 3
$1\frac{1}{2}'' \times 8''$ . . .	12 3	11 7	10 8	10 0
$2'' \times 8''$ . . .	13 11	13 3	12 7	11 9
$2\frac{1}{2}'' \times 8''$ . . .	14 10	14 3	13 9	13 0
$1\frac{1}{2}'' \times 9''$ . . .	13 10	13 0	12 0	11 3
$2'' \times 9''$ . . .	15 7	14 11	14 0	13 2
$2\frac{1}{2}'' \times 9''$ . . .	16 8	16 0	15 3	14 7

Common Rafters and Ceiling Joists

	Nominal size	Clear span when spaced at centres of			
		16 in.	18 in.	21 in.	24 in.
		ft in.	ft in.	ft in.	ft in.
RAFTERS (i) Plain tiles, 40° pitch or steeper.	$1\frac{1}{2}'' \times 3''$	6 0	5 8	5 3	4 11
	$2'' \times 3''$	7 2	6 9	6 2	5 10
	$1\frac{1}{2}'' \times 4''$	8 2	7 8	7 1	6 8
	$2'' \times 4''$	9 9	9 1	8 5	7 11
(ii) Single-lap (interlocking) tiles, 35° pitch or steeper.	$1\frac{1}{2}'' \times 3''$	6 10	6 5	5 11	5 6
	$2'' \times 3''$	8 0	7 6	7 1	6 6
	$1\frac{1}{2}'' \times 4''$	9 3	8 8	8 0	7 6
	$2'' \times 4''$	10 9	10 2	9 5	8 9
CEILING JOISTS . . .	$1\frac{1}{2}'' \times 3''$	5 6	5 4	5 1	4 10
	$2'' \times 3''$	6 2	5 11	5 7	5 4
	$1\frac{1}{2}'' \times 4''$	7 6	7 2	6 10	6 7
	$2'' \times 4''$	8 4	8 0	7 7	7 3

Purlins

Nominal size of Purlin	Spacing of Purlins				
	ft in. 6 0	ft in. 7 0	ft in. 8 0	ft in. 9 0	ft in. 10 0
	PURLIN SPANS for Plain Tiles				
	ft in.	ft in.	ft in.	ft in.	ft in.
2″ × 4″	4 7	4 3	4 0	3 9	3 7
2″ × 5″	5 9	5 4	5 0	4 9	4 6
2″ × 6″	7 0	6 6	6 1	5 8	5 5
2″ × 7″	8 2	7 7	7 1	6 8	6 4
2″ × 8″	9 4	8 8	8 1	7 8	7 3
2″ × 9″	10 6	9 8	9 1	8 7	8 2
3″ × 8″	11 5	10 7	9 11	9 4	8 11
3″ × 9″	12 9	11 10	11 1	10 6	9 11
	PURLIN SPANS for Single-lap (interlocking) Tiles and for Slates				
	ft in.	ft in.	ft in.	ft in.	ft in.
2″ × 4″	5 0	4 7	4 4	4 1	3 10
2″ × 5″	6 4	5 10	5 6	5 2	4 11
2″ × 6″	7 7	7 0	6 7	6 3	5 11
2″ × 7″	8 11	8 3	7 9	7 3	6 11
2″ × 8″	10 2	9 5	8 10	8 4	7 11
2″ × 9″	11 5	10 7	9 11	9 4	8 10
3″ × 8″	12 5	11 6	10 9	10 2	9 8
3″ × 9″	13 10	12 10	12 1	11 5	10 10

OBSOLESCENT CONSTRUCTION

The drawings that follow have been included because:

(*a*) Architects and builders have to cope with old buildings where this type of construction is met with.

(*b*) There is a certain interest in seeing how problems of, for example, spanning, were tackled in earlier times.

These forms of construction are not offered as good construction to be used nowadays, since though they were satisfactory in days when labour and material were cheap, they would be very uneconomical in all respects now.

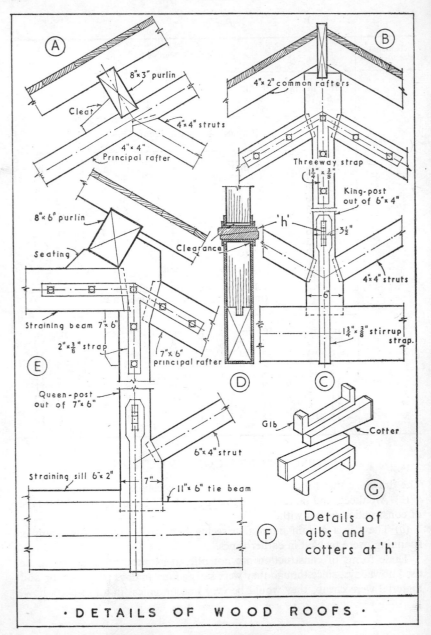

Details of gibs and cotters at 'h'

· DETAILS OF WOOD ROOFS ·

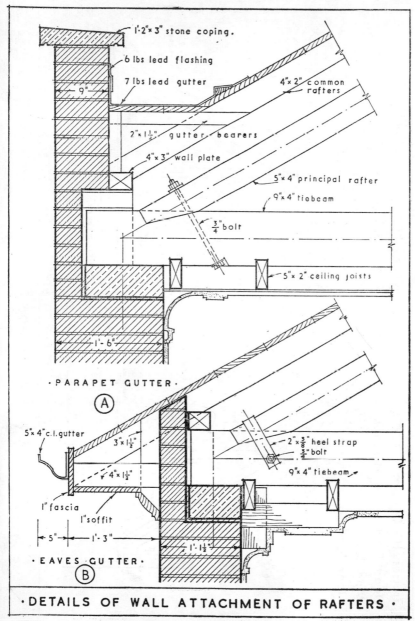

1'·2"× 3" stone coping.

6 lbs lead flashing

7 lbs lead gutter

9"

4"× 2" common rafters

2"× 1½" gutter bearers

4"× 3" wall plate

5"× 4" principal rafter

9"× 4" tiebeam

¾" bolt

5"× 2" ceiling joists

1'- 6"

· PARAPET GUTTER ·

Ⓐ

5"× 4" c.i.gutter

3"× 1½"

4"× 1½"

2"× ⅜" heel strap

⅝" bolt

9"× 4" tiebeam

1" fascia

1" soffit

5"

1'- 3"

1'- 1½"

· EAVES GUTTER ·

Ⓑ

·DETAILS OF WALL ATTACHMENT OF RAFTERS·

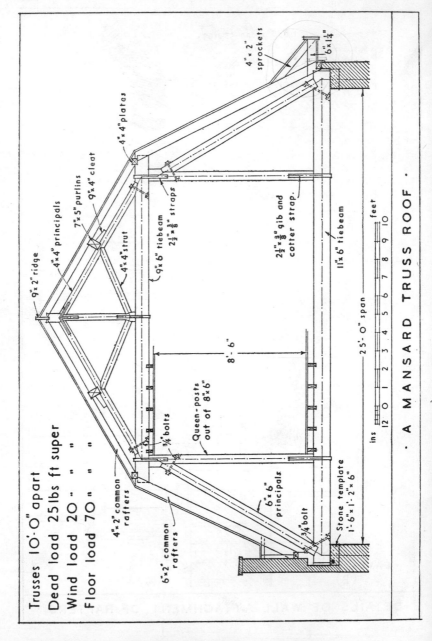

Trusses 10'-0" apart
Dead load 25 lbs ft super
Wind load 20 " " "
Floor load 70 " " "

4" × 2" sprockets
6" × 1¼"
4" × 4" plates
9" × 4" cleat
7" × 5" purlins
4" × 4" principals
4" × 4" strut
9" × 2" ridge
9" × 6" tiebeam
2½" × ⅜" straps
2½" × ⅜" gib and cotter strap.
11" × 6" tiebeam
25'-0" span
4" × 2" common rafters
8'-6"
Queen-posts out of 8" × 6"
6" × 2" common rafters
¾" bolts
¾" bolt
6" × 6" principals
Stone template 1'-6" × 1'-2" × 6"

ins 12 0 1 2 3 4 5 6 7 8 9 10 feet

· A MANSARD TRUSS ROOF ·

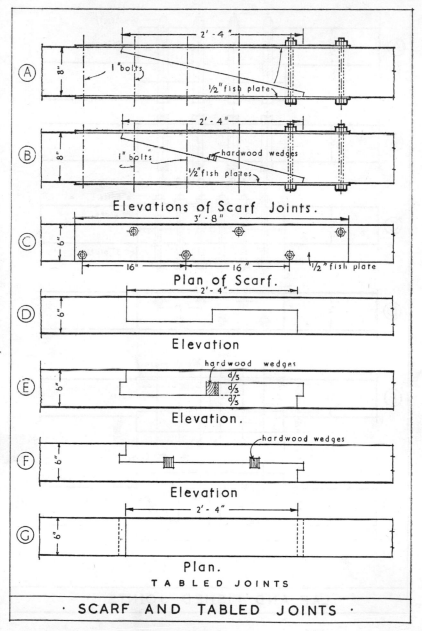

Elevations of Scarf Joints.

Plan of Scarf.

Elevation

Elevation.

Elevation

Plan.

TABLED JOINTS

· SCARF AND TABLED JOINTS ·

AA2

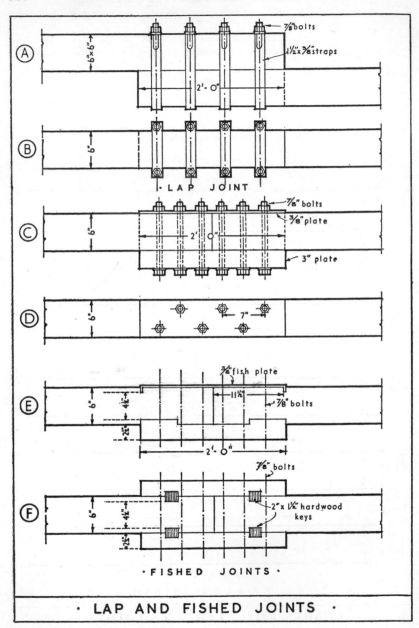

· LAP AND FISHED JOINTS ·

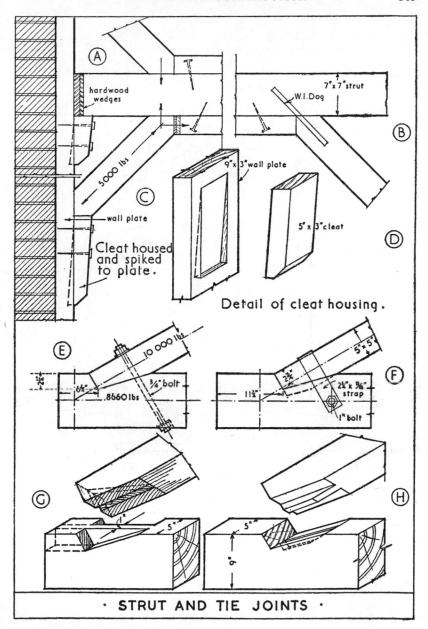

· STRUT AND TIE JOINTS ·

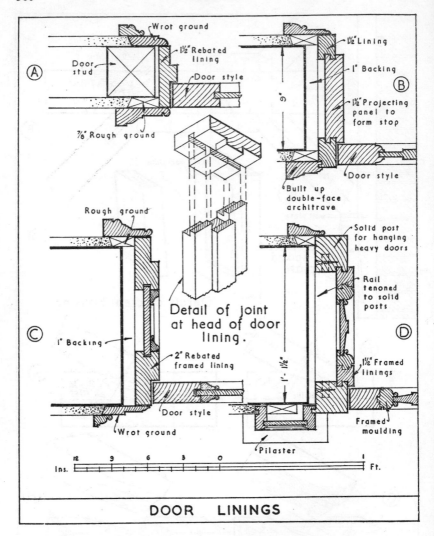

Wrot ground

1½" Rebated lining

Door stud

Door style

⅞" Rough ground

1½" Lining

1" Backing

9"

1½" Projecting panel to form stop

Door style

Built up double-face architrave

Rough ground

1" Backing

2" Rebated framed lining

Door style

Wrot ground

Detail of joint at head of door lining.

Solid post for hanging heavy doors

Rail tenoned to solid posts

1' - 1½"

1½" Framed linings

Framed moulding

Pilaster

Ⓐ Ⓑ Ⓒ Ⓓ

Ins. 12 9 6 3 0 1 Ft.

DOOR LININGS

Index